B
940.
481
94
BEVA

(1667360) 818101 2945 38

WENTWO

S0-AHZ-440

JUM'S WAR

FINDING MY FATHER
WILLIAM 'JUM' BEVAN 5TH FAB AIF

GEORGE BEVAN

PIER
9

...SIER'S PAY BOOK.

Pay Book No. 185801

Surname BEVAN

354

Christian Names William

Reg. No. 10235 Religion C. of E. Rank Driver

Enlisted in 2nd. Military District. Age on Enlistment 23

Date of Attestation 23.8.15. Date of Embarkation 17.12.1.

Unit 14th Batty. 5. F. A. B.

Transferred to	Date.	Authority.	Signature.

RUNO

Commonwealth Aud...
Of ... S...

Book opens on

If the sol...
Discharge

CANCELLED

15/1/16   at Sea
2 3/1/16   Absent without leave 24 hrs fined forft 1 days pay total 10/-
29/12/15   Improper Conduct on Orderly Room fined 2/6 total fine 2/6.
10/1/15
31/2/16   Zeitoun
15/2/16
28/2/16   Etaples
15/4/16   In the Field
11/5/16

DEDICATION

Dedicated to my grandson, Pasha Pizazz Bevan, born 14 August 1999, whose great-grandfather, William Charles 'Jum' Bevan, was born on 14 August 1892 and suffered the insane tempest of the Great War.

FOREWORD
by General Peter Cosgrove, AC, MC (Ret'd)

Over my many years in uniform I got to know thousands of soldiers of all ranks, many of them very well. It is true to say that there is no archetypal digger just as there is no archetypal Australian. Each person is unique not only in their innate character but in the way they serve and the way they relate to each other. That said, in that wonderful way we human beings tend to aggregate characteristics and behaviour, we all of us create mental images of 'typical' people – people who typify a profession or a place or a time. Jum Bevan, in this beautifully drawn account, typifies those many thousands of 'accidental warriors' who fought and bled, who laughed and cried and died and survived as part of the Australian Imperial Force in Flanders in World War I.

George Bevan as a man of mature years freely tells us that he had almost let the last memories and records of Jum slip from his grasp, perhaps to be lost forever. We are grateful to him for drawing Jum from the fading shadows into the reverent and respectful light of this new millennium. I have recently visited the battlefields of Flanders and seen them punctuated as they are by those many acres of military cemeteries with their countless thousands of silent warriors. George's respectful, affectionate, insightful and occasionally pungent characterisation of Jum's war and that of his colleagues rings to the echo with truth, accuracy and understanding.

Jum is no saint and George would not have it so. There were few saints in the AIF, just as there are few saints in life. Yet courage and comradeship, selflessness and sacrifice there

4

were in abundance – but all at a cost. We understand from this sensitive and absorbing description of one man's war, the profound and dreadful damage these experiences wrought to his psyche and we start to understand and to glimpse a similar damage to the many thousands who came back from those killing fields – the flower of a generation dead or physically maimed or deeply scarred emotionally.

I was much moved by reading this absorbing account. You will be too. We need to travel back from time to time through the pages of stories such as Jum's War. *For only by doing so do we meet to some degree the unpayable debt of their deeds and sacrifice.*

PROLOGUE

Accusing as I do, without exception, all the great Allied offensives of 1915, 1916 and 1917 as needless and wrongly conceived operations of infinite cost, I am bound to reply to the question, 'What else could be done?' And I answer it, pointing to the battle of Cambrai. 'This could have been done.' This, in many variants, this in larger and better forms ought to have been done, and would have been done if only the Generals had not been content to fight machine gun bullets with the breasts of gallant men, and think that that was waging war.

Winston Churchill, *The World Crisis, 1911–1918*

The Western Front of World War I was one of history's most horrific battlefields. In a war of attrition that stretched over four long years, Allied and German armies battled for territory that was won and lost by each many times over before the Allies, with the help of the Americans, finally prevailed in late 1918.

The losses were horrendous. In the Battle of the Somme, between July and November 1916, over 1.2 million men were killed. On the opening day of the Allied attack – 1 July 1916 – the British alone lost 20,000 men; around 40,000 were wounded.

The war on the Western Front was like a bushfire – men and equipment toiled up and down the front lines to contain the shifting blaze of battle, which rolled back and forth over a devastated landscape, punctuated by obscene forests of stripped and splintered tree trunks.

The men fought not only each other but also gas, mud, rain and rats. They fought disease from the shredded corpses that were often left to lie where they fell. Buried corpses were frequently exhumed from shallow graves by heavy shelling as battles criss-crossed the same ground repeatedly. Soldiers often fought next to rotting corpses or body parts for days, or even weeks.

While one direct shell hit could kill many men instantly, gas killed them slowly and painfully. If they survived, their lungs were damaged for the rest of their lives. The battle zones, denuded and pockmarked by shelling, became pernicious fields of mud that prevented movement and collected in shell craters so deep that men and animals drowned. Rats, fat and sleek from feeding on the corpses of soldiers, were bold enough to gnaw at the helpless wounded.

The living conditions were appalling. The trenches were largely cramped and unsanitary. Following heavy rain, they became stinking cesspits. Soldiers, usually on duty for four to six days at a time, but often for much longer, fought hunger, thirst and sleeplessness as well as the enemy. Trench foot was rife. Lice were constant companions, spreading trench fever. In the absence of antibiotics, many wounds were treated by amputation to prevent gangrene.

There was little consideration given to a soldier's mental wellbeing. This critical aspect of a man's health was often con-veniently ignored.

The terms 'trauma' and 'post-traumatic stress disorder' were unknown then. Shell shock was the general diagnosis, although sometimes terms such as 'neurosis', 'hysteria' or 'psychotic behaviour' were used to describe men who showed no physical injury but who were obviously mentally disturbed by the horrors of the Western Front. Many simply thought that these men were cowards or malingerers.

Whatever the label, there were only two options for these men: front-line service or incarceration in an insane asylum. It followed that a percentage of men who were sent back to the front line should never have been returned to active duty. The ability of these soldiers to perform was, to say the least, dramatically curtailed.

At the end of the war, estimates of the number of men killed ranged between 8.5 million and 10 million. Per capita, Australian troops suffered the greatest losses. Many soldiers returned home and were able to live fruitful lives, but many were permanently scarred. What the casualty estimates didn't consider was the damage done by the unimaginable trauma of battle, which echoed down the lives of so many returned soldiers in a grimly familiar pattern of violence, alcohol abuse, ruined careers, ruptured families and despair.

This work does not intend to glorify war, although inevitably glory fell upon a great number of the participants involved in the conflict of World War I. There is no glory in death. To consider death glorious is absurd and a contradiction in terms. There is only glory in life.

In the beginning, this project was exciting; but then I began to feel annoyed, then angry and finally disgusted as a picture of criminal waste of human life on a scale of unprecedented proportion unfolded. The suffering of the men was unimaginable, the devastation beyond belief.

William Charles 'Jum' Bevan, an ordinary artilleryman, arrived in France in February 1916 and left in 1919. He survived the carnage. This, then, is the story of the man as he travelled down the path of physical and mental destruction during and after the Great War.

Jum Bevan was my father.

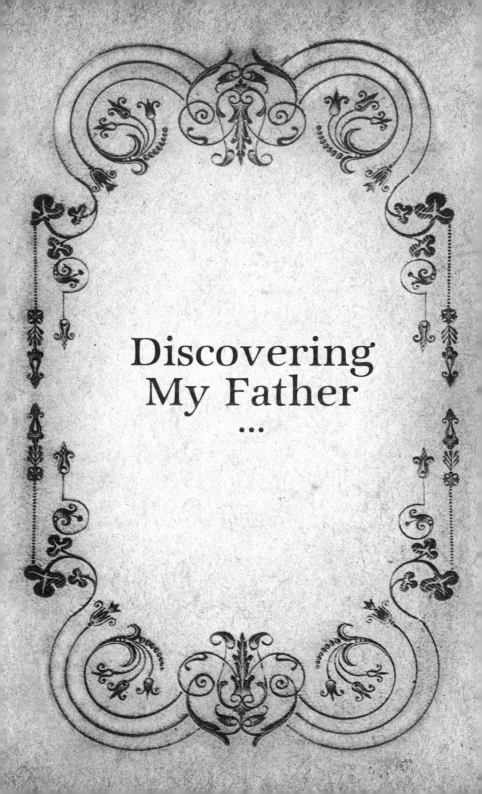

Discovering
My Father

...

14 August 2002

A winter chill settled over Sydney as the cold, heavy sou'wester sent white horses scurrying across the waters of the harbour. The expected rain was a definite threat to the afternoon of golf I had planned; but I was happy not to play, as a small third birthday party for my grandson, Pasha, had been scheduled for the evening.

I was clearing my desk of rubbish, placing some papers in a lower drawer, when I spied a cardboard box hidden beneath a few old company receipts. I recognised it: taped closed, it had been moved from place to place with the family for many years.

With light rain now falling, and golf cancelled, I had some spare time. I took the box out of the drawer. I remembered that my mother had given me the box in late March 1953. It was the month my father died.

I had not attended his funeral. We had left the family home in 1947, with my parents divorcing in 1949. The recollection I had of my father at that time had not endeared his memory to me. During my childhood, I had come to be terrified of my father: my lasting impressions were of a man given to fits of violence and abuse, mostly when alcohol was involved. I hadn't thought much about him in the fifty years since he had died. I realised that I knew very little about him.

My curiosity aroused, I split the box open. First I saw three medals, hung with coloured ribbon – a three-pointed Star medallion, 1914–1915; the British War medal; and a third, the Victory Medal. There were also two books of similar size: a brown Australian Imperial Force soldier's paybook and a glossy, black cardboard-covered diary.

The inscription in the paybook informed me that it belonged to Bevan, William Charles, Regimental No. 10235, Religion C of E,

Rank Driver, Enlisted in the 2nd Military District, aged 23 years on 23.8.15, Unit 14th Battery, 5th FAB. There followed various pages of entries, fines, cash payments of 2 shillings per day on embarkation, rising to 3 shillings per day when he was 'mustered as Driver'. I put down the paybook and opened the diary. Written in a legible, boyish scrawl in indelible pencil, it commenced:

Left Sydney 17.12.15

I was intrigued. Fifty years after his death, I began to read my father's diary, written nearly ninety years before. I realised with some shock that my father had been only twenty-three or twenty-four years of age at the time.

I cast my mind back to 1953 – I was then eighteen years of age – and the day in late March when my mother approached me, saying, 'I have something for you.' I'd looked up from my evening meal.

'What is it, Mum?'

'A few mementoes of your father's from the First World War – some medals and a diary.'

I didn't respond; I was more concerned with getting to the Friday night movie than looking at my father's old personal effects.

'I understand why you didn't go to his funeral,' Mum continued, 'but you are his son!'

'Why would I be interested in anything to do with him?' I said, angrily. 'My last recollection of the man was of him belting the crap out of me with his bloody horsewhip! Why don't you see if Reg wants it?' Reg was my brother.

'He's not interested. All he cares about is the house he's building,' said my mother, looking at the small box in her hands. She'd never mentioned it again.

My grandson Pasha's birthday was a great success. It was during the singing of 'Happy Birthday' that I realised, with some surprise, that my father's and Pasha's birthdays were on the same day – 14 August, albeit 106 years apart.

The following morning I awoke with a strange urge to visit my father's grave. I had never seen it, but I knew he was buried in the Botany Cemetery at Matraville. I considered my feelings: those early years had remained behind a closed door – did I now wish to open this door to a frightening past that had no place in my life of today? With some trepidation I made my decision. I drove to the cemetery near La Perouse, south of Sydney. I knew it was highly possible that my father's grave would not be traceable.

The attendant was polite. 'Yes, Mr Bevan, here is your father's plot, Grave No. 761, Presbyterian B Section.' He handed me a printed map that showed the position of all the grave plots.

I stepped out into the sunlight, feeling a strange mix of emotions. Here I was, about to stand and face the grave of my father, who had lain at rest for fifty years.

I quickly got lost and, after an hour of fruitless wandering, had all but given up my search. The grave numbers appeared incorrect. Where my father should have been was an empty plot. I sat down on the granite edge of an encased grave and glanced northwards, up the slope of neatly constructed grave sites. There, at the end of the 'empty' grave, sat a finely carved headstone. These were reserved for Armed Forces personnel who had succumbed to war injuries.

I was sitting on the edge of my father's grave! I read the inscription:

Dvr. William Bevan 5th FAB A.I.F.
6th March, 1953

What I felt was indescribable. So many years had passed before I had made this trek. During those years, I had suppressed all memories and thoughts of my father. I decided now that there had to be a reconciliation, a closure of the enmity that I had burdened myself with for so long.

I considered what we had never addressed as a family: the mental damage that my father had suffered for three years on the Western Front and his continual, residual suffering for the thirty-five years from then until his death in 1953. Our family had not recognised his illness; nothing had been done to alleviate his suffering. A distressing lump arose in my throat. It was three hours before I moved from his grave.

What had my father really been like? How did I remember him? (Certainly, I had never forgotten the horsewhip.) How would

I have wanted my father to be? Of course, when I was a child, the Saturday afternoon movie matinees featured many heroes with whom I could align my father.

In fact, I was about to embark on a journey with my father – my father as I remembered him, my father as he really was, and my father as, perhaps, I wished him to be.

I realised that to fully understand my father's life during the Great War, I would need more information. A phone call to the National Archives Service Records in Canberra sent me off to the Australian Artillery Museum at North Fort at Manly in Sydney. The museum is housed in a smallish building, and I browsed through the material rather quickly. The librarian, Danny Toplis, a retired warrant officer class II, asked me, 'What are you really doing in the museum?' I explained that my father had served on the Western Front during World War I in the Fifth Field Artillery Brigade.

'Just a moment.' He smiled, and soon returned with three small journals. 'These are the diaries of the Fifth Brigade, 1916 to 1918. We've just received them through an estate bequest.'

I began to read the neatly handwritten entries. A picture of these three years of war began to emerge, and with it facts and figures that I could not have obtained from any other source. I spent the next six weeks studying the Brigade Diaries.

It was satisfying that the brigade entries coincided with the entries from my father's diary. I realised that the information I had would be the key to deciphering this man, my father, and in understanding the type of man he had become. Here was a story that had to be told.

As I began to write, it became obvious that there would be holes and gaps in the factual story. I have taken some liberties in filling these in.

The Great War

...

October 1918

As the Germans retreated in defeat, and only a few weeks before the signing of the Armistice, some of the most desperate encounters of the Great War were fought. The Battle of Busigny, east of the Somme River, was one such firestorm.

In the wake of the conflagration, two Allied artillerymen emerged from a shell-damaged trench, half-supporting, half-carrying a slumped figure. He was soaked with blood from the chest down.

Captain Harold McErbain, attempting to find his way back to the 5th Brigade, saw the trio staggering towards a horse-drawn dray, where a corporal and a lieutenant stood waiting.

'Jesus!' he said suddenly, recognising the injured man. 'It's Jum! Jum Bevan!' Running to Jum's side, he took one arm. 'You all right, Jum?'

A burble of unintelligible words flowed from the wounded man's mouth.

'You know this man, sir?' asked the lieutenant.

'Yes,' said Captain McErbain. 'He's a gunner in my Battery.'

'We're taking him to the CCS,' said the lieutenant. 'There's one about half a mile down the track towards Busigny.'

'I'll come with you,' said McErbain.

They carefully lifted the crumpled figure into the dray and moved off towards the casualty clearing station. McErbain sat in the dray with Jum's head on his thigh.

1915

The pony's tail streamed out as the young rider, hair flying in the wind, dug his knees into the pony's flanks. With his blue-grey eyes glinting and his mouth set in a determined line, he urged the pony on. Light, with a lean, muscular frame, he had no trouble handling the galloping mount. The rider, an even-featured young man, now gave the pony his head. Horse and rider became one. Without breaking stride, they cleared the fence with ease. The rider eased the pony to a canter, swung around and headed to a post-and-rail fence where another young man sat on his mount, waiting.

'Gee, you were going fast at that fence, Jum,' said Bob Buchannen.

'Don't worry, Bob. He's a great little horse, this one,' replied Jum.

Prancing lightly, the pony was snorting, flanks heaving, catching its breath.

'You like riding bareback, don't you, Jum?' said Bob.

Jum smiled. 'The horse knows what you want before y'realise it yourself.'

'Wish I could ride as well as you.'

'You ride as well as any young bloke around,' laughed Jum. 'Come on, I'll race you!'

As they galloped, a dusty Chevrolet with its back open thumped along the dirt track to Douglas Park. With six or so passengers hanging on in the rear, Jum's father George held the vehicle steady, despite the many potholes he encountered. A passenger in the back yelled over the noise of the vehicle, 'Look't those two mad bastards!'

They could see two horses, galloping towards the bouncing car. The young riders, yelling and whooping, divided and thundered past the car, one on each side, meeting again at the rear before disappearing in a cloud of dust and muffled hoofbeats.

'Jesus, George, wasn't that Jum and young Buchannen?'

Bevan turned with a grimace and nodded. 'One day one of them'll get badly hurt, mark my words.'

The two riders suddenly veered right off the track, clearing a low mound without faltering. Up a slight slope, over the crest and down into a steep gully, barely checking their breakneck speed, the two sprayed their way across a shallow ford. Halfway up the next rise, Jum eased to a canter. Bob slowed and slipped in beside him.

'Good ride, mate!' called Jum.

Bob grinned and replied, 'I'll catch you one day, you bugger!'

George Bevan was an engineer. Having worked for many years as an assistant engineer on various projects throughout New South Wales, he had secured a worthwhile position on the construction team at the Cordeaux Dam, south-west of Sydney and not far from the village of Douglas Park. The Cordeaux Dam was a major New South Wales government project requiring a large and varied labour force.

Through his father's influence, Jum Bevan was apprenticed as an electrical engineer, and worked five-and-a-half days a week at the dam.

George Bevan had arranged bed and meals for Jum with the Buchannen family, as the trip from Sydney was two hours each way, and costly. Jum's weekly wage of 4 shillings was a welcome addition to the family's meagre income. He lived in a comfortable outbuilding, sparsely furnished with essential items. It was clean and warm and Maude Buchannen provided solid Irish cooking. Jum soon settled in.

Most Saturday afternoons, he would travel to Sutherland by the two-car rail motor, and thence by train to Sydney's Central Station. A short tram ride to Randwick would deliver him to his family's home in Albion Street, Waverley. The house was crowded with Jum's four siblings, but it was a happy, friendly home.

He would spend Sundays frolicking in the surf at Coogee or Bronte Beach, or lazing about in the quiet waters of Clovelly Bay.

William Charles Bevan, born to Amelia and George Bevan on 14 August 1892, was the eldest child of five. He was a wild child – an unruly handful, aggressive and fiercely competitive. He was also extremely strong – so strong that his friends nicknamed him 'Jumbo' (as in the elephant), which was soon shortened to Jum.

At 5 feet 8 inches, Jum Bevan was not tall, although his athletic build served him well in various sports. He taught himself the basics of boxing and wrestling, and became a very handy middleweight boxer and a virtually unbeatable wrestler in his weight division.

With his slight but strong frame, Jum was very acrobatic. His skill on the 3- and 6-foot diving boards was exceptional, winning him a state diving championship in 1911. For Jum, diving was the quintessential activity, allowing him to exercise both his imagination and skill in an unrestricted, unbounded way.

The entire family was musical. Jum's younger brothers could both play a range of instruments while Jum, with his fine ear for music, could thump out a great accompaniment on the piano to any tune you could whistle, sing or hum.

His other love, riding bareback, had become a daily routine. Riding to and from work at the Cordeaux Dam on the Buchannens' ponies honed his expertise.

Jum's younger brothers were content with an easy life; they liked to laze about and play music, but Jum was a purely physical type who enjoyed being active in the outdoors. Bob Buchannen was more like Jum, and the two young men became as close as brothers themselves. During these carefree days they developed their skills and formed their strong, direct personalities.

But these days were coming to an end. World War I loomed. To a young Australian male, it seemed as thrilling, faraway and heroic as a *Boy's Own* tale.

One night, following the evening meal, Jum sat with the Buchannen family around the fire.

'The men at the dam have been talking about the fighting in Gallipoli, and the Kaiser in Germany,' said Jum.

Stoking his pipe with a cracked and gnarled finger, Hector Buchannen replied, 'Germany's a long way from here. If there's trouble in Europe, they can work it out for themselves.' That was the end of the discussion.

The next day, enjoying the sun during a lunch break at Cordeaux Dam, Jum noticed Harold McErbain reading the local newspaper.

'What's new, Harold?'

'Not much. The boys at Gallipoli are doing it tough, though,' said McErbain. He looked up at Jum. 'Jim Gillies and I are thinking of enlisting for France.'

Jum stared hard at McErbain. 'What would make you want to go to war?'

'That'd take all day to answer, Jum.' He paused, then continued. 'Men our age and younger are fighting and dying over there, and they're doing it to protect our freedom. I feel guilty not being part of it. And I think it's wrong for one country to attack another without any just cause. I feel like I have to do something about it.'

'Hadn't thought of it that way,' replied Jum. 'Why is Jim going?'

McErbain looked at Gillies, who was lying on the ground listening intently to their conversation.

'The pay's great,' said Gillies, with a broad grin. 'There's lots of lying around with nothing to do, and plenty of sheilas to keep you happy. Also the recruiting feller who spoke to us said the food will be first class.' He looked south to the enormous gaping hole in the valley. The scarred earth walls of the dam stood out in stark contrast to the rich greens of the gum forests. 'Besides all that, it sounds exciting. And Harold will need someone to clean his boots,' he concluded.

A wave of laughter rose from the group as George Bevan emerged from his office. 'OK, boys, enough of the war – we've got a dam to build. Let's go!'

The men rose and moved off to their respective jobs. Jum stood at his bench with McErbain's words echoing in his head, unable to concentrate on the large electric motor he was rewiring. Though he didn't realise it then, the conversation had set his destiny in motion.

Throughout the year, the news from Europe became increasingly grim, but the appalling loss of life at Gallipoli was not fully explained by reports in the Australian newspapers: the casualty lists were outdated virtually by the hour, and the government's trumpeting call-to-arms would have been severely compromised if the perceived adventure were to be marred by the realities of violent death and injury.

Despite the cold of June, Bob and Jum were splashing about in the waterhole on the Buchannen farm. The weak, wintry sun did little to warm their shivering bodies as the cool afternoon set in. After drying off, they dressed and sat on the rock overlooking the waterhole.

'It looks like these Germans are serious about the fighting,' ventured Jum.

'I don't know much about it, yet, mate,' said Bob.

'Well, we're right in it now. The Australian troops are getting the shit kicked out of them at Gallipoli. A few from the dam have enlisted already. I know Harold and Jim have gone in for the artillery. It's not a bad idea. I'm thinking about it too,' he added.

Bob stood and looked down; he was thoughtful. 'I turn nineteen this month, so I can do whatever I want. I'm not too welcome around here, anyway. My father thinks I don't exist.' Bob and his father had never got on.

The pair made their way to the farmhouse, Bob engrossed in his own thoughts. Before turning in to the gate, he put his hand on Jum's shoulder.

'If you go, mate, I'm going with you,' he said.

'We'll see,' said Jum, dubiously. Then he said, laughing, 'How would you go in the army? You can't even wear your boots for more than a couple of hours now.' Work regulations at the dam made the wearing of boots compulsory. As Bob had gone barefoot all his life, he found the footwear heavy and cumbersome.

'I'll manage,' Bob said seriously.

During a lunchbreak later that week, Jum steered Bob aside from the group.

'I'm going to enlist tomorrow,' he said.

Bob's heart thudded in his chest. 'Well, I'm coming with you, Jum,' he answered.

Jum thought carefully. 'You realise that this is real – real bullets, not the little .22s we shoot bottles with?'

'Like I said, there's nothing to keep me here,' said Bob. 'And I can't imagine it here without you, Jum.'

'What about your mum?' said Jum, and Bob's face clouded. 'You know she's not going to like it.'

That night, Jum sat quietly in a corner as Maude Buchannen prepared the evening meal, dreading the imminent confrontation. Bob went to the sink and poured a glass of water, which he quickly gulped. He then moved to the fire and placed a small log in the flames. He walked back to the sink and poured another glass of water.

'What's on your mind, Bob?' asked his mother.

'Nothing, nothing at all,' he stammered.

His father looked up. Bob swallowed hard and blurted out, 'Jum and me are going to enlist tomorrow.'

The crash of a bowl smashing on the brick hearth broke the silence. Maude Buchannen, her face ashen, could only blink and look at Bob. Then she said, in a harsh voice Bob had never heard before, 'No, you're not!'

She sat heavily in the nearest chair and began picking up the pieces of broken crockery.

'I've made up my mind, Mum,' said Bob.

She looked straight at Jum. 'This is your doing, isn't it?' she said, her voice venomous.

'No, missus,' replied Jum. 'I told Bob I was going, and he said he wanted to go too. It was his idea. I tried to talk him out of it, but he wouldn't listen.'

Maude began to sob, and Jum moved to her and put a hand on her shoulder. 'Come on, missus,' he soothed. 'Maybe he's got flat feet and they won't take him.' Maude pushed Jum's hand away, and sat gazing intently into the fire.

Breakfast the following morning was a tense and silent affair. Maude's eyes were bloodshot and red-rimmed, her hair in disarray.

'You haven't changed your mind, Bob?' she asked quietly.

'No, Mum, I've made up my mind. Don't worry, I'll send my pay to you every week,' he said, tears starting in his eyes.

Maude half-smiled. 'Damn the pay, Bob, I want *you*.'

Bob turned to Jum. 'I'm going to get my gear.'

'I'm ready,' replied Jum. Then he turned to Maude. 'Well, I suppose this is goodbye, Mrs Buchannen.'

Maude moved to Jum and clasped his hands in hers.

'Promise me, Jum, that you'll look after him. He's my only child, he's just a boy ... Promise me!' Her voice wavered and tears filled her eyes.

Jum looked anywhere but at the beseeching eyes riveted on his face.

'I promise, Maude,' he said, using her name for the first time. 'I'll watch out for him, I promise.'

Maude rinsed her face in cold water, brushed her hair and walked out into the yard where the two were waiting by the buggy.

'We can walk, Mum,' said Bob.

'Don't be silly,' she said, as she climbed into the driver's seat. The pony tossed its head as Maude slapped its rump, aiming for the gate and the station at Douglas Park.

Working in his barn, Hector Buchannen heard the horse and buggy. He did not stop working, look up, wave goodbye or even acknowledge Bob's departure.

He never mentioned Bob's name again.

Maude Buchannen didn't speak as the buggy bumped softly over the dirt track behind the trotting pony. The boys were quiet, looking at the blue gums occasionally appearing through the early morning mist.

'I wonder if they have gum forests like this in France,' said Bob.

'I'm sure they have some trees,' replied Jum, 'but maybe not as tall as ours.' He cast his eyes skywards to the flowing, leaf-laden branches of the gums moving slowly in the breeze. When would they see this magnificent countryside again? Would Bob and he ride the wild ponies again? Swim in the waterhole?

'Not far, now,' called Maude over her shoulder. The pony trotted to the main street, where few people were about on this early winter's morning. Maude hauled on the reins, easing the pony to a halt, and climbed down from the buggy.

'Come into the store, boys, before you leave. There may be something you need to buy,' called Maude.

They entered the store, casting glances around. Bolts of cloth, clothes on hangers, more clothes neatly stacked on shelves. In the far corner, bags of flour, salt, oats and all manner of consumables were neatly arranged.

A display cabinet was set up in the middle of the shop. It was a great attraction for the young boys of the area, as it offered penknives, belts, buckles, sets of brightly coloured marbles, cases of leather-working tools, open-bladed knives and fishing tackle.

Maude moved to the counter. She spoke quietly to Tom Grady, the proprietor of the store, as they made their way to where Jum and Bob stood examining the display counter.

With a smile, Tom unlocked the cabinet top and extracted two of the best clasp knives. Turning to the boys, he held out one knife to each. 'You may need these where you're going,' he said.

'I can't afford this, Mr Grady,' said Jum.

'You don't have to. It's a going away present,' Tom replied with the same soft smile.

Maude stood close to the storekeeper, her eyes averted. Shakily, she said, 'Come on, boys, time to go.'

Jum and Bob collected their small bags and the four travelled the short distance to the station. 'I hope that old train will get us to Sutherland,' said Bob, in a faint attempt to lighten the farewell.

Maude took her son into her arms. 'Please be careful, Bob,' she whispered in his ear.

'I will, Mum,' he replied.

Tom Grady shook hands with Jum. 'Take care, Jumbo,' he said.

'We will,' said Jum, with a wry smile.

'Write to your mother,' said Tom to Bob, holding his handshake a trifle longer.

The train driver gave one quick blast on the whistle as the train moved forward. Jum and Bob hung out the windows, calling and blowing kisses. The boys were quiet on the train ride to Sydney, each immersed in his own thoughts.

Jum had always made his decisions independently, and had been surprised when his father recoiled in anger. 'Have you thought about anyone but yourself, William?' he'd asked. 'I worked hard to get this position for you, and now you're just going to throw it away?' Deep down, George Bevan was resigned. He knew his son's temperament, knew he would refuse to change his mind.

'I do appreciate what you've done for me,' said Jum, 'but I've gotta experience other things. I've got itchy feet!'

'What about your mother?' George asked.

'You and Mum have four other kids to occupy you. You know I'm not a stay-at-home boy,' said Jum. Then, 'Wish me luck, Dad?' he asked gently.

George couldn't speak, but pulled his son towards him.

'You'll be proud of me, Dad,' said Jum.

He leapt onto his pony and looked back at his father standing in the doorway of his office.

'See ya, Dad!' he called. He wheeled the pony and galloped off into the late afternoon and away from the dam forever. He did not see the tears brimming in his father's eyes.

The train hammered its way north to Sydney. 'Well, there's Redfern,' said Jum. 'Next stop, Central.'

'At least it's not raining,' said Bob.

As the train slowed to a halt, the boys stood and reached for their bags in the overhead rack. Walking through the turnstiles after handing in their tickets, they moved into the cavernous concourse of Central Railway Station.

Jum looked around and said to Bob, 'The recruiting office is at Victoria Barracks in Paddington. We'll catch a Bondi tram.'

As they approached Victoria Barracks, they saw a large infantryman with polished brass, shiny boots and sergeant's stripes standing rigidly to attention at the gate. He smiled as he directed the boys to a large room. A dozen or so young men were standing around. A tired corporal behind a large desk motioned Jum and Bob over.

'Have either of you attempted to enlist here before?' he asked in a bored tone.

After names, next of kin and addresses were given and recorded, another corporal addressed them. 'You will report to Holsworthy Army Camp tomorrow. Here are two train tickets to Liverpool. You'll be met at the station. You leave Sydney on the 8 am from Central. Understood?'

Jum nodded as he took the tickets. 'We understand,' he said. Then he turned to Bob. 'Well, that was a bit of an anticlimax, but it's done!'

'What happens now?' asked Bob.

'Basic training at Holsworthy, I suppose,' said Jum. The pair walked up to Taylor Square and boarded a tram to Randwick.

As the tram moved off, Jum said, 'We'd best stay with my mother tonight before we leave. She'll be happy to have us.'

Amelia Bevan opened the door and greeted the boys warmly, but with some tension in her face. 'Come in, come in. Like a cuppa?'

'No thanks, Mum. But do you mind if we stay here tonight?'

'Not at all, your father telephoned last night and told me all about it. So, off to the war, are we?' said Amelia.

She knew her son well, and didn't attempt to dissuade him. Jum had inherited his mother's stubbornness and iron will.

'We thought we'd give it a try,' said Bob.

'Millie has gone to stay with a school friend, so Bob can sleep in the front room,' said Amelia, as Bob murmured his thanks.

'We'll go for a walk to the beach, Mum,' said Jum. 'Should be back about 5.'

The boys left the house and walked the mile and a half to Coogee Beach. Sitting on the sand, they watched the small shore-break as the surf curled and dumped along the beachfront.

'We might not see the beach again for a while,' said Bob.

'I guess so,' was the terse reply. Jum, who loved the freedom of the water, would miss the ocean much more than Bob would.

The cold winter wind decided them against a last swim. They watched as the white water crashed across Wedding Cake Island, then walked to the cliff at the north end of the beach. 'Let's go and check out Clovelly,' said Jum.

They walked around the cliff edge to Clovelly and continued on past the clifftop cemetery. Bronte would be their last call. Sitting on the grass behind the beach, the boys talked whilst the seagulls wheeled and screeched overhead.

'After basic,' said Jum, 'we should try for the artillery.'

'Why not?' said Bob.

The next morning, after a brief and unemotional farewell from Amelia, the pair headed for Liverpool, where they joined a throng of young men moving to the station's exit. After loading into large horse-drawn drays, the group headed for Holsworthy Army Camp.

There the men received clothing, boots and equipment and were allotted to various tents, sleeping twelve men each.

Falling in prior to lunch, dressed in their ill-fitting tunics, each man had to recite the Oath of Attestation. Jum nervously repeated after Captain Harrison: 'I swear that I will well and truly serve our

Sovereign Lord, the King, in the Australian Imperial Force from the 23rd August, 1915 until the end of the war and a further period of four months thereafter unless sooner lawfully discharged, dismissed, or removed therefrom and that I will resist his Majesty's enemies and cause his Majesty's peace to be kept and maintained and that I will, in all matters appertaining to my service, faithfully discharge my duty according to law. So help me God.'

It was 23 August 1915, one week after Jum Bevan's twenty-third birthday. Bob Buchannen had turned nineteen in June.

The ensuing weeks were a blur of drills, weapons training and endless parade-ground marching. The most enjoyable part of training for Bob and Jum was working with the camp horses. Showing their natural talent for handling animals, they were soon spending much of their time in the stables. The days passed quickly, with their brief basic training coming to an end in September.

As the boys had agreed previously, they applied for artillery school. And as fate would decree, artillery personnel were in demand. The troop carrier HMAT *Berrima* was scheduled to leave for Egypt in late December, as reinforcements were desperately needed in Europe in the worsening theatre of war.

They had no trouble being inducted into the artillery school, where they learnt the intricacies of the 18-pounder QF gun and the 4.5-inch Howitzer. Weighing in at about 2,830 pounds, the 18-pounder required a team of ten men. The teams soon became adept at moving the weapon around, with or without horses.

Live firing training commenced soon after, with detachments rapidly becoming highly proficient in weapons use and maintenance. Jim Gillies and Harold McErbain had gone into the artillery school in the same intake as Jum and Bob and the four men were the core of an 18-pounder artillery detachment of ten men. They applied themselves assiduously.

In late November, before they embarked for Egypt, the artillery replacements were sent to a bivouac at Randwick Racecourse on the outskirts of Sydney.

The day of 16 December 1915 saw Sydney suffering hot, westerly winds. Although the wind subsided late in the afternoon, the air still hung heavily as the sun – a blood-red ball – slowly sank below the

Blue Mountains west of Sydney. The centre of the racetrack was a hive of activity as khaki-clad figures hurried in all directions between tents, carrying, packing and calling excitedly to each other.

Hundreds of tons of equipment, horses, feed and field guns had been loaded onto the HMAT *Berrima* over the past week. About 200 artillery replacement personnel were due to arrive at 1000 hours at Circular Quay. Bevan and Buchannen were already packed and waiting to leave the next day. Lying on his stretcher, Jum said to Bob, 'What say we slip across to the Doncaster Hotel for a few quick beers? We've got till 6 o'clock.'

'Jum, we're confined to barracks, no leave, you know that,' replied Bob. The 'confined to barracks' order had been in operation for over a week while the men underwent various inoculations and the pay books were finalised.

'We'll only be gone for an hour. Come on, let's go,' said Jum.

Nonchalantly, the pair sauntered past the main stand opposite the finishing straight, ducked over a small fence and sprinted towards Doncaster Avenue. Arriving at the Doncaster Hotel a few minutes later, the two elbowed their way to the bar and ordered beers. Only forty-five minutes remained till 6 o'clock closing and they wasted no time.

'My shout, Jum,' said Bob. 'Don't worry, mate, Mum gave me a fiver before we left to tide me over.'

By 6 pm they'd consumed a large quantity of beer, which left them heady, light-hearted and eager for the adventure ahead. They clambered over the rear fence of the barracks, stumbling and bumping into each other as they tried to move quietly. Creeping around the corner of the main stand, they were confronted by a sergeant and two privates wearing the dreaded insignia of the Military Police.

'Wondering where you were,' said the sergeant crisply. Jum and Bob stood there, looking sheepish.

'We've just been for a walk,' said Bob.

'What, they serve alcohol on walks do they?' replied the sergeant. 'Come with us.' The group marched towards the large Headquarters tent. The sergeant nodded to the two privates. 'Keep them here.'

After a few minutes in the tent, the sergeant returned.

'Get to your tents,' he said. 'You're both on charges tomorrow.'
Inside their tent, Bob said, 'Wonder what they'll do, Jum.'

Jum smiled. 'Most likely a firing squad. Let's get some sleep.'

Reveille sounded at 6 am sharp the next morning and the barracks exploded with movement. A non-commissioned officer appeared at Jum and Bob's tent. 'You two are to report to HQ at 0700 sharp.'

'Here we go,' thought Jum. 'Get cleaned up,' he said to Bob. 'We've got to front the brass.'

The sergeant marched them into the Headquarters tent. The temporary officer commanding, an older captain, wearily read the charge sheets.

'Absent without leave, drunk and disorderly,' he said. 'What have you to say for yourselves?'

'Just a quick drink at the local before we left, sir,' said Jum.

'Orders are orders, Private, and AWL is no laughing matter. If orders are disobeyed in the front line, it could cost countless lives. The fact that you both leave today is in your favour; it's your lucky day. But a repeat of this will have you both in serious trouble. Fined one month's pay each. Dismissed. Get them out of here, Sergeant,' he finished.

The sergeant marched them outside and barked, 'Get your gear together and get ready to move out.'

Jum and Bob hurried back to their tent.

'Well, we got off that one,' said Bob.

'Nothing else he could do,' replied Jum.

The scene at the quayside bordered on pandemonium. Two hundred troops, complete with equipment, waited at the rear of the wharf. Stores, provisions and the last of the heavy cargo were being roped aboard, the stevedores having worked through the night.

Finally, as midday approached, the troops started filing up the gangplank of the HMAT *Berrima*. With hawsers cast off, the vessel went astern out of Woolloomooloo Bay into the main harbour. Slowly coming about, the ship moved east at half-speed towards Sydney Heads.

The horror of the Western Front was approaching. But the untried warriors from Australia felt a great adventure was about to begin.

2002

With a vague feeling of uneasiness, I opened my father's diary and read the inscription and first entry.

Dvr W. Bevan 14th Battery 5th FAB AIF

Left Sydney 17.12.15

Left Fremantle 1.1.16

JANUARY 1916

The *Berrima* troop carrier – a small, converted coastal steamer, loaded with 200 men, horses and equipment, and numbers of artillery pieces – ploughed into the slight Indian Ocean swell. A warm, sunny January afternoon attracted a large contingent onto the deck; stripped to the waist, they would suffer from sunburn that night.

On deck, the makeshift boxing ring had already hosted two bouts. Two bantamweights, punching mostly fresh air, had entertained the crowd and exhausted themselves over three rounds. The next bout, a total mismatch, saw the overweight heavyweight dropped in the first round.

The two boxers for the final bout slid under the ropes. Jum Bevan sat in his corner, eyeing his opponent.

'Watch him, Jum,' said Bob Buchannen. 'He looks mean.'

'He's carrying a bit round the belly,' Jum observed. 'We'll see.'

Introductions made, the seaman acting as referee waved the boxers to centre ring as the bell rang for the first of the three rounds. Jum slipped into his orthodox stance and probed with a snappy left, followed by a right cross. His opponent took the left in the face and the right on his left elbow. The round continued with Jum landing solid body blows to the other boxer's unguarded midsection.

'What do you think, Jum?' said Bob, wiping Jum's face with a towel at the end of the round.

'He's wide open. I don't want to hurt him.'

Round two followed much the same course as the previous one.

Halfway through round three, the tired opponent dropped his guard, leaving himself wide open for a left hook. Jum instinctively moved his weight to his right foot as he started the punch. At the last moment, he pulled the punch and clinched instead. He growled into the other's ear, 'Get your bloody hands up,' and broke cleanly, pushing his opponent away.

With ten seconds left in the round, Jum let go a flurry of left–right combinations that had the other boxer on his heels. Jum moved in. As the bell rang, he dropped his hands and moved to his corner. The referee raised Jum's hand, declaring him winner on points to a smattering of applause.

'Why didn't you drop him, Jum?' asked Bob.

'I didn't need to, mate; he was gone in the second round. Besides, he's not a fucking German.'

For the next week, the *Berrima* battled a heavy, south-west gale coming off the Antarctic. Most of the troops suffering severe seasickness. The ship arrived in Cairo, Egypt, in January 1916. Jum and Bob, part of the contingent that was to join the 5th Field

Artillery Brigade – the FAB – left Cairo for Zeitoun, arriving at Le Havre in France in early February.

The column moved by train north to Étaples, thence to Hazebrouck and finally, in horse-drawn wagons, to Saint-Lys, a forward staging area used to ready the troops for front-line action. Spreading out into the encampment set up for them, the replacements for the 5th Field Artillery Brigade were allowed no time to laze about.

The commanding officers of the various units believed that after eight weeks cramped on a ship and several more weeks spent travelling, the men needed to practise and fine-tune their weapons. The daily slog of drills on the 18-pounders and the 4.5 Howitzers continued unabated for many days. The various gun detachments regained their swiftness and dexterity, but the officers expected still more improvement in readiness for the heavy action taking place near Armentières.

Jum Bevan, along with Bob Buchannen, Gillies and McErbain, were staged in camp at Saint-Lys until 10 March 1916. The 2nd Divisonal Ammunition Column then received orders to move to Fleurbaix, where fierce battles with the Germans were taking place.

There was a strong rumour that the German front line and artillery were securely dug in, with an extensive system of trenches that allowed both infantry and artillery free, unseen movement.

On 10 March, Jum and Bob were transferred to the 22nd Howitzer Brigade, which then staged with 1 Anzac Corps on 1 April to Fleurbaix. Jim Gillies and Harold McErbain were moved to the 5th Field Artillery Brigade, which arrived at Fleurbaix on 9 April 1916. At this time, the fighting between the Australian forces and the German troops had just begun.

The late winter rains had turned the badly ruptured road system into a quagmire, the mud making troop or artillery movement almost impossible. Some tracks had been improved by English engineers, who had reconstructed roads from thousands of destroyed trees.

Thick, deep mud and heavy rain greeted the brigade replacements at Fleurbaix.

Captain Conrick of the 14th Battery waited whilst the men unloaded from the open horse-drawn carriages.

He addressed the group.

'I want the following to move out: Bevan, Buchannen, over there.' He pointed to a small group of tents. 'You're now in the 105th Mortar Battery. Gillies and McErbain, report to Sergeant Hill at HQ – you're headed for the 14th Battery.'

He waved his hand in the general direction of a large, symmetrically arranged tent encampment. The four men trudged along duckboard walkways, which allowed some ease of movement away from the gluc-like mud, towards the largest tent. Behind the rows of tents, the dark, cloudy sky was lit continuously by flashes that leapt skywards.

'Almost like an early summer electrical storm,' thought Jum.

The deep rumble of distant gunfire punctuated an eerie skyscape that was to become familiar in the years ahead. A few light snowflakes swirled about as the distant storm slowly headed towards the camp.

Sergeant Hill stepped out of the Headquarters tent. 'Follow me,' he said. 'Bevan and Buchannen, 50 yards down there in Tent 1. Gillies and McErbain, over there to the left.'

Jum and Bob dropped their gear and lay down on their camp stretchers. The chill in the tent soon displaced the slight warmth generated by the walk.

The tent flap opened. 'You two are relieving in about thirty minutes. Move quickly to the mess tent and get a hot meal before you stand to.' The flap closed.

'Here we go, Jum. Guess that means we're on,' said Bob.

Both men moved towards the mess tent with their eating utensils. They slipped behind the flap. A kerosene lamp cast an odd pallor on the faces of the men. Confronting the two was a steaming cauldron of stew. A number of weary men were sitting at one table, eating.

'What time you on?' asked a small, thin corporal.

'About thirty minutes,' replied Jum.

'Nightwatchmen, eh? Tough on your first night.'

Jum and Bob loaded their cans with stew, sat down and started to eat. The corporal moved to their table.

'Good tucker, this,' said Jum.

'It should be,' said the corporal. 'Fresh this morning. A Boche shell knocked over two horses.'

Jum looked up, his mouth full of stew. He glanced at Bob, who was looking pale.

'Can't waste fresh meat here – you'll get used to it,' said the corporal, laying a friendly hand on Bob's shoulder. 'Make sure you're dry and wear two pairs of socks – tonight will be very cold. Put an extra shirt on too.'

'Thanks for the advice,' said Jum.

'I'm Henry Larkin,' said the corporal.

'Jum Bevan and Bob Buchannen, Henry,' replied Jum as the men rose and shook hands. Henry Larkin was corporal in charge of the 18-pounder No. 3 Gun of the 14th Battery.

'You'll be relieving No. 1 Mortar Gun tonight. It's quiet, nothing doing today; too bloody cold for the Boche,' said Larkin.

As he turned to go, he called, 'Keep warm, you buggers!' A wave and a grin and he was out of the tent.

Jum, Bob and two other gunners made their way to the gun positions situated some 800 yards from their wagon lines. As the cold and dark descended, the light snow continued to swirl about, coating the ground and equipment with a feathery, slippery sheen. For the moment, everything seemed clean and fresh.

'Time to go, boys,' said Jum as he stepped into the position.

'About time,' was the curt reply. The four men who were being relieved moved eagerly out of the position and away towards the hot food and warmth of the mess tent.

Sergeant Hill had explained to the four new recruits that they expected no action tonight, as intelligence had reported German stores and ammunition were being moved forward to their wagon lines. He'd cautioned them to be alert, though, just in case.

Jum noted where the ordnance lay, the position for the mortar shells when the action was on and the general layout of the position. A makeshift tarpaulin cover had been erected on a few pieces of timber, enough to provide comfortable cover for the four of them.

Jum turned to the other gunners. 'Why don't you blokes get some shut-eye? I'll take first watch.'

'You sure, Jum?' asked Bob.

'No need for all of us to be awake.'

'Suits me fine,' said one of the others.

The three crept under the recently vacated tarpaulin cover and, if the snoring were any indication, were soon deeply asleep. Jum moved around the position and walked some 30 yards, just enough to keep warm.

Time slipped by quickly as Jum, immersed in thoughts of home, remembered the morning they had left Douglas Park, and how Maude had asked him to look after Bob.

'She's a good woman,' mused Jum. 'Too good for her bloody husband.'

Jum felt the clasp knife that Tom Grady had given each of them. From that day, he had always worn it on his belt and felt undressed without it. He wondered why Grady had given them the knives. They were worth at least 10 shillings each.

A voice broke his reverie. 'Jesus, Jum, what time is it?' Bob was rubbing his eyes.

'I think about 0400, mate,' said Jum, as he glanced at his watch.

'Why the bloody hell didn't you wake us?' said Bob.

'No need to, mate, nothing happening.'

'You get some sleep now, Jum,' Bob replied. 'You must be buggered.'

Jum patted Bob's arm as he slid under the tarpaulin. He was asleep as his head touched the makeshift pillow.

At 0700 hours, four shadows appeared in the growing dawn light. The snow had eased, but the dark grey sky promised further bad weather.

'Saved the world, did we?' came the first remark.

'All yours, boys,' said Bob.

Jum was instantly awake and gently nudged the other two. 'Come on, you sleeping beauties, time to eat.'

The four tramped back to the tent lines, stamping savagely to get their circulation moving.

Captain Terry Conrick was conversing with Lieutenant Colonel Tideswell, the Commanding Officer of the 5th Artillery Brigade.

'Sir, we have two runners arriving today.'

'About time, Terry! Where do you suggest we place them?'

'Well, sir, I think Bevan and Buchannen could move from the 105th to No. 1 Gun, 14th Battery, and the new bods take their place in the 105th.'

Tideswell nodded in agreement. 'I'll leave it to you.'

APRIL 1916

BRIGADE DIARY

15.4.16 Enemy incendiary shells set fire to billets, no injuries.

Two weeks later, the new team were on night watch in No. 1 Gun position when Bob Buchannen called, 'Runner coming very fast!' The panting pony slithered to a halt, but the rider was already out of the saddle.

He ran to the GPO, the gun position officer. 'Urgent SOS from 6th Brigade, gas attack, get your masks on, commence rapid fire on Ref. Coordinate C7,' he gasped.

The detachment went instantly into action.

'What range, Jum?' called Harold.

'Range is coming, get a few away. Our current range is 600 yards clear of the sixth,' replied Jum.

The breech of the 18-pounder, already opened by McErbain, was slammed shut as Jim Gillies rammed home the first shell. McErbain wound the traverse of the gun to its new bearing at C7.

'Fire!' screamed McErbain, as he twitched the firing cord. The gun exploded into life, sending the 18-pound, high-explosive projectile some 2,000 yards on its way towards the south-east.

The gun bucked under the impact recoil of the shell, tossing lumps of damp clay across the position.

Jum was moving the shells into position for Jim Gillies to load, while Bob leapt about ensuring a constant flow of ammunition. 'I'll check the range, Harold,' called Jum.

'Spot on 2,000 yards, Harold.' He looked around. 'Christ!' he thought. 'The gas!' But he pushed the threat from his mind as the well-rehearsed team slipped into gear. Shell after shell was sent on its way. Eight rounds per minute was a high rate of fire for a reduced gun detachment that normally consisted of eight to ten men per gun.

The barrage had lasted over an hour and the detachment was sweating profusely before a second runner jumped into the position.

'Boche infantry is advancing on a wide front, now at 1,800 yards,' he panted. 'Drop your range to 1,700 yards and let them have it, shrapnel!'

'What about the gas?' screamed Gillies. But the runner was already sprinting towards the remaining guns.

At this time, gas warfare was frequently used to the north of the Messines Front. Following German gas attacks, the Allies had installed gas cylinders near their front-line trench.

The guns of the battery increased their fire rate, working feverishly to repel the German offensive. For five minutes the rate rose to twelve rounds per gun per minute. The original mounted runner had galloped to Brigade Headquarters and returned. He ran to Captain Conrick in his dugout, 100 yards to the rear and centre of the battery position.

Conrick blew his whistle and screamed, 'Cease fire, cease fire!'

Silence settled over the positions. Exhausted, the detachments collapsed in and around their dugouts.

'Well done, you buggers!' called Captain Conrick. 'The wind changed, the gas went back into their faces and our 18-pounders did the rest!'

Gillies, gasping and smiling, said, 'We did it boys, we did it! Our first action and we did it!'

McErbain, looking at his watch, remarked, '1700 to 1915, two-and-a-quarter hours.' He carefully counted the empty cartridge cases lying in a large heap. 'We got away about 120 rounds.'

'Not bad,' said Jum, with a smile. The other detachments reported similar rates of fire.

'That's about 450 rounds in just over two hours,' said Gillies, his chest still heaving. 'Give those German bastards something to think about!'

'Wouldn't want it every night of the week,' Bob said quietly. As darkness settled over the gun detachments, they replaced the clothing they had hastily cast off during the action. The well-timed storm, which had blown the gas attack back into the German front line, was moving slowly towards the east.

Sitting on the edge of the gun position, Jum Bevan lit a cigarette and contemplated the large pile of empty cartridge cases. 'Our first engagement. What an intro,' he thought.

His back ached from the two-hour effort of keeping up the ammunition. Each shell weighed about 23 pounds. He did a quick calculation: he'd moved just under one ton of ammunition in two hours. He noted that a large load of shells would be needed tomorrow morning. Another session like the last one would see them out of ammunition.

'Harold, we've got to tell the GPO what ammo we used.'

Harold nodded. 'Already written it down, Jum. We'll need it early morning.'

The positions settled down for the uneasy night ahead. It was not known whether the enemy was to launch a second offensive that night. Sentries were doubled and instructed to report any enemy movement that would indicate the start of another attack.

The night passed uneventfully, with morning bringing grey skies and a light breeze from the north-west.

The fifty men had been relieved at 0700 hours and were eating breakfast back at the wagon line. The group stood in the occasional burst of wintry sun, quietly smoking and talking.

Lieutenant Colonel Tideswell approached the group with two junior officers.

'Well done, boys,' he said. 'You certainly let them know we're here. They'll remember the night of 15 April 1916, when you blew the gas back in their faces. You new men of the 14th Battery did an excellent job – over 400 rounds in just over two hours. Your efforts, along with the 105th Howitzer Battery, halted a major attack by the enemy. Our shells, and determined fighting by the 6th Infantry Brigade, have pushed them back to their original positions.

'Enemy casualties, on a rough count, appear to be 300 plus. Our infantry had fifteen men killed, ten unaccounted for and sixty or so wounded. Their artillery couldn't find our range, which is unusual, so we only suffered one casualty – Gunner Gillies burnt his thumb on a shell casing.'

A cry came from the back of the group. 'He burnt his thumb lighting a bloody fag in the middle of the action!'

Laughter and smiles as the Lieutenant Colonel dismissed the men with a wave of his hand.

Bob said to Jum, 'How come the Boche didn't get our range?'

Jum nodded at Henry Larkin, who had joined the knot of men. 'Ask Henry, he's got the experience.'

'Well,' said Larkin, 'firstly, they may have decided to go without artillery as a surprise factor, which is unusual. Or being under offensive orders, there may have been a mix-up in the range their artillery was given. You know, when our own men are attacking and we're laying on a barrage, it's easy to drop a couple short into our own lines. Better to hold off until the range is confirmed.'

'Maybe they thought the gas would do the job and save ammunition,' commented Sergeant Hill, on the edge of the group. 'Anyway,' he said, 'we were bloody lucky not to cop some retaliation.'

'What's it like, Sarge, under barrage?'

Sergeant Hill turned to Bob, who had asked the question. 'After an hour, you'll stop praying for it to stop, because that won't work; three hours, you'll be crying for your mum; and if you're still alive after that, you'll start to piss in your pants.'

The colour drained from Bob's face.

'Don't worry, Bob,' laughed Jum. 'I'll be your mum, but don't piss in your pants – I'm not washing your clothes!'

The men headed off towards their tents for some well-earned rest and sleep.

At the end of May, the snow and chilly north winds began to abate. The mud, as thick as ever, began to exude a pervasive bad odour as the earth warmed slightly.

The opposing forces were in stalemate, with artillery securely dug in on both sides, pinning infantry in their trenches for days on end. Life became a continuous round of eat, sleep and stand to. Shelling was sporadic, with both infantry armies gearing up for the spring offensive to come. In World War I, the chief method of attack by both sides was to employ a massive artillery bombardment to protect an infantry attack.

Jum had hoped that he and Bob would be transferred to Transportation. He approached Captain Conrick outside Brigade Headquarters one morning.

'Excuse me, sir.'

Conrick turned as Bevan saluted. 'Yes, Jum, what is it?'

'Wondering, sir, when Buchannen and I will get to be amongst the horses? We're qualified as drivers, and we know about horses,' he finished.

'You, Buchannen and McErbain are my best gunners. I can't let you move from your present job right now,' Conrick responded. 'However, one of our mounted runners has been transferred, and we have some replacements arriving next week. I'll see what I can do for you.'

'Thank you, sir,' answered Jum.

That evening, lying in their tent, Jum turned to Bob. 'I spoke to Conrick today, about us being mounted runners.'

Bob rolled over on his stretcher. 'What'd he say?'

'He's going to try and do something next week, when the replacements arrive.'

'You beauty!' said Bob, as he drifted off to sleep.

Brigade Diary

27.4.16 10.30 pm. Gas attack! 6th INF. Brigade.
All Batys fired all along the line until 11.00 pm.
Right group fired 180 rds. 11.00 pm gas
attack over.

Later that week, Jum and Bob's pleasant sense of anticipation was spoilt by a heavy bombardment. The men jumped for their tin hats as the shelling increased in intensity. 'They haven't got our range yet,' thought Jum, as the shells continued to scream overhead.

For over an hour, the gun detachments waited underneath the screeching shells, at the ready for orders. Then a mounted runner arrived at the positions.

'You characters are lucky and unlucky,' he said.

'Well, give us the news,' said Buchannen, stripped to the waist and stacking newly arrived ammunition.

'That last stunt, over your heads, was sent "direct mail" to your lines,' said the runner. 'Eighty per cent of your tents were hit by Boche incendiary shells, most tents were burnt out, and all your gear's gone up in smoke.'

'Well, what's the lucky part?' said McErbain.

'You poor silly bastards weren't in your tents,' the runner laughed.

Two wagons had been destroyed, with a stack of shells receiving a direct hit and igniting a spectacular fireworks display. Luckily for the brigade, the men not on duty were taking delivery of a large consignment of ammunition and no casualties were suffered.

The offensive continued. A few days later, the German artillery began shelling with its favourite weapon – the 77-millimetre gun. It had a large range of ammunition that included incendiary, high-explosive and high-burst shrapnel devices. While two battery outposts were completely destroyed during the heavy bombardment, no casualties were suffered.

During a few days' lull in the action, the batteries took the opportunity to deepen their positions and add heavy sandbag fortifications. This ensured that only direct hits would be able to inflict serious injuries.

A new approach to artillery warfare was evolving, with air observation being used more frequently. Allied aircraft made sweeps over the enemy lines and signalled back to Brigade Head-quarters the whereabouts of enemy placements. Mounted runners were then despatched to the various battery outposts with information that gave the individual outpost officers more precise targets.

Aircraft pilots took enormous risks as they flew at low altitudes over the trenches, gathering information about troop numbers and deployment. It was a great step forward when aircraft were finally fitted with radio and could transmit the information back to artillery Brigade Headquarters.

Fierce hostilities had recommenced. Artillery bombardments were often non-stop for twenty hours or more. During one such engagement, Jum and Bob were on day duty in the No. 1 Gun position when the shelling started. McErbain and Gillies, now very experienced gunners, had both been promoted. McErbain was promoted to corporal and Gillies moved to driver. They were replaced in the 14th Battery by two raw-boned brothers from Wagga Wagga in New South Wales.

Jum was not considered for promotion. His service record, showing the drinking and AWL before the contingent left Sydney, ensured he was passed over at this stage.

As the shelling intensified, the gun detachments sought cover as best they could. The heavy work that had been carried out on the positions days before was paying off.

Midday came and went with no weakening of the attack. Caught under cover in the positions, the men endured shells within yards of the detachments.

One of the Wagga brothers, James Roberts, who was about eighteen years old and known as 'Wagga', was watching carefully as a high-explosive shell landed on top of the position parapet, very close to the large stack of shells.

'Bloody hell!' he whistled as he turned to Bob. 'What happens if the stack cops it?'

'Won't bother us,' said Bob. 'We won't know a thing about it.'

Wagga glanced about, looking for some area of greater protection as shell after shell exploded nearby. As the barrage continued throughout the afternoon, each close hit made Wagga jump nervously. Jum moved over to him.

'Settle down, mate. We'll be OK,' he said reassuringly.

'How much longer will it last?' There was real fear in Wagga's eyes. Wagga didn't scare easily, but in the muddy trenches of France he was frightened by what he could hear, but not see – the approaching 77-millimetre shells.

Bob Buchannen said, 'Mate, when you piss in your pants, the shelling will stop.'

Jum smiled. Bob had done just that a week ago, as predicted by Sergeant Hill.

Night closed in, but the intense shelling continued, though fewer shells were falling on the area. More shells seemed to be heading westward towards the wagon lines. The makeshift Brigade Headquarters had been pinpointed by the enemy artillery.

The wagon lines at Brigade Headquarters suffered severe losses. Two officers were killed, as were four men in ordinary ranks. Some fifty horses were lost, and fifteen injured. Five wagons were destroyed.

At 2000 hours, the barrage from the Germans ended. Mounted runners arrived at the battery outposts with orders to commence firing in retaliation. The brigade was about to unleash a reply that was to last all night.

'Fire!' screamed Jum. The 18-pounder bucked and jumped. The detachments fell into the well-practised movements of continuous fire: breech open, eject, reload, fire. The range had been reset to accommodate the new target bearings. The four batteries commenced a barrage to match what they had suffered all day, the men relishing the activity that had been denied them during the German assault.

Spread in a line that extended for half a mile, the four batteries fired in a steady rhythm. The twelve 18-pounders now fired non-stop.

The four Howitzers of the 105th Battery also contributed to the bombardment. These 4.5-inch weapons were a deadly force. They threw their shells high in the air so that they landed directly in the enemy trenches, causing havoc and death on a frightening scale. A rapidly descending 4.5 shell allowed no escape.

Wagga jumped everywhere, clearing ejected cartridge cases. Jum noticed a damp stain at Wagga's crotch. 'Welcome to the Fleurbaix club, Wagga!' he shouted as he ripped the firing lanyard.

The activity continued unabated throughout the night, with fresh teams of relief artillerymen taking over as exhaustion overwhelmed the original crews. Wagonloads of new ammunition arrived at the positions. Each position received some 400 shells during the night. The firing rate slowed to four rounds per minute, but the bombardment was unremitting in its intensity.

The ceasefire came at 0500 hours that morning. The detachments, totally exhausted after nine hours, slowly removed cotton-wool ear plugs with leaden arms. So completely spent were the men that the reliefs came out on wagons to allow the night detachments to ride back to central camp. The men stumbled to their tents, too tired to even contemplate food. Most slept where they dropped, fully clothed, their boots still on.

Since early 1900, there had been rapid advances in weaponry, guns and machine guns, so this war developed into a new style of conflict. In France the old charges of mounted horse brigades were a dismal failure when faced with the murderous German Maxim machine guns. During World War I, only a few charges were made by mounted brigades, early in 1916. The losses of men and horses were so appalling that commanders changed their tactics dramatically, relying on artillery, both heavy and light, to inflict death and destruction on the enemy. It had become a war of attrition. Both sides were firmly ensconced in extensive trench systems that were many miles in length.

German and British armament factories desperately designed and produced larger and longer-range guns that could be fired from 12 to 15 miles behind the front lines. The final absurdity was the 'Paris Gun', designed by the Germans to destroy Paris. It had a range exceeding 80 miles, with shells of massive destructive power. Luckily for the Allies, the gun was inaccurate and hard to set in position. It also had only a short life, as the weapon's barrel, subjected to intense heat from the massive propellant charges, was destroyed after only forty rounds had been fired.

In early 1916, the French leader, Marshall J. J. C. Joffre, was in agreement with British General Sir Douglas Haig that a massive offensive would be undertaken by both their armies north and south of the Somme River. The French Higher Command was worried by the German build-up of divisions east of Verdun. The planned attack would take place on a 45-mile front. The British, with twenty-five divisions of men, were to cover 15 miles of the front. Joffre's thirty-nine divisions were to attack on the remaining 30 miles of the German front line. The conference of 14 February 1916 confirmed the agreement to attack on 1 July 1916.

But on 21 February 1916, the German war machine struck at Verdun. General Von Falkenhayn, the Chief of the German General Staff, believed that to strike the French at Verdun with overwhelming force would inflict such gross chaos that the French army would either bleed to death or be forced to seek peace. Without their support, the English would be unable to continue the war.

Indeed, the Battle of Verdun was a disaster for the French. With French losses double that of the Germans, the French were forced to throw in their reserves. The German offensive overran the French lines and occupied the armoured fort of Douaumont.

Even more disastrously, the French had used most of the proposed infantry intended for the Somme attack.

General Petain, the defender of Verdun, lost sixteen of his thirty-nine divisions between February and June. The appalling losses suffered by both the Germans and the French were amongst the highest of the war. Four hundred thousand Germans were killed and injured, with the French casualties amounting to 272,000 injured and 270,000 dead – a total of 942,000 men either dead or injured.

Germany's plan was on the way to success. The British would have to attack at the Somme without French support.

June 1916

Brigade Diary

18.6.16 Raid by Brigade took place, enemy trenches. Many Germans killed by gunners acting as infantry.

The morning was warm, with a clear sky and no sign of rain. The artillery, rested for two days, had slept, eaten and relaxed in the unusual lull in the fighting. Rumours were rife, as the idle gunners sought to explain their inactivity.

'We're heading for Saint-Lys for a rest,' said one rumour.

'Bullshit!' was the reply. 'We're going to the Somme.'

Under intense barrage from German artillery, the 7th Brigade had planned to attack the enemy north-east of Albert on the main Amiens–Arras road. But the proposed offensive was in doubt because the 7th Brigade was under strength, with no infantry reinforcements available. Discussions at division level proposed a number of artillerymen be called on to enable an attack by the 7th Brigade on the entrenched enemy front line.

Sergeant Hill passed amongst the artillerymen. 'Muster in ten minutes outside the Headquarters tent. Pass the word, all personnel, I repeat, all personnel to attend!'

Fifteen minutes later, Lieutenant Colonel Tideswell emerged from the Headquarters tent and addressed the battery. 'Tomorrow, you men will get a chance to come face to face with the enemy. The 7th Brigade are mounting an attack south at the Somme on the German centre front. They are under strength. We have been ordered to join them in their attack on the enemy front line. You all remember your basic training with the .303 and the bayonet. Well, tomorrow you are going to use them. As at 1400 hours, you will all be infantrymen under the command of the 7th Brigade Infantry. I wish you well,' he concluded.

A quiet murmur went through the assembled men. Tideswell returned to the Headquarters tent, leaving the officers commanding the batteries to explain the details. 'What the bloody hell?' said Wagga. 'I thought we were bloody gunners!'

'Soldiers first, gunners second, Wagga,' said Jum.

Ron Roberts voiced their collective concern. 'I haven't touched a .303 since basic training. I forget which end to hang on to!'

Wagga laughed. 'Bob'll have no trouble hanging onto his weapon after what we saw in the bath house!'

Bob blushed awkwardly.

'Straight left arm and drive hard forward on the left foot, Ron,' said Jum. 'And if the bayonet sticks, boot the bastard in the chest as you pull the bloody thing out.'

'Just like sticking a wild pig, eh, Bob?' Ron laughed.

Jum turned and faced the group, a serious expression on his face.

'We all know what to do if the bayonet does get stuck. Pull the bloody trigger, two jobs at once. The bastard is sure to die and the bayonet releases easily.'

Bob turned away, his face pale. 'I don't think I could kill anyone with a bloody bayonet!'

Jum looked at Bob. 'If it's him or you, I'll bet you will.'

Captain Conrick had his men move to an area where he could be heard.

'Well,' he said, 'you heard the CO. Tomorrow you become infantrymen for I don't know how long – a few days at the most, I'd expect. You'll be moved out by wagon about 80 miles south. You'll be under the command of Captain Harry Haverstein, Australian Pioneers. Our troops will boost his company from 180 to 230 personnel. We will be under his direct orders, and subject to his command.'

'Will you be there, sir?' asked Jim.

'Yes, Gillies, but I'll take my orders from Captain Haverstein also. You'll receive weapons and ammunition upon arrival.'

The men were given 20 minutes to pack their gear and move to the truck lines, where they were to be transported south to Belloy-sur-Somme, north of Amiens.

Wagga climbed aboard beside Jum and Bob. 'Anything's better than that bloody shit fight we went through a week ago,' he said.

'You'd prefer a cold steel bayonet up your arse?' said Jum. 'This is the real thing, man to man, so get yourself ready.'

The hive of activity south of Albert reminded Wagga of the anthills on his father's property. From the hill crest overlooking the 7th Brigade, thousands of men were deploying in all directions.

When they had reached the flat area, a sergeant approached them. 'Where're you heading?'

'A Company Pioneers,' said Captain Conrick.

'Go 300 yards down there,' he said, pointing, 'and about 100 on your left.'

A nod from Conrick and the wagons moved forward.

Captain Conrick stepped down from the wagon as a tall figure wearing captain's rank approached and addressed him.

'Harry Haverstein. And you are?'

'Terry Conrick, 5th Field Artillery, your willing and able reinforcements,' he smiled.

Haverstein glanced at the wagons and saw young men with set, determined faces who had already seen enough.

'I'm glad for any help, Terry. Happy you could come,' said Haverstein.

As the two officers moved to the Headquarters tent, Conrick called to Sergeant Hill, 'Stand the men down, Sergeant. They can smoke if they like.'

Hill acknowledged and passed on the order.

In the tent, Haverstein and Conrick surveyed the contour map on the table. Various hand-drawn lines indicated the troop and artillery positions of both sides.

'We've been given this area to capture,' said Haverstein, pointing to the map.

'Uphill to the trenches, I see,' said Conrick.

'Yes, parapets and barbed wire, just for good measure.'

'Artillery?'

Haverstein smiled. 'We have most of you here. But we do have two batteries about 1,000 yards behind. They're going to lay on a barrage prior to us going in.'

Conrick examined the map. 'I see there's a dip about 400 yards in front of their first trench.'

Haverstein nodded. 'You've got it. We'll move up under cover of darkness into that defile, wait there for the barrage to finish and hopefully catch Fritz with his pants down.'

'We have another problem, Terry,' he continued, 'a major one. We have no jumping-off trench, and as you well know, that's not the best way to start an attack.'

A jumping-off trench usually ran approximately parallel to the opposing front line. It was joined in the centre by a communications trench that could be up to a mile in length. This allowed the attacking force to gather under cover prior to an assault. It was not unusual for lives to be lost in the jumping-off trenches, as their own artillery bombardment could fall short onto their lines.

Trenches facing the enemy were usually dug in zigzag formation. This ensured that artillery or mortar shell explosions in each trench were contained to about 20 yards, limiting the possible damage. The excavated soil was deposited on the side facing the enemy, and at times sandbagged for greater height and stability. One hundred yards or so of barbed wire entanglement usually completed the defence.

This all made an attacking force's job nearly impossible, unless the barbed wire had been cut and destroyed by artillery fire. Opposing troops snagged on the wire became easy marks for machine gun and rifle fire.

Conrick pondered. 'At least, Harry, we'll be attacking from behind that defile and hidden from the Boche!' Haverstein nodded in agreement.

'Can you show me the German artillery positions?' asked Conrick.

Haverstein moved his pencil back behind the forward trenches. 'About here, 1,600 yards behind. The artillery is noted as 77-millimetre guns.'

'You know, the Germans will have trouble landing the .77s in that defile,' said Conrick.

'Really? So the defile we're using as our jump-off may not cop any artillery?'

'That's the way I see it.'

'It's great to have your artillery experience,' said Haverstein. 'We weren't quite sure.'

'If we keep the men forward on the upslope,' said Conrick, 'the enemy artillery will be useless. That is, if they don't have trench mortars nearby.'

'Yes, vertically descending mortar bombs would be a worry, but we have no intelligence reports to indicate mortar batteries, unless they have them hidden.'

'When are we on, Captain?' asked Conrick, becoming more formal as two sergeants moved into the tent.

'We move out towards the defile at 0200 hours. We're at about three-quarter company strength, so it won't take us long to cover the 1,200 yards to our position.'

Haverstein turned to the two sergeants. 'This is Captain Conrick of 5th Brigade. He has about 80 boys hot to go, haven't you, Captain?'

'We'll do our best sir,' replied Conrick.

The four studied the map. Haverstein pointed to one area and said, 'I want Captain Conrick and his men in the centre. They'll then have cover from both flanks. Two platoons on either flank and two more behind. The gunners will beef us up into a solid force.'

Again, he addressed the sergeants. 'Keep up tight in the defile. Captain Conrick agrees Fritz artillery will have trouble pinpointing our force. Get the men fed and bedded down.'

The sergeants nodded and retired from the tent.

'I'll do the same for our men once the rifles, bayonets and ammunition have been issued,' said Conrick. The men shook hands. Conrick left the tent and approached his men, who were waiting patiently by the wagons. The hazy sun now settling over the western hills cast a soft shadow over the troops.

Conrick called Sergeant Hill. 'Charlie, let's get our boys issued with weapons and ammunition.' Conrick and Hill led the men to the stores wagons and they lined up in single file. Jum and Bob were the first two in line.

The armoury sergeant lifted a shiny new .303 Lee Enfield out of its box and handed the weapon to Jum, who moved to the next wagon. Here he received two full bandoliers of cartridges, a carry strap and a bayonet. Fixing the strap to the rifle was simple, as was hanging the bayonet in its scabbard from the webbing belts. As groups of men formed, they stood the rifles in small pyramids, with muzzles touching at the apex.

Conrick called the men to order and described what course the action would take.

'Any questions, men?'

Corporal Henry Larkin spoke up. 'I just hope the boys from 8th Battery are as good and accurate as us when they start tossing the heavies over our heads!'

'I'm sure they will be,' smiled Conrick.

Sergeant Hill then stepped forward and addressed the men. 'Get your meal from the mess wagon, come back here and settle down,' he said. He glanced up at a clear sky. 'We will be moving out from here at 0130, so get some rest.'

In the mess wagon, a large cauldron of the usual stew was bubbling. Jim Gillies looked into the pot and exclaimed, 'Excuse me, cookie, what have we here?'

'Stew, hot and tasty, mate,' replied the cook.

'The meat looks very familiar to me.' Gillies spun around to face the men. 'Jesus, it's Darkie! He was my lead horse on the ammo wagon yesterday. He must have bought it!'

He dipped his finger into the pot, then into his mouth, turned back to the group and said, 'I always liked Darkie, but I'm going to like him a lot better now!'

The cook glared at Gillies. 'All right, smart arse, get your food and piss off.'

Amid laughter, the men loaded their dixies with the stew and grabbed lumps of dry hard bread.

Later, they eased into restless sleep. Awakened at 0100 hours, the men stood and slung their gear into position. Greatcoats were left behind in neat piles to be collected later.

Bob laid his folded greatcoat next to Jum's, saying, 'I hope I come back for this.'

'Don't be stupid, of course you'll be back,' said Jum harshly.

Captain Haverstein passed the word to his platoon commanders. About 250 men started moving quietly towards their objective, about 1,500 yards to the north-west of their position. The attack had been scheduled for the first moonless night available. Reaching the crest of the first hill, the leading lines of troops dropped to their stomachs and crawled forward over the rise in total silence.

Reaching the lower ground, the leading lines of infantry, now hidden from enemy view, rose to crouching positions and moved forward much more quickly. As the rear lines caught up, the men massed into a tightly knit bunch.

'Like a herd of sheep back home,' muttered Wagga. The sergeant glared at him and waved his fist, and Wagga did not open his mouth again.

After what seemed an eternity, the lead lines slid over the crest of the final hill before the defile. Captain Conrick, in the front line of his men, was sweating profusely as he waited for the enemy machine guns to open up in their faces.

The darkness hid them as the first lines reached the eastern upslope of the defile. Two spotters moved forward up the slight crest to observe the enemy, then slowly slithered backwards. 'All dark,' one spotter whispered to the officers. 'Can't see any lights or activity from the enemy lines.'

Harry Haverstein looked at the luminous dial on his watch: 0150 hours, ten minutes to the start-up of the barrage. Unbeknownst to Haverstein, the two original Allied batteries had been increased to seven – a total of twenty-eight guns. The batteries had spent all day moving into their positions. This artillery assured a blanket cover of the 1,200 yards of enemy front-line trenches stretching north and south.

Following a tried and true tactic, the twenty-eight guns supporting this attack were to fire for thirty minutes preceding the infantry attack. Eight rounds per gun per minute would see approximately 6,000 rounds fired.

At 0200 hours, a high-pitched screech announced the arrival of the first high-explosive shell. The screech grew to a continuous scream as the seven batteries turned on their full fire power.

Bob Buchannen's hands trembled as the battalion began fixing bayonets. With full magazines and one round in the chamber, safety catches were supposed to be on. 'Take it off safety, Bob!' screamed Jum into Bob's ear above the din. The half-hour barrage had one minute to run. Captain Haverstein crawled his way to the top of the mound.

At exactly 0230 hours, the din ceased as abruptly as it had begun. Haverstein stood and started trotting over the crest of the defile. Hundreds of infantry rose as one and followed.

Jum and Bob were running forward towards the leading German trench some 300 yards away when the enemy machine guns started to respond. Whistling, snarling jabs plucked at their clothes, and spurts of earth erupted in their faces.

'Don't run straight, swerve about!' yelled Jum. A star shell exploded overhead, its brilliance lighting the attack area and blinding the men with its sudden intensity. 'Down, down!' shouted Jum as he dropped behind a small clump of earth.

'What the hell?' yelled Bob.

'Just a star shell, keep still!' As the glare faded, Jum rose and grabbed Bob by the collar. 'Come on, let's go!'

As quickly as they could, the two ran the last 100 yards to the slope leading uphill to the parapet. The barbed wire lining the enemy trench appeared intact. Traversing the slope, Jum spied an opening blown by the shelling. Without hesitation, he leapt into the trench. Four dark figures turned towards him. Screaming, half in terror, half in anger, he pulled the trigger. Three of the enemy faces were suddenly lit by a second star shell. The fourth figure lay inert in front of Jum.

He felt Bob slide in behind him. As Jum reloaded and fired again, one of the figures struggled to raise his weapon in the confined trench.

As the enemy rifle came up, Jum realised he could not reload and fire in time. Without thinking, he leapt forward and drove his bayonet deep, feeling the steel slide into the thick chest of the German. A scream rose from the man's throat as Jum dragged the rifle back out of the pitching body. One of the figures left in the trench ran to the next corner; the other stood, mouth open, fixed to the spot. His white face and wide eyes were highlighted by the next star shell. He slowly raised his hands, palms open – not in surrender, but in a silent plea for mercy.

Jum had ejected and reloaded when he was nearly deafened by the blast from the .303 beside his ear. Bob had fired point-blank, hitting the man in the lower neck.

Jum swung around to check the other end of the trench. A head appeared.

Jum snapped his rifle up as a voice called, 'Easy mate, I'm here to help.' A Pioneer sergeant came into view, his face lit by the continuous star shell bursts.

'Well done, boys, you got three of 'em.' The sergeant moved past them. 'The end section back there is secure. You two stay here and keep a lookout for any other cheeky bastards that want to mix it with us,' he said, and moved to check the other end of the trench.

Jum was trembling uncontrollably. He had never seen a dead body before, let alone killed a man. Sweat poured into his eyes; his breath rasped in his throat. He wiped his eyes on his tunic sleeve and made sure his .303 was loaded. As he propped the rifle against the earth bank, the sounds of fighting receded.

He looked at Bob, whose trembling hands clutched his .303 in a vice-like grip. He was staring at the man he had shot in the neck.

'Jesus!' Bob said, 'He's just a boy!'

Jum saw that the body was indeed that of a boy, no more than sixteen or so.

'He's younger than me,' whispered Bob.

Jum put his arm around Bob's shaking shoulders. 'You saved my life,' he said. 'Look, Bob, if he wears a German uniform and carries a German gun, he's old enough to kill or be killed.'

Jum reached for a cigarette, but couldn't light it with his shaking hands. An arm reached out with a lighted match and held it steadily to the cigarette. The Pioneer sergeant had returned. He nodded as Jum inhaled deeply.

'You gunners have done a great job, mate, make no mistake. We wiped them completely. It looks like there were only about 500 in the front trench. Stay on guard, though – they may counter-attack and try to regain this position.'

The sergeant moved away, leaving Jum and Bob to stand watch from the eastern side of the German trench.

The first streaks of a grey dawn appeared. Jum looked around him. Large numbers of Allied men were in the field. Various small groups of German prisoners, hands on their heads, were being marched west towards Albert. Jum turned to look at Bob, who was gazing at the young German he had killed.

Groups of Pioneer men had moved through the trench, past Jum, Bob and the still bodies of the German infantrymen. Three men, including a corporal, appeared.

'What do you make so far?' asked the corporal of the man behind him.

'I've got eighty-five dead, Eric's got the wounded,' he replied.

'These three dead?' the corporal asked Jum.

'Think so,' said Jum.

The corporal rolled the first body over. With no obvious injuries, the man could have been sleeping.

'He was the first I hit,' said Jum.

The other two were laid out next to the boy, who was already face-up on the trench floor.

'All young, ain't they?' observed the corporal nonchalantly. The private nudged the young boy with his boot.

Bob moved suddenly. 'Leave him alone!' he screamed, pushing the private into the trench wall.

Jum grabbed Bob and held him tightly. 'Easy, Bob, easy.' He motioned with his head for the three to move on.

'What's the problem, mate? He's only a fucking German!' said the private, rubbing his shoulder where Bob had crashed into him.

As dawn's soft light blossomed into the brightness of early morning, Jum and Bob climbed from the trench and stood on the parapet, peering east towards the route of the German retreat.

Turning, they surveyed the scene to the west, back to their own lines. Dotted along the ground, back to the defile they had left at 0230, were some twenty to thirty figures. Stretcher bearers were moving amongst the group as the dead, dying and wounded were taken to a number of wagon transports.

Jum and Bob crossed to the front parapet on their way back to their own lines. With a last glance at the gaping mouth of the dead German youth, Bob followed Jum through the break they had entered in the attack.

At 200 yards out from the German line, they spotted Captain Conrick lying on a stretcher. The two hurried over.

'How are you, sir?' asked Jum.

'Not too bad, Bevan. You're both OK?' asked Conrick. They nodded and he continued, 'Caught one in the top of my leg, just a graze. I'll be back in a few days.'

The stretcher bearer looked at Captain Conrick. 'Three weeks at least before you're back,' he said. 'Why don't you two make yourselves useful and take the captain over to the wagons?'

Jum and Bob quickly slung their rifles, lifted the captain and headed for the wagon line.

'How did you make out as infantry?' asked Conrick.

'That's the first time I've ever killed a man,' said Jum. 'I don't think I'll ever forget it.'

'There'll be a lot more of that before this is over,' said Conrick grimly.

Once they had lowered the stretcher to the ground, Bob moved away by himself and lit a cigarette.

'He's quiet,' Conrick commented.

'He just killed a German in that bloody trench, a young feller, and unarmed,' said Jum. 'I don't think he feels too good.'

Conrick rolled onto one elbow. 'Bob'll grow up pretty fast being part of all this.'

Jum nodded and patted Conrick on the shoulder. 'Get well, we'll see you soon.'

Jum and Bob sat in the open truck, heading back to camp. They had handed in their weapons and were now rattling along the main road to Amiens. The trucks were quiet, with only the occasional sound of quiet conversation.

'We were pretty lucky, Bob,' said Jum. 'Conrick's wounded, and only one gunner got killed, so all in all we got off lightly.'

'Those poor German bastards in the trench weren't so lucky.'

Jum put his arm on Bob's shoulder. Bob looked ahead and said nothing.

Jum and Bob lay in their tent after returning to Belloy-sur-Somme. Jum sat up and said, 'I'm going for a feed, mate. You coming?'

'Maybe later.'

Jum walked to the mess tent, collected his food and sat at the trestle table.

Henry Larkin moved beside him and asked casually, 'How'd you go?'

'Bob and I got a few. He's not feeling too well,' replied Jum.

'Understandable,' said Larkin. 'That your first close combat action?'

'You bet,' replied Jum.

'I've had three,' said Larkin. 'Sort of grows on you a bit.'

'You mean you get used to it?' asked Jum.

'No – but the other blokes, the Germans, they just become things in grey. You don't hate them; you're just relieved if you get them before they get you.'

Getting up to go, he added, 'There's a whisper we're due for a spell. Be good to get away from this shit hole.'

30 JUNE 1916

Thiepval and Beaumont-Hamel, a mile west of Pozières and Mouquet Farm, were held tightly by the German forces in deep trench systems. They enjoyed the high ground, so attacking infantry would have to force their way uphill into extensive barbed wire defensive lines protecting the first line of trench.

Despite their strong position, Carl Junge, a captain of the 4th German Division, Prussian Guard, had misgivings. A number of top-line German divisions had been removed and sent to the Eastern front to combat the renewed vigour of the Russian armies.

The massive Allied bombardment had continued for eight days without respite. The evening of 30 June 1916 was no different.

Junge and his command were aware that the Allies had been massing division after division of troops west of the Somme area of Picardy. If the barrages were any indication, an Allied attack was imminent.

Deep in the fortified trench line at Contalmaison, near Pozières, Junge was anxious for the expected encounter to begin.

At 0625 hours on 1 July 1916, his instincts were aroused by a heavy increase in the Allied shelling. 'This may be it!' he barked. 'Prepare yourselves!'

At 0728 hours, the eight-day bombardment ceased. The silence was uncanny. Junge screamed at his men, 'Up! Up! Into position! Into position!'

His crews – deafened, eyes wide with fear – ran up the parapet steps with their Maxim machine guns and ammunition, quickly settling into their line.

'Wait for my command!' Junge ordered.

The faint, soft blasts from the Allied trench whistles sounded thin in the clear morning air.

Captain Junge had served at Ypres in Belgium in 1914 and 1915. He had seen a lot of action at the Meuse River, Verdun, in early 1916. He was a hardened, professional German officer, highly experienced in the demanding role of commanding officer of an elite machine gun company.

But as the Allied trench whistles continued their shrill call to action, Junge stood for a moment, amazed. As far as the eye could see, from the right at Ovillers and left to Fricourt and Mametz, a khaki line of Allied infantry appeared, marching abreast from the British front-line trench, rifles firmly gripped at the high port and held diagonally across the chest – the accepted carrying position of a rifle when enemy engagement was imminent.

'*Mein Gott!*' exclaimed Junge. 'What are they doing?' He spun around, anxiously scanning the area to the north-west, thinking that Allied troops must be approaching from behind in a flanking move.

Bu there were no Allied troops coming to trap them. He turned back to face the south-west, just able to discern the destroyed road to Albert. The khaki figures of the Allied troops began to fall under the machine-gun fire. Still they came, in a second wave.

'Fire, fire!' he shouted. The chatter of the machine guns filled the trench. Khaki-clad figures fell and fell.

A third line appeared, and then a fourth. Junge noticed that one of his detachments was firing on a group of wounded, motionless men.

'*Nein, nein!*' he shouted. 'Leave them, they are injured. Go down, sweep the line, back and forth. Aim high – if you get the first line, good; if not, you'll get the second.'

The dark ground began to turn khaki as bodies covered the despoiled landscape. Still they came. And still they fell, most without firing a single round.

The Allies had anticipated that after the eight-day barrage the German front line, blasted by two million artillery shells, would be destroyed. Instead, the easy walk to the German lines as proposed by Haig and Haking was a slaughter. By 0930, two hours after the attack commenced, it was estimated 20,000 British troops lay dead or dying in No Man's Land.

After continuous action for four-and-a-half hours, Junge's men were cramped and exhausted, and the muzzles of the Maxims, although water-cooled, were overheating. One group had ceased firing.

'Why have you stopped?' Junge demanded of the operator.

The boy, no more than nineteen, turned his tear-stained face to Junge. 'This is madness. This is murder. I can't do it any more.'

'You stop only when I tell you to stop,' said Junge. 'When I tell you, understand?' The boy slumped behind the Maxim, shaking and sobbing. Another of the detachment attempted to console him.

'Leave him alone,' said Junge. 'Commence firing!'

The youth slowly shook his head. Captain Carl Junge unclipped his holster and withdrew his Steyr revolver. 'For the last time – commence firing!'

Again the boy shook his head.

Junge took one pace forward, placed the Steyr behind the boy's right ear and pulled the trigger. The shot could not be heard over the cacophony of twenty Maxim guns operating at full pressure. He gestured to the remainder of the detachment with the Steyr. The men moved the body of the boy with alacrity, and his position was quickly filled.

A momentary lull in the British infantry advance allowed respite. Junge said loudly, 'Rest and let the weapons cool, and be ready to recommence.'

As the stillness settled, another fearful sound was heard. It began as a low hum, then grew in volume, expanding until it filled the air with its vibration. Junge stood, slowly turned his head and cocked his ear towards the fallen bodies in No Man's Land.

His lieutenant moved beside him. 'What is it, Captain?'

Junge was a battle-hardened warrior, but his voice broke slightly as he said to the lieutenant, 'That is the sound of thousands of men in mortal agony. They are calling for help.'

The German lieutenant's shoulders slumped and he whispered, 'May God forgive us.'

Junge smiled grimly and turned as he spoke. 'This is only the beginning.'

The Allies looked on in horror. Recovering the casualties at this stage was impossible. The drone of the dying was joined by the drone of the swarms of black flies that flew in to settle on the dead and the injured.

Along the 13-mile front of the attack, about 110,000 Allied troops had marched out. The total casualty list for the day was 60,000 dead or wounded. But for two weeks, the attack persisted in its original form. Losses amounted to 100,000 men.

The proposed Allied breakthrough at the Somme had failed. This was the most horrendous day, the blackest day the British Army had ever experienced.

July 1916

Brigade Diary

3.7.16 The Brigade being relieved by Brigade of New Zealand Artillery.

Another week passed with very little action taking place. Following the large offensive north of the Somme, both sides had dug in. They fired a few shells at each other, but in a civilised way – not before 0700 hours and certainly not between 1300 and 1400 hours.

The days were dull and drawn out. Bob, although still quiet and reserved, had become part of brigade life once again, and had even been heard to laugh at one of Jim Gillies's silly jokes.

Jum threw the tent flap open. 'Bob, quick! I think we're in for a spell!'

Bob moved out with Jum, who pointed to a large wagon line approaching, with a number of 18-pounder guns in tow.

'It looks like two batteries,' said Jum. They watched as the line drew nearer. 'They're bloody Kiwis!'

Australian personnel lined the track into the camp, waving and calling to the men on the transports. It transpired that the two batteries were the first of a complete artillery brigade, fresh from the Land of the Long White Cloud.

The 5th Field Artillery Brigade was given one hour to move out. The men rushed to their tents and put together their kits. After assemblying at the wagon lines, the men were moved to Amiens, a few miles west of Belloy-sur-Somme. Billets had been arranged for them in various houses, sheds and hay barns.

Jum and Bob were assigned to a large hay barn on the outskirts of Amiens. Clean and dry, the building offered welcome relief from the mud, damp and shell fire they had endured.

A low steel container had been dumped in the yard, 50 yards from the farmhouse. For two hours, a continuous bucket line had filled the tank with steaming water, supplied by a boiler from Brigade Headquarters.

A quartermaster wagon team collected the men's filthy clothing and issued complete new sets for the thirty-odd personnel billeted at the farm. Raw lumps of coarse soap got rid of some of the filth and lice as the men scrubbed months of grime from their exhausted bodies.

Eventually, clean and attired in fresh, new clothes, the men were ready for action. A different kind of action, as Sergeant Hill explained to them.

'The Boche was nearby a few months ago and left a pretty awful impression around here. There are a few places in town where you can get a drink and a meal. Don't carry on like idiots – show some respect for these people,' he said.

In high spirits, some sixty or so men from 5th Field Artillery Brigade converged on the village about half a mile to the northwest. Belloy, a smallish village, still boasted four inns and a few bistros where the food was excellent, given the severe shortages caused by the war. The innkeepers and restaurateurs had been alerted to the men's arrival and extra supplies of food and drink had been secured in anticipation.

A light breeze filtered through the tree-lined main street on this warm, late summer's day. Villagers greeted the men with waves and smiles.

'This *estaminet* looks OK to me, boys,' called Jum over his shoulder as he mounted the steps to a largish inn and pushed open the door.

'What's a bloody *estaminet*?' asked Wagga.

'It's French for pub, Wagga,' laughed Jim Gillies.

A few locals were enjoying an early evening aperitif. When the men went inside, there was much backslapping and many cordial greetings, especially from the innkeeper, who spoke passable English.

Before the men had left for the village, the paymaster had issued them with francs in lieu of English pounds, the usual payment currency for the Australians. The men were ready to enjoy themselves.

Breasting the bar, the soldiers ordered large jugs of beer. The innkeeper quickly decided more waiters were required.

Wagga was grinning from ear to ear. With two glasses almost out of view in his huge hands, he had firmly planted both feet and was in the process of creating a world speed record for the consumption of alcohol.

The merriment grew as the drinks eased the painful memories of the past few months.

The innkeeper's two daughters had joined him behind the bar, attempting to keep up with the demand for drinks.

Bob, euphoric and a trifle unsteady, grabbed Jum by the arm. 'Over here, mate,' he insisted, as he dragged Jum away from the group to a battered upright piano in the corner.

'Christ, Bob, I forget how to do it,' laughed Jum as Bob bounced the cover back.

As Jum softly played a few chords, the piano came to life, sounding surprisingly well-tuned. One of the men grabbed a stool and pulled Jum down onto the seat. Turning to the men around the piano, Jum said, 'If I'm going to bloody work, I want beer!' Amid laughter, a litre jug of beer appeared on top of the piano. Jum gripped the jug in both hands, took a huge gulp, then began to play.

He attacked the instrument with gusto, punching out a rollicking popular tune. The men gathered around the piano raised their voices raucously. Song after song echoed around the inn, while the innkeeper beamed at the bulging money drawer.

At nineteen years of age, Wagga was not really accustomed to the fierce drinking. He staggered to the piano.

'Jum,' he said, shaking Jum's shoulder. Jum looked around, grinning. 'Play "Where the Tuckerbox Sits on the Dog",' he slurred.

After the laughter had subsided, Jum said, 'You mean "Where the Dog Sits on the Tuckerbox"?'

'Just play it,' Wagga said, and burped.

The crowd took up the chorus.

Where the dog sits on the tuckerbox,
Five miles from Gundagai ...

And so the night continued.

By 9 pm, the group had dwindled to about six. In a break in the conversation, Harold McErbain asked, 'Anybody seen Wagga?'

'He's out the back, unconscious,' someone said. 'Pissed as a fart.'

'We'd better make sure we get him back to the billet,' said Jum. The others nodded.

McErbain moved to the bar and spoke to the innkeeper. 'We are all starving hungry,' he said, cheerfully, pointing to his mouth. 'Food, food, please!'

He dropped a number of francs onto the bar. One of the daughters picked up the francs, carefully counted the money and handed about half of it back to McErbain.

'One moment, please,' said the innkeeper. Within moments the girl reappeared with a large cane basket loaded with fresh, crusty bread, a large tub of butter and a round of cheese. Then she brought plates and a handful of knives. She watched as the men set about devouring the food.

'More beer!' someone cried.

'More bloody food!' was the echo.

The girl quickly brought a large jar of pickled onions, more bread and cheese and some red wine. Francs changed hands, with the girl carefully counting out each amount of change to the men.

The other daughter was speaking animatedly to her father in French behind the bar. She seemed surprised at the amount of food and drink the men were consuming.

Replete, the men agreed that sleep was next on the list. As they staggered away from the inn, Bob paused. 'Bloody hell – Wagga!'

McErbain headed back with Jum. A few minutes passed, then out of the laneway appeared McErbain, pushing a wooden-wheeled farm barrow with Wagga slung inside. His arms hung over the barrow sides and he snored gently.

'We'll take him in turns,' said Gillies.

The five headed unsteadily towards the billet.

The following morning, Wagga was the only man who was not happy to discuss the night over breakfast. He had gingerly moved from his billet, found a large old rainwater container and dunked his head into the chill water.

Sergeant Hill addressed the large group. 'Where did this contraption appear from?' he said, pointing to the wheelbarrow.

'That's Wagga's taxi, Sarge,' said Gillies, and told Sergeant Hill the story.

'You'd better return the taxi to the inn, Wagga,' said Sergeant Hill, restraining a smile.

'Maybe someone else will need it tonight, Sarge,' said Wagga.

'They won't,' said the Sergeant, serious now. 'We've been ordered six hours standby. Be ready to move.'

The men looked at each other in disbelief.

'We were expecting three weeks, not one night!' said Jum.

'There's a big action going on about 25 miles north. The Boche are moving infantry and artillery on a 6-mile front.' He paused. 'The entire 2nd Division is in danger of imminent attack. Be ready to move.'

A mounted runner cantered into the yard and slid to a stop beside Sergeant Hill. A few quick words and the runner galloped away towards Belloy-sur-Somme.

'Let's go!' said Hill loudly. 'ETD has changed to five minutes!'

The troops ran to the wagons, pulling on shirts and tunics as they went. As each wagon filled, it headed for Amiens railhead at a fast clip.

The train steamed and puffed as the carriages filled. The guns and large loads of ordnance that had arrived during the night lay in the open wagons, ready for the impending battle.

Some 20 minutes later, as the train slowly moved towards the first junction of the railhead, a number of latecomers jogged beside the train, eagerly grasping the helping hands that reached to pull them aboard.

The train picked up speed as the engineer slammed the throttle valve wide open. The men had no idea of their destination, but knew it meant being back in action – and, by the way Sergeant Hill had spoken, heavy action and plenty of it.

An hour later, the train charged through the small station of Bresle. Jum Bevan looked at Sergeant Hill. 'Pozières?' he asked. Hill nodded. Jum's mouth went dry.

They had heard rumours of the fierce fighting in the Somme region, with the British, Australians and New Zealand troops struggling desperately to maintain their positions. The reports enumerated extremely heavy losses, especially in the English and Scottish regiments, which were encountering heavy and accurate German artillery bombardments. The infantry, pinned in their trenches for many days, had been urgently seeking artillery support for weeks. Only recently had the Allied command realised the importance of retaliatory artillery fire.

The 2nd Division AIF had also hung on tenaciously. With the bombardment lasting twenty hours per day for the past two weeks, the situation had become desperate.

The train loaded with the artillerymen and weapons arrived at Albert close to midday. Unloading guns, ordnance and ammunition engaged the troops for some hours.

Loaded wagons set off for the Central Command south of Pozières. There was no time to dig gun positions. The batteries set up in an area that offered protection to Headquarters, which faced the German front line, a mile to the east.

Pozières was immeasurably important to General Haig and the Allies. General Sir Henry Rawlinson, General Haig's Second-in-Command in the Somme, believed that Pozières was the key to the area. The small agricultural village sat on Pozières Ridge, which ran to Thiepval to the west. It was situated on the Amiens–Bapaume Road at its highest point, known to the Germans as 'Hill 160'.

Pozières had gently graded slopes for 1,000 yards in all directions – north to Mouquet Farm and Thiepval, south to Ovillers and Contalmaison, and east to Bazentin and Delville Wood.

The Germans had consolidated their position here in early 1916, with their artillery commanding uninterrupted views of any Allied movement.

The Fourth Army, commanded by General Rawlinson, consisted of eleven British infantry divisions, and one Indian cavalry division. Four brigades formed one division so, in effect, Rawlinson's Fourth Army consisted of forty-eight infantry brigades – approximately 200,000 men. General Haig anticipated success in the upcoming Somme Offensive, but Rawlinson was not so optimistic.

Brigade Diary

10.7.16 Fifth FA Brigade moved to Pozières.

28.7.16 Heavy bombardment in support of attack by 2nd Div Infantry carried out as per Official Order No. 41.

At this stage of the war, the frontal system – the 1st and 2nd Trenches of the Allies – was strung between Albert and Beaumont Hamel. The German defensive line was well dug in, protecting a lush area known as 'Mash Valley' and, to the east, 'Sausage Gully'.

Opposing them was a forward trench line harbouring infantry of the 2nd Australian Division, who had been pinned there for eight days under constant shelling.

Movement to or from the line to Headquarters was almost impossible. Only two mounted runners survived the run of a mile back to Headquarters, where they reported horrendous conditions. The dead and the wounded were jammed in the trenches. Sometimes the living used the bodies of their fallen comrades as cover. Attack after attack by enemy infantry had been repelled, but at great cost.

Three battalions of the 2nd Division were desperately short of ammunition, food, water and medical supplies. There were only six Lewis machine guns left, and the covering rifle fire had been greatly depleted. These were the mainstays of the Allied defence. At one stage, the Germans had advanced to within 300 yards of the Allies, only to be thrust back by the unrelenting determination of the Australian battalions.

Then rain arrived, and continued unabated. The cratered fields soon collapsed into a sea of mud.

Still the enemy shelling continued. It had become suicidal to attempt to move from the trenches. Thirst, another great enemy, had seduced some into sipping the filthy water lying in the trenches, resulting in dysentery. Relays of men held their tin hats upside down in the heavy rain to capture a little fresh water.

Lacking artillery retaliation, the 2nd Division was hopelessly and ruthlessly contained, desperately awaiting the arrival of the 5th Brigade.

Finally, in a burst of frenetic activity, the 5th Field Artillery Brigade guns were hauled into position, 500 yards east of the Central Command. Wagon after wagon dropped shells on the positions.

The 14th Battery personnel had another agenda. They were ordered to move forward in wagons, waiting until the enemy artillery had been silenced before proceeding to the front line. Approximately thirty wagons were loaded with food, water, ammunition and medical supplies. The same wagons were to evacuate the wounded and the dead, and return them to Headquarters.

The men were determined to reach the survivors of the 2nd Division. But the ferocity of the onslaught had destroyed the landscape, making it almost impossible to reach the front line by horse and wagon.

On 3 August 1916 at 1700 hours, the Allied barrage began on the enemy gun positions pounding Sausage Gully. The four batteries sent a formidable reply to the German bombardment. The barrage continued until 0900 the next morning, with detachments relieved twice during the night by gunners brought forward from Central Command.

The group of gunners under McErbain were ready and waiting patiently for the enemy fire to be silenced. A mounted runner appeared, moving fast towards the wagon group. McErbain rose to his feet.

'This might be it!' he said.

'Get moving, McErbain,' the runner panted. 'Boche artillery is having a rest!'

The wagons loaded with stores moved quickly towards the front line on roads that remained firm and solid. The men in the wagons waved as they passed the four batteries in the firing area. The gun range was set at 3,000 yards; the wagons moved towards the front-line trenches as shells shrieked overhead.

McErbain galloped his wagon to 200 yards short of the line, then stopped abruptly. Jumping down, he spread his arms wide to indicate that the wagons following should move to either side. 'This is as far as we go,' he called. 'We won't get through that shit!' The men had to proceed through the last 200 yards of mud on foot.

Staggering under heavy loads of stores, the men picked their way among the water-filled shell holes. They were to dump the equipment at the rear of the trenches and return to the wagons for a fresh load.

McErbain and Gillies entered the first trench. The nauseating stench of decomposing bodies was like a physical blow. With elbows wrapped around their faces, they stepped over and around corpses. Gillies saw a movement from one inert shape and started. A large, sleek, black rat appeared and looked at him, unafraid. As Gillies and McErbain stared, they realised that the trench was alive with vermin. Well-fed rats slowly crawled over the still bodies.

McErbain picked up a trench shovel and slashed at the voracious swarm. The rats were too fat to move quickly. He disposed of five or six before the rest sensed danger and fled. Open-mouthed, the two men surveyed the scene in shock and disbelief. Then a croaking voice from further down the trench sent them running. A half-conscious man lay on his back, still grasping his bayonet, a blood-soaked leg stuck out at an unusual angle. His eyes, half-closed, tried to focus as he heard the voices.

'All right, mate,' said McErbain, 'we'll get you out now.'

'Watch out for the rats,' the man whispered. The bayonet slipped from his grasp as they carefully lifted him. The leg jarred and moved, and a high-pitched shriek tore from the man as he lapsed into unconsciousness. McErbain and Gillies soon had the infantryman on a stretcher. Calling to two bearers, McErbain pointed to the unconscious youth. 'He's still alive, but just.'

As the carriers picked up the stretcher, the rear bearer spoke to McErbain. 'He'll be lucky to make it. His leg certainly won't,' he said bluntly.

'Do your best,' said McErbain.

He placed his hand on Jim Gillies's shoulder. 'Was that your mate Collins down in the trench?'

Gillies, white-faced, turned to McErbain. 'Yes,' he said, 'that was young Eric.'

They re-entered the trench and discovered many more wounded as they moved along the half-submerged duckboards. The first Lewis gunner they encountered was exhausted beyond belief, too tired to move.

More wagons and men arrived, toiling all day and into the night to clear the mass of humanity from the nightmare of the trenches. Wounded soldiers were helped to the wagon lines in a continuous stream.

The Saturday evening meal was eaten in total silence. Not one of the rescuers could speak or discuss the scenes of carnage they had had to endure. Words could not describe what they had witnessed. Emotions were held in check by sheer willpower. All knew that to let go now would be their undoing.

'Pass a lump of bread, Bob?' asked Jum. Bob reached out to the plate with a shaking hand and had trouble picking up the crust.

'Got the jimjams, have we?' asked Jim Gillies. Buchannen retracted his hand, looked at Gillies and nodded.

'Don't move, Bob,' said Jum, as he rose and left the tent. He arrived back in a few minutes and sat down. Reaching into his tunic pocket, Jum slipped out a medium-sized bottle and poured a healthy nip of the amber fluid into Bob's pannikin.

'Drink this, mate,' offered Jum.

'What is it?'

'Special medicine. It'll calm you down.'

Bob tossed the contents down his throat. Coughing badly, he staggered into the cool night air. He returned after a few minutes and sat back down.

'Pass me a lump of bread, Bob?' Jum said again. Buchannen reached out, picked up the crust and passed it to Jum. His hand now steady, he picked up his fork.

Later, Sergeant Hill and Jum sat alone at the trestle table in the dim lamplight, talking quietly.

'What's in that concoction?' asked Hill. Jum smiled and brought out the bottle. Hill took it, held it to the light, then smelled the contents.

'Christ, what's in it?'

'A mate of mine is a cook in 4th Division,' said Jum. 'He makes it up.'

'What's in it?' repeated Hill, taking another sniff.

'Metho, lemon essence, four spoons of sugar and just the smallest bit of boot polish.'

'Why the boot polish?'

'To give it some colour.'

Hill looked at Jum. 'May I?' he said as he lifted the bottle. Jum nodded. Hill cautiously took a small swig. 'If the bloody Boche don't kill us, that will!' he said in a hoarse voice, and grinned.

An overcast sky, with dark storm clouds building in the west, soured the Sunday morning in late July. Captain Claude Jenkins, the Brigade padre, carefully picked his way across the rough, broken ground to a group of men standing and smoking. He wore a white smock over his army issue tunic and his wispy hair floated in the breeze.

Jenkins was thirty-eight. Slight and bespectacled, he had been the rector in the parish church of Wenden Village, near Sydney, for two years. Some eighty parishioners had enjoyed his Sunday services since 1913.

He was a devout Christian and firmly believed in the religious principles he espoused each Sunday. Whilst no pulpit-thumping evangelist, he was committed to his church and his following. The parishioners enjoyed his courteous disposition and he was often sought out as a patient listener.

It came as a great surprise to all – himself included – when suddenly, after a Sunday sermon in which he had made many references to the war, he decided to enlist as a padre. It seemed to him that his parishioners could dispense with guidance for a couple of years whilst he saved the poor, wretched soldiers in France. He had no idea of the nightmare unfolding in Europe. None of Rector Jenkins's parishioners had enlisted, so he had had no contact with the bereaved wives or parents of men killed or wounded in action.

He was welcomed and inducted as an honorary captain into the AIF. He had arrived at the Western Front only weeks before this dark Sunday morning, full of idealism and ready to dispense the gentle solace of God's word.

'Good morning, boys,' he said, cheerfully. None of the men responded. 'I have noticed that when I conduct Sunday Services, you young men do not join. God is everywhere, you know, watching over all of you, protecting you ...'

The heavy silence continued. Gillies lit a cigarette and McErbain studied his bootlaces. Buchannen merely stared at the padre, causing him to stutter into silence.

Gillies stood and jabbed his cigarette into the steel wheel of the wagon.

'God, eh?' he said. 'God is everywhere, you say? Tell me, Padre, where was God yesterday? On holiday?' Gillies moved to within arm's length of Jenkins.

'What do you mean?'

'Yesterday,' said Gillies, 'we came across this trench, Padre, front-line area, Sausage Gully it's called. One of our trenches. It'd been under constant shelling for eight days. Nobody could leave and no food, water, medical supplies or ammunition could get in. Eight days, Padre, the men hadn't moved. Most of them couldn't, because they were either badly wounded or dead. I got to that trench first.

'Ever smelt dead bodies, Padre? The first six I saw were dead all right. Then I saw young Eric Collins, same age as young Buchannen here.' Gillies pointed to Bob. 'I thought he was alive. I thought I saw him move. I jumped forward to help him sit up. But he couldn't get up because he wasn't alive. That movement I saw was a big black rat climbing out from under his tunic. It had been eating out Eric's stomach. It was covered in Eric's blood, and so fat it could hardly move.' Gillies' voice rose to a rasping snarl.

'Where the fuck was God yesterday, Padre, when a fucking rat was eating my mate's body?'

Gillies moved closer to the Padre and McErbain, and Jum moved to restrain him. The Padre, visibly shaken, took a step backwards.

'Come on Padre, where was He? Sitting up there looking on while the rats ate our mates? And not only the dead – some of our wounded had holes in their cheeks and lips where God's little black bastards decided to have a meal while they were unconscious.'

Jum moved between Gillies and the padre. 'Padre, Jim here's had a bad two days – we all have. Why don't we leave it alone for now?'

The padre looked stunned. 'Don't come back here, you sanctimonious bastard,' Gillies yelled over Jum's shoulder, 'with all your talk of God, religion and all the bullshit you feed those poor mongrels every Sunday!' He pointed to the group waiting patiently for the padre. 'Don't waste our time. We have Germans to kill and I'm going to enjoy every minute, understand?'

Bevan and McErbain each grabbed one of Gillies's arms and led him behind the wagon, as the padre turned and stumbled to the waiting congregation.

'There will be no service this morning,' he said. 'I don't feel very well.'

He turned and walked back along the line until he reached his billet, where he threw himself onto his stretcher and buried his head in the pillow, giving himself up to convulsive sobs.

The brigade continued the clean-up of Sausage Gully, and some 800 of 3,000 men originally in the front line were brought back on wagons to Central Control, where their bodies were neatly lined up in rows across the boards.

Removal, identification and tallying of the dead had become so gruesome that the clean-up squads were equipped with gas masks to allow the work to continue. White crosses began to sprout; they looked as innocent as flowers at the start of spring.

Row upon row of grave markers crept their way back from Command and up a gentle slope towards Pozières. The graves faced east, where the conflagration had begun, in Sausage Gully. For the fallen, it would be an eternal view of the murderous Somme.

A few days after Gillies's run-in with the padre, Jum sat gazing over the field of crosses. Hundreds of young men, who only a few days previously had been full of life, now lay buried, their lives viciously cut short. 'And for what?' he mused. 'The front line has gone nowhere! A few grubby yards of mud!'

He shook his head to erase a building dread of what the future held, then picked up a handful of pebbles, his target a lone shovel left by a reluctant gravedigger. The *ding* of the pebble hitting the metal blade had an eerie ring, as if it were summoning the dead back to life to fight again.

'What did the bloody padre expect?' he thought. 'All of us to sink to our bloody knees just so we could make him feel good in front of his God? No wonder Gill went off his brain, those fucking rats eating the dead!' He shuddered. 'So many ...' His eyes lowered. 'There is no God,' he thought. 'No God could stand by and do nothing about the way our boys died in the trenches!'

Then, standing on the rise of Pozières Ridge, he looked out again over the sea of graves. 'Where the bloody hell are we going to bury them all? Soon all France will be covered with white crosses.'

EARLY AUGUST 1916

'You in, Padre?' Captain Conrick stood at the entrance to the padre's tent. Jenkins emerged. 'Always for you, Terry,' he smiled.

'The CO would like a quiet word with you, sir, when you are available,' said Conrick.

'No time like the present!' replied Jenkins, and together they walked to the Headquarters tent.

Conrick entered first and addressed Lieutenant Colonel Tideswell.

'The padre is here, sir.'

'Thank you, Conrick. Please show him in.'

Tideswell, a mass of paperwork on his desk, sighed deeply. He could do without this at the moment. He rose and greeted Jenkins.

'Sit, Padre, please be comfortable.' Jenkins sat and looked inquiringly at the CO. 'It has been reported to me that you suffered an embarrassing scene Sunday morning last?' said Tideswell, getting straight to the point.

Jenkins looked down, then raised his eyes. 'Well, Colonel, upon reflection, that outburst may have been something I deserved.'

Tideswell stopped tamping tobacco into his pipe. 'I beg your pardon?'

'I think it was unfortunate that I spoke to them in that way at that particular time,' said Jenkins. 'I understand the men had been under great pressure.'

'I heard that you were abused, that God was denounced by Gillies – is that correct?'

'No, sir,' replied Jenkins. 'Gillies simply asked me the toughest question that any minister of God can be asked, which is "Where is God?" I must say he asked me that very forcefully, leaving nothing to the imagination by his choice of words. But, Colonel, this is my job. I fell down badly in not offering this young man the help or comfort that he required in his time of enormous need.

'I'm sure you're aware of the appalling conditions the men experienced when clearing the trenches of the dead and wounded last Saturday?' Tideswell nodded and Jenkins continued. 'Gillies had come across a young friend in the trench who had died during the attack. I understand that the 14th Battery were the first assigned to clear the dead and wounded?'

Tideswell leant back in his chair.

'I ordered the 14th Battery to start the task,' he said. 'When it became too much for that number of men, 200 from 4th Division had to be brought in to help finish the job.' Tideswell paused, then went on. 'The 14th Battery have shown themselves to be a very competent unit, cohesive, with a strong degree of individual strength. I was of the opinion they'd handle this difficult job well, but I wasn't aware of the extent of the casualties.'

'I don't think anyone had expected the loss of human life that we experienced,' said Jenkins. 'And these men are really only boys. I don't think they're equipped with the mental strength to handle these situations.'

Tideswell's face set into a hard, resigned mask. 'Padre, I have to set aside personal feelings and make decisions that will help end this conflict as quickly as possible. I'm called on to act for the greater good of all concerned, even if it means individual men have to suffer.'

'I am concerned for the mental wellbeing –'

Tideswell held up his hand. 'Mental wellbeing is not a consideration when it comes to a soldier's ability to fight. If he's not visibly injured, he'll front up to the line, follow orders and fight. If not, he'll be taken out of the field, court-martialled and executed for desertion. That is the law as I understand it. How many dead bodies had you seen before France, Padre?'

'Maybe a dozen or so,' said Jenkins, 'when I carried out burial services.'

'All neatly laid out in their coffins, nicely dressed and surrounded by flowers?' Jenkins nodded. 'Well, Padre, there are no flowers here, and most times the injuries would preclude even a glimpse in a funeral parlour. Legs missing, arms and heads missing. Often a soldier's remains will fit easily into a water pail, which we then tip into a small grave. This is a fact of war; it won't change. All we can do is try to end this unholy mess as quickly as possible.'

Jenkins rose to his feet. 'Thank you, Colonel. You've reinforced what I decided yesterday. My job here is to look after the spiritual and mental wellbeing of the soldiers; yours is to keep them physically healthy. We should make a good team.'

'Certainly,' said Tideswell, 'but be aware of how difficult these men will become as the killing and suffering get worse by the week. And for how long, no one knows.'

Both men moved out of the tent and stood in the weak sunlight.

'Sir,' said Jenkins, 'I would like to be with the men in action. I think it would allow me a greater insight into what they are experiencing.'

'We'll see, Padre. I don't want you to risk injury or death. A dead padre is no use to us.'

'Sir, if a live padre isn't doing his job, he might as well be dead for all the good he'll be,' said Jenkins. The two shook hands, and Jenkins walked towards the mess hut.

Terry Conrick emerged from HQ's tent and stood alongside the CO.

'You hear all that, Terry?' said Tideswell.

Conrick nodded. 'Yes, sir.'

'If Jenkins goes up the line, I'll bet the first half dozen shells will send him scampering back to safety.'

'I don't know, sir – he sounded fairly determined,' said Conrick.

'Anyway, keep him out of harm's way,' said Tideswell. 'The last thing I need is to have to explain a dead padre to the Division.'

AUGUST 1916

With unit. In action unit on Somme,
Sausage Gully/Albert.

The Australian 2nd Division, along with French and English troops, was holding the front line from east of Bapaume through Sausage Gully, down to Montauban on the Somme.

Both the German and Allied forces eased hostilities. German troops had been the subject of fierce bombardment by the Allies, resulting in enormous casualty lists, and their efforts were focused on bringing in much needed supplies and men. In late July, General Haig decided that the proposed offensive thrust east of Pozières was to be delayed. The congestion of the roads north of the Somme had halted any projected advance. All operations on the Somme Front were postponed until free movement was possible.

After completing the work required to bring the brigade up to battle-readiness, the men were very happy to laze in the improving weather.

But the break was to be short-lived. Lieutenant Colonel Tideswell summoned the battery captains and other officers to a brigade briefing. Looking around the sombre faces, he said, 'Well, the holiday is over, for the moment. The Boche are moving many weapons and large amounts of equipment back to the area we thought we had dislodged them from. Aircraft reconnaissance has given us detailed positions of troops and artillery, along with stores, wagons and a large fleet of motorised trucks. Their motorised equipment allows them to move much heavier guns more quickly than we can our 18-pounders. We attack tonight.'

He turned, and lifted a pile of sheets from his desk. 'All the information you need is here.' He tapped the pile with his pipe, then addressed a major nearby. 'Freddie, your Howitzer Battery is to going to be the first to start up, at 1730. That gives you two hours to prepare. Might I suggest you get going?'

Major Freddie Dawson nodded, took his information sheet, grabbed his lieutenant by the arm and headed outside.

As they moved away, the lieutenant said, 'Not much bloody time to prepare!'

'We'll be OK, mate,' said Dawson. 'Grab that wagon and get a driver while I arrange some ammo.'

Dawson headed for the magazine store situated some 200 yards away, protected by a low surround of sandbagged walls. He entered the store, his eyes trying to adjust to the gloom as the store sergeant greeted him.

'Sergeant, we're on in two hours. I'll need 400 high explosives urgently.'

'You're the 105th, aren't you, sir? Dawson nodded. 'Short notice, sir?'

'Can't be helped. The Old Man's been given orders.'

'Right, sir.'

Turning, the sergeant called into the rear of the store. 'Donald and Harris, here, quickly!' Two men ran forward. 'We need 400 4.5 Howies, now.' He turned to Dawson. 'Half shrapnel, half HE, sir?'

Dawson nodded, then asked, 'You want the wagon out the back?'

'Yes, sir,' replied the sergeant.

Dawson's second-in-command had positioned the wagon and driver at the store front.

'Around the back, driver,' called Dawson, waving his arm.

The men quickly started loading the ammunition.

'You'll need four trips, sir,' said the sergeant.

'Haven't got time. Lieutenant, organise another wagon. They can do two trips each.' The lieutenant nodded and headed for the wagon lines.

Wal Donald had secured his plate of food and sat down at the trestle table. A few gunners had eaten and were quietly smoking.

'Fireworks tonight, boys,' he said quietly. McErbain and Bevan looked up. 'The 105th have just grabbed 400 rounds, have to be in position by 1715.' It was 1700.

Jum looked at McErbain.

'I guess that's us, too, Harold,' said Jum.

'I reckon so,' replied McErbain. 'We must be on later. Anyway, we've got enough ammo for a full night.'

Padre Jenkins approached the table. 'Did I hear correctly?'

McErbain nodded. 'Looks like things are hotting up again.'

'Thank you,' said Jenkins, and moved slowly out of the tent.

'I feel sorry for him, poor bastard,' said McErbain.

'Don't feel sorry for him,' said Jum. 'He's back here out of harm's way!'

'I think he just doesn't realise what it's like up front, Jum,' said McErbain. 'The other night,' he continued, 'I was out walking and having a fag and I thought I saw a light in the cemetery.'

'I've seen that light,' said Gillies. 'I was too bloody scared to mention it before. Thought somebody might think I'm crazy.'

'I've seen it too,' said Bob Buchannen.

'Well, I went to have a look, and it was the Padre, kneeling at one of the crosses. He stood up after a bit, held this little candle in a bowl to my face and said, "Good evening, McErbain. I'm just saying goodbye to these boys." Then he said, "If you'll excuse me, I still have a lot of prayers ahead of me." And he waved his arm across the graveyard. The Padre intends to talk to and pray for every one of our 800 mates out there.'

Captain Conrick entered the mess tent. 'We're on, boys,' he said. 'Nineteen hundred to 0500 tomorrow morning.' He sat down at the table. 'The 4.5 Howies are about to start.' Then, looking at his watch, he murmured, 'They already have.' The soft *whump* of the Howitzers could be heard in the distance. 'Their target is a large fleet of motorised trucks running supplies like crazy. Our target is the front line of Boche infantry. We'll run at a rate of one round per minute each gun. That should be enough to keep their heads down.'

'Understood, sir,' said McErbain. 'You have new coordinates?'

Conrick nodded. 'You'll have them half an hour before we start up.'

The men rose glumly and walked to their tents to prepare for the night's action.

At 1850 hours, Captain Conrick moved up to No. 1 Gun position. 'I have the coordinates for you, Harold,' said Conrick.

McErbain stepped out of the position and studied the orders by the dim light of an oil lamp.

'Keep it one round every minute, Harold,' said Conrick before moving to the next position.

As the firing rate was low, only four men were required to man the gun. Relief detachments were due at 0200 hours. Ammunition stacks were checked, the range and coordinates were checked, and the men waited patiently for the command.

With one minute to go, Jum heard a scraping noise behind him. He glanced over his shoulder. 'What the fuck!'

The other three turned.

'Sorry, Padre, you startled me,' said Jum.

'What the hell are you doing here, Padre?' said McErbain, dragging Jenkins unceremoniously into the position.

'I just want to see what you boys do. I've never been in a gun position before.'

McErbain swung around as Jenkins settled himself in the position. 'Don't move!' he said. Then, to the other men, 'Let's go!'

The breech was swung open, Wagga slid the first shell into the gaping hole and Jum slammed the breech shut.

'Fire!' yelled Jum, as he snapped the lanyard.

Padre Jenkins's feet were resting on the curved recoil plate of the gun as it sent the first shell hurtling 4,000 yards to its target with a thunderous report. The gun bucked and smashed back, and the padre's feet were clouted by the recoil plate. Hastily he dragged his feet up under his backside as the reload commenced. The detachment was equipped with cotton-wool ear plugs, but the padre wasn't. The deafening blast of the firing and the brilliant muzzle flash had left him temporarily deaf and blind.

McErbain helped Jenkins to his feet. 'You OK, Padre?'

Jenkins waved his hands over his ringing ears, shaking his head.

McErbain grinned. 'The first shell is the worst.' He handed Jenkins a lump of cotton wool and indicated how to insert the plugs in his ears.

With one minute between rounds, the men of the detachment had enough time to relax, smoke and talk. When the padre's ears had stopped ringing, he joined in the conversation.

'You shouldn't be here, Padre,' said McErbain. 'If we cop a direct hit, we're all gone.'

'I assumed that would be the case, Corporal,' said Jenkins. 'I can't believe how loud that gun is!'

'Wait till we get to rapid fire,' said Jum. 'And when the Boche are returning our fire as well, it seems like the end of the earth.'

By this time, the four batteries of the 5th Field Artillery Brigade had fired some eighty or so rounds. Jum was rolling a cigarette, and the others lazily waiting for the next round, when an enormous explosion destroyed the No. 2 Gun and position 50 yards to their left.

McErbain sat up, winded and dazed. Jum, who had been hurled across the position, crawled out and stumbled towards No. 2. Captain Conrick was sprinting from the outpost to the enormous crater where the No. 2 Gun had been.

The 18-pounder was a twisted mess of smoking debris.

Jum looked up at Conrick. 'Looks like three dead, sir. Ron Roberts is conscious, but only just.'

Conrick and the rest of No. 1 Gun moved quickly into the position. Wagga carefully eased his brother onto an ammunition box.

'You OK, Ron?'

Ron nodded slowly.

'I can't leave you alone for a moment, can I?' said Wagga, cradling his brother gently in his arms.

Jenkins stepped into the position, looking aghast.

'What was it, sir?' asked Jum.

Conrick, grim-faced, replied, 'Looks like a 150 Krupp, the biggest field gun the Boche has. Quick, Jum, back to HQ – we must let them know.'

Jum leapt out of the position and sprinted to the outpost, where two horses stood saddled and tethered.

'Watch the potholes,' called Sergeant Hill as Jum leapt onto the first pony, dug his heels in and headed towards the Brigade Headquarters at full gallop. To be in the saddle again on a wildly galloping horse made Jum's spirits surge.

There was still enough light in the northern summer late evening to illuminate any potential pitfalls for a galloping horse and rider. As he thundered his way along the road made of tree trunks, Jum was up in the stirrups, low over the horse's neck. The pony seemed to relish the wild ride, and kept up the pace without faltering as they approached the Headquarters encampment.

Colonel Tideswell and two officers emerged from the tent as Jum slid off the pony's haunches and hit the ground.

'What was that explosion, runner?' asked Tideswell.

'We think it was a 150 Krupp, sir,' panted Jum. 'At least, Captain Conrick thought so. It destroyed No. 2 Gun. Three dead, the others look all right.'

'Fuck!' said Tideswell. 'They've caught us with our pants down. If the Krupps are in action, we can't reach them; we're at their mercy. They'll be sitting back at 10,000 yards, laughing.' He said to Jum curtly, 'Big job for you, son. Get back to the 105th first, then across to the others. They have to lay on everything they have until further orders from me, understand?' Over his shoulder he added, 'Same range, runner.'

Jum ran from the tent. Springing astride the horse, he flailed its flanks with his heavy boots. The horse, its ears back, snapped into a full gallop in a couple of strides. Three hundred yards out and going fast, Jum did not notice the rain squall approaching from the east. He gasped as he was hit by a solid wall of water. Easing the pony back, he shielded his eyes with one hand as he carefully cantered amongst the shell holes. Arriving at the 14th Battery Outpost, he tossed the reins over the post and ran for the entrance.

Wet to the bone and shivering, Jum accepted a dry cloth from Sergeant Hill.

'What's the story, Jum?' asked Conrick.

'The CO wants the whole brigade to rapid fire, current range. He's nervous about the Krupp 150, though,' said Jum through chattering teeth.

'Diversionary tactic. Wants us to keep the front line pinned down whilst he considers what to do about the Krupps.'

'I'd best go, sir,' said Jum.

'Yes, away you go. I suggest the 105th drop some star shell and shrapnel. Let them think something is on.'

'Right, sir.' Jum ran to the pony and headed towards the Howitzer Battery while the rain continued unabated in windblown, drenching squalls. Thunder and lightning were now a violent accompaniment to the deluge.

Sergeant Hill brought each gun corporal back to the outpost, and Conrick addressed the four men. 'Orders are to lay it on thick and fast. A steady rate of eight rounds per minute should do it.'

A massive explosion in front of the 14th Battery made the outpost walls shake and the ground shudder.

'Another 150,' said Conrick.

'My God, they're big!' exclaimed McErbain.

'I've never experienced them before,' replied Conrick, 'but I've read about them. Their range is an easy 10,000 yards. They have a number of shell types, from high explosive to shrapnel; I don't know about gas. What I do know is that the gun weighs about 15 tons and is a bastard to move. It's equipped with an advanced range-finder and, when it's set up, it'll drop its rounds in a 150-yard circle from 10,000 yards away. The ordnance sits on a 20-millimetre steel plate to absorb the massive recoil. From what I understand, they're hard to set up, but when set right, they're murderous.'

'How big are the shells, sir?' asked the No. 4 Gun corporal.

'Enormous – 6 inches in diameter, and they weigh over 100 pounds. The projectile distance can be up to 7 miles. The charge needed is very large, pre-packaged and comes in a variety of strengths to allow for range. Anyway, get moving. Eight rounds per minute per gun.'

The men trotted back to their positions in the unrelenting rain.

Claude Jenkins was still in the crater that had once been the No. 2 Gun. Two of the dead gunners had been carried out and covered by a tarpaulin.

Bob Buchannen looked down at Henry Larkin's body, which still lay in the crater with the mangled remains of the 18-pounder. 'We met him on our first night in action at Fleurbaix,' he said. 'He told Jum and me to wear two pairs of socks for the cold.'

Claude Jenkins was close to retching. Henry Larkin was missing both legs from the thigh down. His chest was a gaping hole where a large shell fragment had passed through.

'Leave me with the corporal for a few minutes,' he said. 'I must pray for him.'

The gunners moved out of the crater.

Wagga's brother, Ron, was unhurt. Later, it was discovered that he had stepped out to relieve himself only moments before the 150 had hit. As the sandbagged wall was higher than his head, he had miraculously escaped the main blast. Knocked semiconscious, he had wandered, dazed, back into the crater.

Captain Conrick waited for Jenkins to leave the crater, then ordered the No. 3 Gun detachment to remove the body while Jenkins, his face drawn, sat at the edge of the outpost.

'That was nasty, Padre,' said Conrick, putting his hand on Jenkins's shoulder. He could see that the padre was on the verge of breaking down. 'That kind of injury is hard on everyone,' he said. 'But we must be strong and stand together. We're all going to need each other's support.'

Jenkins swallowed and twisted his hands together. Conrick quickly changed the subject.

'Look out there, Padre,' he said, pointing to the ferocious weather building up in the east. The black cloud line was rolling and churning in a fearsome display of elemental power. Lightning slashed across the black background of the heavens, creating a dazzling spectacle.

'We're in for the biggest storm of all time. You'd best move in here until it passes over.'

After a moment, he said, 'What made you come to the line, Padre, if you'll excuse me asking?'

'Gillies called me a sanctimonious bastard that Sunday morning, and I was shocked,' said Jenkins. 'But it made me think. I asked myself whether Gillies was right. I wondered what had prompted him to turn on me so savagely. Then I realised, there I was, back at Command, out of danger, espousing love and forgiveness when I had no genuine basis or right to preach this to the men. I was a fool to expect any other attitude than what I experienced. I decided I need to be on a level footing with the men, be accepted by them, if I'm to carry out my work with any meaning.'

'I've never seen a padre or chaplain dodging around 77-millimetre shells before, just to keep the men happy.'

'I think what I'm really talking about is respect,' said Jenkins. 'If the men respect me, I believe they will respect what I have to offer in God's name.'

Jum had carefully delivered the CO's orders to each of the battery gun position officers. He slowly picked his way through the deluge and the heavy mud towards his position. After hitching the pony and easing the girth strap, he entered No. 1 Gun position. Jenkins had once again placed himself behind the men, but found the overpowering smell of cordite made him queasy. He climbed from the position and stood watching the detachment.

The gunners were fast-moving shadows in the dark, appearing wraith-like as the muzzle flashes and lightning bolts illuminated them for an instant at a time. A pale green shroud hung around the gun. Wagga's shirtless muscular frame was highlighted by the flashes, and the rain poured against his upper body. His relief at his brother's survival had turned to fury. 'Here's another one, you bastards!' he screamed as he rammed home the round.

Jenkins stared as the gun bucked under the recoil and the men seemed to jump and dance to the tune of the gun. He felt ill, and his mind whirled as the noise grew. He slumped to his knees, his hands clasped in front of him. 'A dance of death,' he whispered. 'O Lord, forgive them.'

Then he stood, swaying, the rain pounding his body. Stumbling, he made his way over the small rise towards Central Command Headquarters. He tripped and fell into the mud, rose and fell again. It was two hours before he stumbled into the Headquarters entrance.

While the bombardment continued, the officers at Headquarters analysed the crisis. Tideswell turned to his adjutant, his face pale and drawn. 'Round up every officer you can find. I want them all here, now!' he said.

The lieutenant ran from the tent towards the officers' lines, returning with a group of men. In a strained voice, Tideswell addressed them. 'Gentlemen, we face a crisis of the gravest nature. As you may have heard, there's been a very heavy impact on the 14th Battery area. It's been confirmed by Captain Conrick that they received what they consider to be the first of possibly many Krupp

150-millimetre artillery shells. I feel sure some of you will know the ramifications of this?'

A few of the officers nodded.

'For the others, let me inform you: once the gun is fixed in its position, the accuracy of the weapon is frightening, even from 10,000 yards. It can deliver firepower that a full battery would have trouble keeping up with.' Tideswell paused. 'We know the Germans have three 150s, ready to destroy everything within their range. With proper sweep and search tactics, these three weapons are capable of destroying our brigade within a few hours.'

The officers were silent.

'I have decided our only course of action is to lay on an intense bombardment from full brigade strength. I have sent a mounted runner to all batteries with that order. We cannot reach the Krupps, but we will keep their heads down in the forward trenches.'

Major Freddie Dawson, Battery Commander of the 105th Howitzer, stepped forward. 'Excuse me, sir, could you say at what time the first 150 shell was received?'

Tideswell glanced at his watch. 'About an hour ago now.'

'Assuming the Boche has his 150s set up, what firing rate could we expect, sir?'

'Response rates would vary, but five to eight minutes per round would be a fair firing rate.'

'Sir, if the Boche realises we're building up for a large infantry operation – which he will, of course, by our artillery barrage – would he not do all in his power to contain our artillery?'

'Yes, Dawson,' said Tideswell impatiently.

'Then why has the Boche only sent one 150 over? They'd calculated the range correctly, so why only one round in over an hour?'

'Other rounds might have fallen short, and we wouldn't have heard them,' replied Tideswell.

'Yes, sir, but any sight-layer worth his salt would drop his first round on the agreed target, the second round 100 yards over target and the third round 100 yards short. Classic search, sweep and destroy.'

Tideswell stood up abruptly. 'You may have something. We have only heard, and confirmed, one round received. Get me a mounted runner on the double!' he said to his adjutant. Within moments, the officer and runner appeared in the tent. Driven by fierce winds, the rain swept across the fields in great white sheets.

'Get to the 14th, runner, I want to know how many 150 shells the battery has received. Quickly, fast as you can, but get back in one piece!'

Not bothering to salute, the runner sprinted to the waiting pony tethered under a makeshift cover, grabbed the reins and had the pony leaping forward as he expertly hit the saddle.

'Is he good enough?' Tideswell said to his adjutant.

'Good enough!' The adjutant looked at Tideswell and grinned. 'Sammy O'Brien, he's twenty, been mustering cattle in North Queensland with his father since he was four years old. He has more horsemanship in his big toe than anyone in the brigade. Apart from Bevan, I suppose.'

The conversation in the tent centred on the Krupp gun. It had originally been used as a secondary gun on German battleships, then a massive gun carriage had been designed to transport the weapon for use in the field. Its extreme weight – over 15 tons – made the Krupp cumbersome and unwieldy. It had to be moved using a motorised lorry or tractor, as it quickly became obvious that horses could not handle the enormous dead weight. Taking into account the loading rack and rails, relocating the Krupp presented a formidable logistical problem.

Tideswell was discussing the pros and cons of heavy field artillery and the decided advantages of much lighter weaponry for hit-and-run operations in the field. 'One problem with the Krupp, I recall, is the towing pole, which also acts as the recoil arm. A large plate of 20-millimetre steel must be set on a firm base under the end of the pole for recoil absorption,' he said. His eyes suddenly widened and he turned to his adjutant. 'John,' he said, 'let's calculate the rain!'

The officers heard the excitement in his tone and gathered around him. 'We know where the Krupps are,' said Tideswell. 'Their position would mean that they were hit by the storm before we were. So how long have they been under this downpour?'

The adjutant examined the map, made a number of calculations, then turned to Tideswell and said, 'Given 8,000 yards, gun to target, we're a further 1,000 yards back. I estimate the front is moving at about 15 miles an hour. The rain started here' – he checked his watch – 'one hour and twenty-five minutes ago. Allowing forty-five minutes for the storm to hit here, it means they've been under heavy rain for about two hours and twenty minutes sir.'

'Good! Now, step outside, John. Walk 20 feet off the boards and tell me what happens.'

Bemused, the adjutant trotted into the pouring rain, returning a few moments later.

'As you can see, sir, mud up to my shins.'

'Wonderful,' beamed Tideswell.

Dawson suddenly slapped the desk with his open palm. 'That's it!' he crowed. 'They can't secure the base plate in the mud, so they can't stabilise the bloody gun!'

'Spot on, Dawson. Keep your fingers crossed until the runner returns. Then we may confirm our hopes.'

When O'Brien re-entered the tent, hair streaked over his forehead and face spattered with mud, Tideswell said quickly, 'What have you got, runner?'

'Two rounds only, sir, the last one over an hour ago and about 300 yards short.'

The group broke into excited conversation. Tideswell addressed his adjutant. 'Pour this man a drink, Lieutenant,' he said, indicating Sammy O'Brien. 'Only two rounds, eh? That's excellent news!'

O'Brien self-consciously took the whisky glass and drained the contents. 'Thank you, sir. Captain Conrick says they'll need reliefs soon if the fire rate is to continue.'

'One more despatch for you, O'Brien. To Captain Conrick. Orders are for the four batteries to stand down. Relax for the night. When you return, go straight to the mess, get some food and sleep.' With a grin and a wave of his hand, O'Brien sprinted for the pony waiting patiently under the shelter.

Tideswell looked up to see Jenkins, shaking, exhausted, covered in mud. As he watched, the padre's eyes rolled back and he fell, unconscious, into the tent entrance.

'My God, it's the padre! Lend a hand here!' called Tideswell.

A few of the officers jumped forward and carefully laid Jenkins on a reserve stretcher kept in Headquarters.

'Get some towels and dry clothes or he'll freeze,' said Tideswell.

Willing hands quickly stripped, dried and dressed Jenkins in warm clothing. He slowly regained consciousness and struggled to sit up.

'Here, drink this, Padre,' said a young captain as he held a very stiff brandy to the padre's lips. Shutting his eyes, Jenkins gulped. The raw spirit slammed into the back of his throat and he gasped for air. The captain poured another, and this also quickly disappeared.

The next day dawned in brilliant sunshine. The guns were quiet on both sides. No infantry activity disturbed the stillness. The men moved about quietly, hanging soaked clothing over tent lines to dry.

The infantry was preparing to re-occupy the trenches where hundreds of men had died a few weeks before. Three more crosses appeared that morning as the three gunners from the 14th Battery joined their comrades in French soil.

With little movement from the enemy lines, the men enjoyed the rest and inactivity during a week of fine weather.

Intelligence from an air reconnaissance plane that had made a dangerous, low-altitude run over the enemy lines reported that enemy infantry had retreated some 1,000 yards to regroup and establish a solid front at their second line.

Tideswell and Freddie Dawson had been right. Photographs taken by the plane's navigator showed the three Krupp 150s to be in disarray. One gun was on its side; another faced north, away from the Allied line; and the third was attached to a towing lorry, 200 yards east, sporting what appeared to be a heavy coating of French mud. The fierce storm had saved the brigade from certain large-scale damage.

The warm week came to a close with orders for resumption of action. The 5th Field Artillery Brigade had taken time to overhaul and service their weapons and were ready to re-engage. The 13th Infantry Brigade was to attack the enemy trenches early the next morning at 0530 hours. To cover their attack, the artillery was ordered to lay a heavy barrage onto the new enemy line from 0300.

At 0255, Jum looked at McErbain. 'The padre coming this morning, Harold?' he quipped.

McErbain turned and grinned. 'Don't think so, mate. The night of the 150s was enough for him for a while.'

'I heard he was in the 7th Field Hospital for three days,' said Jum.

'Why did he put himself at risk like that?' asked Gillies.

Bob spoke up. 'I reckon he came here to shut you up, Gill, after you abused him that Sunday morning. That got his back up.'

'He's stronger than he looks,' said Jum. 'Remember how he prayed over Henry Larkin, lying in that shell hole – that took some doing.'

The conversation lapsed. Jum snapped the lanyard as McErbain called 'Fire!'

The barrage lasted until twenty seconds before 5 o'clock in the morning, with the 13th Brigade Infantry advancing slowly under its cover. But fierce German retaliation drove the 13th back to the front-line trenches the Germans had vacated four days earlier. There the infantry dug in, preparing for a German counterattack. The brigade artillery was now 2,000 yards from the 13th Brigade front line, well away from the action.

September to November 1916

Brigade Diary

1.9.16 Command satisfied with our barrage on enemy trench system.

3.9.16 05.10 am Bombardment in support of 13th Infantry Bgde during attack on enemy.

Rain was falling lightly as the No. 1 Detachment slopped their way to the mess tent, eager for breakfast. The men were utterly exhausted. Months of almost non-stop action had taken their toll. Tempers were short and arguments over trivial incidents commonplace.

The men had been briefly relieved of front-line fighting by the 83rd Regimental Field Artillery, an English brigade. After enduring a 10-mile march to billets in Authuille, they were treated to baths, food and a hard-earned, uninterrupted night's sleep. But the sojourn was short-lived. The brigade was ordered to march to a small town north of Authuille, where they were entrained for Proven. From there, they marched a further 8 miles to Busseboom, where the front line, only 3,000 yards to the east, was once again the scene of fierce fighting.

The 5th Field Artillery Brigade, under strength, had received reinforcements from the 2nd Division. With these brand new recruits, the brigade strength was raised to a full complement of men.

The No. 1 Gun still retained the basic detachment of McErbain, Bevan, Gillies, Buchannen, Wagga and his brother Ron, now fully recovered. They squabbled as they headed to the mess tent.

Captain Conrick, aware of the tense situation, sought out Lieutenant Colonel Tideswell in the Headquarters tent.

'What's on your mind, Captain?' asked Tideswell.

'The men, sir,' said Conrick. 'The battery is exhausted. They've had four or five months with only a few days of real rest. They really are at the end, physically and mentally.'

'Captain, I'd be delighted to give the men a month's holiday. But we'd need the Boche to do the same, otherwise thousands of infantry locked in the trenches would be at grave risk. I know they're tired. I am too, and I know you are. The Boche, from Grevilliers Line up to Ypres, have twice the infantry, twice the artillery and twice the ammunition and equipment we do. We're desperate for relief and reinforcements. Let's hope they're not too far away.'

Conrick nodded. 'We'll continue to do our best, sir. I thought I should just quietly let you know the men are doing it tough.'

'Perhaps if some of the armchair experts 10 miles back were to see the conditions the men are fighting in, their attitude might change,' said Tideswell.

The gently rolling hills around the town of Ypres were badly scarred by the ferocity of artillery shells, although vestiges of greenery added some colour to the desolate landscape. To the north, about 30 miles from the town, two armies dug into substantial trenches glared at each other over 1,000 yards of No Man's Land. The batteries had moved to a position that gave them adequate range for their 18-pounder and 4.5 Howitzer guns.

Major Freddie Dawson and Captain Conrick were standing on a slight rise, their binoculars trained on a wooded slope some 1,200 yards to the north-east.

'There he is,' grunted Dawson. 'Right of centre in the trees.'

Conrick moved his glasses. 'Yes, I see him.'

A puff of smoke from the German 150-millimetre trench mortar had signalled the enemy position.

'He's had a battalion of men pinned down for a day and a half with "rum-jars"!' said Dawson.

'Yes, they're a bloody fearsome weapon all right,' said Conrick. 'We've been told there are two mortars and a machine gun detachment there also. I think the 18-pounders will handle them.'

'I'll sight for you, Terry. Lay a couple of rounds on for range,' said Dawson.

Artillery positions usually had an observer or sighter well forward of their guns who relayed information back to the gun position officer about the success or failure of their bombardment. This ensured very accurate fire was concentrated on any given target.

Conrick scrambled down the slope to the No. 1 Gun position.

'Harold,' he called. McErbain turned. 'A Boche gun is about 1,200 yards on that heading,' he said, pointing to the wooded slope hidden from the gun detachment. 'Give Dawson some smoke for a sighter.'

The detachment jumped into action. Gillies lowered the barrel to the correct range and indicated direction. With the shell home and the breech locked, Wagga snapped the lanyard. The customary buck and kick sent the shell shrieking over the hill. Freddie Dawson, training glasses on the slope, noted the cloud of smoke as the round exploded above the wood.

Conrick looked 50 yards down the gully, towards Dawson. Dawson indicated with his thumb down twice. 'Drop 20 yards, high explosive!' snapped Conrick. Gillies had the gun range lowered by the time the high-explosive shell was locked in. Wagga snapped, the gun jumped. The centre of the wood ruptured under the force of the explosion. 'Go!' called Dawson. The detachment leapt into action, getting away some ten rounds in two minutes. Conrick climbed up from the position and ran up to Dawson. 'Bloody marvellous, Terry,' beamed Dawson. 'Look at them run!'

Even without binoculars, Conrick could make out four grey-clad figures, bent double, heading over the crest of the knoll. 'Cease fire!' yelled Conrick. The detachment ceased firing, sat back and lit up cigarettes.

Back at the position, Conrick spoke to Jum Bevan. 'Get this back to Brigade HQ,' he said as he wrote out his despatch.

Jum walked to the GPO Post, gathered the pony's reins, slid into the saddle and cantered towards the Brigade Headquarters some 1,800 yards to the west.

The sun was climbing towards midday. Jum slowed the pony to a walk, enjoying the warmth falling on his shoulders. The slow, measured gait of the pony eased his tension and allowed his mind to drift back to Pozières, which seemed years away, not six months. Bob had become quiet – not morose, but quiet – since the night he shot the young German soldier in the trench. His youthfulness had slipped away, unnoticed by anyone but Jum, who knew him so well.

The men had become set-faced and hard-eyed; there was less conversation and light-hearted banter. These boys had seen and experienced the harsh realities of warfare where men as individuals counted for nothing, especially to the generals of High Command, 20 miles back from the front line. The attack methods of those generals, so successful in the Crimean and Boer wars, were an abysmal failure here. Infantry marching steadily towards the enemy's strongest held point gained little apart from withering machine gun fire, accurate rifle fire from cover, and trench mortars. And to make sure the Germans should be in no doubt about an imminent attack, an artillery barrage anywhere from ten minutes to ten hours long immediately preceded an infantry assault. Jum pondered the fact that a basic rule of combat – protect your force – was ignored, with troops apparently considered nothing more than cannon fodder.

As a quiet observer of the situation, Claude Jenkins saw only too well how many of the men, unable to adjust to the brutal and endless killing, had numbed themselves. They moved away from their faith to a state of mind capable of dulling normal reaction to the horrors of war. He understood that it was an automatic, but inadequate, safeguard against mental breakdown. The death of a friend, a mate, might raise a response such as 'Jack's dead, eh? Pass the sugar. Where'd he get it? Zillebeke, eh? Hear it's tough up there.'

For weeks, Jenkins had battled to formulate an appropriate approach to the men. He had attended other religious services in an attempt to gain insight into how to handle himself and the men under his care. His Sunday service was usually a subdued affair that only the genuinely religious attended.

Since the night of the Krupps, Jenkins had not become involved near the action, either artillery or infantry, again. He felt he needed to find a genuine reconciliation between the killing conducted by 'his' men and the relationship between himself and his God. Accepting the perpetration of death and destruction was not easy.

Late one night, he slowly sat up on his stretcher. A slight breeze stirred his tent flap as he lowered his feet to the chilly duckboard. For the first time in weeks, his mind was lit by a glimmer of hope. He did not have to condone the killing; that was out of his hands. He had no power to control or prevent sin. But he did have a power to forgive.

He must offer succour and hope. Whilst the war progressed, he must be on hand to support the morale of those who had forsaken God, while fervently hoping that, in the future, they could be returned to faith.

The Padre lay back down, rolled to his side and was instantly asleep.

12.9.16 Went to Ypres for a spell from the line.

The slab of barely warm bacon on a lump of stale bread was not the most appetising of breakfasts, though Jim Gillies munched away as if it were his last meal. Light rain drizzled as the padre stepped into the mess tent. He served himself, then headed for the detachment of No. 1 Gun.

Jenkins made for a vacant spot next to Gillies. Since the Sunday of the confrontation, Gillies had been circumspect in the padre's presence, deliberately staying in the background.

As Jenkins moved to sit down, Gillies made an embarrassed half-move to stand.

'Stay there, Jim,' Jenkins insisted. Gillies sat down again. 'Damn rain, again,' he continued.

'Yes, sir,' responded McErbain. 'Looks to be set in, coming from north of Ypres.'

'Are you boys on today?' asked the padre between mouthfuls.

'Nope,' replied Jum. 'We were hoping for a leave pass to Zillebeke. I hear it's a beaut little village.'

'That sounds like a very good idea. Get away from this for a while,' agreed the padre.

Sergeant Charlie Hill's head poked through the tent flap.

'Twenty-four-hour leave passes for No. 1 and 2 Guns, from 1100 hours this morning.' Whoops of delight greeted the news.

'Sergeant, one moment,' the padre called as he rose from the table and moved to the flap. 'Can you get me one of those passes?'

'Sure, Padre,' said Hill. 'I'll speak to Colonel Tideswell.'

The men moved off to their respective tents to bathe and change in readiness for the unexpected furlough.

'He wants to what?' growled Tideswell.

Sergeant Hill repeated, 'Captain Jenkins wishes to accompany the men on their furlough.'

'Well, I suppose it will be another situation like the Krupp shelling. He'll run like blazes when the drinking and fun starts.'

Hill stood waiting for an answer.

'Yes, yes, give him a pass,' the CO said testily, signing the order.

The men of the No. 1 and No. 2 gun detachments were talking and laughing as they waited for Sergeant Hill to allocate the leave passes. Harold McErbain had secured a wagon and two horses for the trip to town, but the return journey would require a walk back to camp the following morning. The men excitedly climbed onto the wagon as Jenkins appeared and headed for the front seat by the driver.

'Off to town, Padre?' asked McErbain.

'You bet, I'm with your crowd,' said Jenkins. As the padre's response sank in, the conversation in the wagon faltered momentarily. The wagon moved off towards Zillebeke at a smart trot.

The loaded cart pulled up in rue de Dorp, the main road through the village. As they stopped opposite the church, the men gazed at the damage the village had suffered, although various stores, shops and a few *estaminets* were still in operation along each side of the street.

The men climbed down from the wagon and split into groups. McErbain, Bevan, Buchannen, Gillies and the Wagga boys went directly to the largest *estaminet*, adjacent to the church. Jenkins smiled when McErbain inquired if he would join them. 'Maybe later, Harold. I'm sure this church could use my presence.'

The men ran into the bar, hung their capes and ordered their beers. The inevitable fresh bread and cheese arrived, along with litres of light red wine. The men relaxed as the drinks and talk flowed freely.

The padre moved across the square to the church's entrance. He entered, closed the large ornate door behind him and moved slowly to a pew, where he sank to his knees and began to pray. A priest even smaller than Jenkins moved quietly down the aisle and waited whilst the padre completed his prayers.

'*Bonjour*,' greeted the Belgian priest.

'*Bonjour, Monsieur*,' replied Jenkins, startled. 'Do you speak English?'

'English, German, French, Flemish – what is your choice?' asked the priest.

The men shook hands. 'I took the opportunity of praying for my men in your lovely church,' said Jenkins. 'Most of the churches I see are only a pile of rubble.'

'Yes, we were lucky. One of the Boche officers who came through here was Roman Catholic and forbade any of the troops to interfere with us or the church,' said the priest.

'How long were they here?'

'About four months, before the French army drove them back.'

'Well,' said Jenkins, 'they are about 5 miles to the east now. We'll try and keep them there.'

The two ministers conversed for some thirty minutes until Jenkins excused himself for overstaying his welcome. The Belgian priest dismissed Jenkins's apology with a wave of his hand and added, 'It has been refreshing to talk with you. I would be happy to do so for hours.'

Jenkins stepped into the light rain, turned up his collar and ran towards the *estaminet*.

The front line was now considerably further east of Zillebeke. During its occupation, formerly by German forces and now by the Allied forces, the village had maintained its commercial life. Restaurants and *estaminets* struggled to stay open, business as usual, even though at times the front line approached to within a few hundred yards of the village.

The German invasion had been close to success in 1915. The French and British forces – underprepared and lacking in men, weapons and equipment – had suffered crippling losses. Villages were blasted to rubble. This mindless destruction, and the indiscriminate slaughter of French and Belgian civilians, ensured that no love was lost between the surviving French civilians and the German invaders. The Allied armies were welcomed as saviours.

Opening the door to the bar, Jenkins moved inside, looking for some familiar faces. The air was heavy with tobacco smoke. Smiling, he removed his hat and headed for the bar. Bob Buchannen, facing the door, was the first to see Jenkins.

'Look out,' he said quietly. 'We've got God in the pub!' All heads turned as the padre approached their group.

'Something to drink, Padre?' suggested McErbain, tongue-in-cheek.

'Thanks, Harold,' replied Jenkins. 'Maybe a small sweet sherry.' McErbain ordered the drink and found the padre a stool.

'How was the church, Padre?' asked Buchannen.

'Beautiful, a lovely place,' answered Jenkins, and went on to describe the church and his conversation with the priest. 'He thought the German soldiers were more motivated by fear than courage. The officers treated the slightest insubordination as treason, and a few executions kept the troops in line.' Jenkins sipped his sherry. 'He also said it was clear how well equipped the men were, that they had clothing and large amounts of stores available.'

'I'll bet they're not short of ammo like us,' said Jum.

'Jum, we have to expect that,' said McErbain. 'They've been preparing for years for this war, and we're playing catch-up at the moment.'

The talk covered various themes, and the padre bought a round of drinks, including a large sweet sherry for himself, which raised a few eyebrows. Jenkins glanced around the room and noticed the piano in the corner. McErbain followed his glance.

'A piano in every *estaminet*, Padre,' he smiled.

'I used to play the church organ when I was young,' said Jenkins.

'Jum can play, but I don't think he does hymns, Padre,' laughed McErbain.

'Give us a few songs, Jum. We could use some entertainment,' said the padre.

Jum, a large beer in hand, made a beeline for the piano. The padre laughed, then sat down, pushing Jum to the other end of the stool. Jum grinned as he thumped into a lively melody. The padre leapt into the treble, and the bar came alive to the rollicking sounds. The men encircled the players, singing verse after verse in a stentorian chorus.

Flushed and excited, the padre smiled at Jum. 'You know this one?' He leapt into a catchy tune that Jum had no trouble accompanying. The padre played until he was exhausted, then begged to be relieved. He went over to the bar, where he sat with a glass of water in his hand.

Gillies had been quietly watching the fun and the singing. He moved over to sit with the padre. He had hardly spoken to Jenkins since that eventful Sunday.

'Padre ...'

'Yes, Jim?'

'Padre, I just want you to know I feel bad about the other day. I was pretty angry and confused.'

'Jim, I was confused too. You asked me where God was, and I couldn't answer you.'

'There is so much killing,' said Jim. It was half question, half statement.

'I know it was dreadful for you to find your friend that way. And when the death of a young person is senseless, brutal and horrific, why wouldn't one ask, "Where is God?"'

'But, Jim, God cannot control our lives. He can guide us, if we have faith in Him, which in turn allows us to select which way we travel in life. The decisions we make are our own, and we must live with our decisions.

'Then there are times, of course, when choices are made for us by others, and we have no alternative but to abide by their decisions. These are the decisions that can eat at our soul, when we are asked to do something that our conscience says is wrong and evil.'

The padre stopped to sip his water.

'We are here now in just such a position. Every day we break the commandment "Thou shalt not kill", but we do it by necessity, as we die or they die, day after day. My answer to your question is that He is here, as He is everywhere, and I feel that my challenge is to retain my faith despite whatever horrific conditions I may suffer. I invite you to do the same – to have faith no matter how hard that may be. It is what will get us through this most testing time of our lives.'

There was a brief moment of silence between the two men.

Then Gillies smiled at Jenkins. 'Thank you for taking the trouble to speak to me.'

'It's the very least I can do,' answered Jenkins. 'Come on, let's join the others in the sing-along.'

The pair moved closer to the raucous chorus that nearly drowned out the piano. The padre sat and bumped Jum along the seat again.

'Where have you been, Padre?' yelled Jum.

Jenkins slipped into the melody easily and said, 'Just doing a bit of much-needed overtime.'

With fresh hands and more drinks, the music thumped along for a further half hour.

Looking at his watch, the padre stood and spoke to McErbain. 'I'll get going, Harold. I'll aim for camp and try to beat the darkness.'

'You won't stay for another drink, Padre?'

'No, no, two were plenty, most enjoyable.'

Jenkins smiled and waved farewell, then stepped out into the chilly afternoon. After the hot, smoky interior of the *estaminet*, the cold breeze whipped his breath away.

With his tunic buttoned to the neck, the padre set off at a brisk pace on the 2-mile trek to camp.

Darkness arrived but the singing revellers were oblivious as they drank, sang and danced their way through the early evening. The dancing was made easier when a number of the young local girls joined them. With their menfolk on the battlefields, they were deprived of male company.

Jum hardly moved from the piano. An accordion player joined him, and the music became softer. Songs of lovers and men lost and away in the fighting filled the *estaminet*. Jum was more than happy to continue whilst the drinks kept coming. The boys made sure of that.

Bob had made great headway with a petite girl of about twenty who had not joined in the singing, preferring to sit and practise her English on Bob.

Initially, bright red with embarrassment, Bob stuttered and stammered his way along, until he discovered that the young lady loved horses, hated Germans and was an avid listener. About a year before, the war had taken her husband after only a few months of marriage.

Jum had also gained a companion. A girl with long, dark hair had claimed the stool next to the piano.

Locals who had joined the entertainment were now drifting home. McErbain was deep in conversation with Gillies. Some of the men had left, in search of a good restaurant. Jum's companion spoke excellent English, and suggested Jum accompany her to a small café for a well-earned meal.

Jum motioned Bob over and said softly, 'Let's get out of here with the girls for some food, and we'll see what happens.'

Bob nervously looked around, even though the girls had gone to repair their hair and makeup.

'Jum, I don't know. Jeanne – that's her name – she rubbed my leg. I nearly went through the roof!'

'I can see how scared you are, Bob,' said Jum wryly, looking pointedly at the noticeable swelling in Bob's pants that he was desperately trying to hide. 'We'll go to that café across the street,' said Jum, then turned to McErbain. 'You and Jim all right, Harold?'

'Yeah, mate,' answered McErbain. 'We've arranged two beds here for the night. You two look like you're set!'

Smiling, Jum replied, 'I hope so! It'll be Bob's first – she doesn't know what she's in for. We've all seen Bob in the washhouse – talk about a weapon!'

The conversation ceased as the two girls, smiling and animated, walked towards the group. Jeanne slid her hand under Bob's elbow while her friend Anna smiled as she pulled Jum to the door.

'Come on,' she said in her lilting English, 'we have plans for tonight.'

'You lucky bastards,' grinned Gillies. 'Be here at 0900. We've got 2 miles to go to get to HQ before 1100.'

Nodding and waving, the two couples left the *estaminet*. In the nearby café, Jum and Bob were content to let the girls order. After the meal, the two boys happily pooled their resources, leaving a small tip for the waitress.

The rain had continued during the meal, with no sign of easing.

'Come, boys, we go this way,' said Anna, as they headed north from the village towards a few dark cottages some 800 yards away. Pulling up their collars against the weather, they walked swiftly towards the cottages.

At the first cottage, Anna steered Jum to the front door as she waved goodbye to Bob and Jeanne, who continued on to a similar cottage further up the hill.

'He is a nice boy, your Bob,' said Anna as she lit a large candle on the main table.

'I hope Jeanne understands that he's young and nervous,' said Jum, as he slowly wound his arms around Anna. She shivered in his strong grasp, and felt once again a stab of grief for the fiancé she had lost six months before. Since that time, she had closed her heart to any feelings of love or care, not wishing to leave herself open to further desolation and pain.

This man with the funny name had caught her unawares. Anna hungrily sought his mouth and was pleasantly surprised by his firm but gentle touch. His hands gently caressed her beneath her coat.

'One moment, my Jum,' she said with a shaking voice, and gently pushed him away.

'I'll sleep on the sofa, Anna,' said Jum softly.

With a tear-stained face and a catch in her voice, Anna whispered, 'No, stay here.'

Once again, the pair held each other, oblivious to anything but their own painful need for comfort and closeness.

After a short time, Anna relaxed, then stood and undressed. She was bathed in the moonlight that shone through a break in the clouds.

Jum's breath caught. For six months, women had been part of another world. Here, in front of him, away from the filth, the horror, the death, the insanity, was the promise of an enchanting return to life.

At the first hint of dawn, Jum awoke from a dream, momentarily confused by his surroundings. The supple warmth of Anna next to him aroused his senses as he gently slid his hands around her body. But he soon fell back into a deep, heavy sleep.

Suddenly, a thumping on the front door made Jum sit bolt upright as bright sun poured through the east window.

'Jum! Jum!' he heard, as Bob pounded on the door.

Leaping out of bed, he pulled on his trousers as he headed for the door. As he swung the door open, he felt the first pang of anxiety.

'Jesus, Jum!' rattled Bob. 'It's nearly 1100 hours, we'll be late and AWL!'

'Fuck!' said Jum, as he sprinted back for his clothes.

'What is it?' cried Anna, as she sat up, startled out of her sleep.

'We're late as hell, we'll be in all sorts of shit – we have to be back in camp in twenty minutes,' gasped Jum as he dressed.

'Don't worry, I have a horse and cart. I will save you much time,' called Anna as she hurriedly dressed and ran out to the harness shed.

'Round the back, Bob!' called Jum. The two boys quickly and expertly harnessed the horse and leapt aboard the cart with Anna, who laughingly slapped the horse into a quick canter. With the wind whipping through their hair, the trio bypassed the village of Zillebeke by a narrow but well-surfaced road, reducing the return trip to Headquarters by about a mile.

Anna eased the horse to a trot as Jum pointed out a small copse of trees some 300 yards from the Headquarters encampment. Leaping from the light gig, Bob nervously tugged at Jum, who was engaged in a fierce embrace with Anna.

'Come on, Jum, we're ten minutes late now!'

'I'll try and get back in a few days,' Jum whispered to Anna.

She watched as the two sprinted towards the camp, then turned the horse and headed back towards her cottage.

Bevan and Buchannen stood stiffly to attention. The dressing-down they received could be heard 100 yards away. 'You cannot be trusted! ... 1100 means 1100! ... Twenty minutes late!' Sergeant Hill, his face flushed, eventually finished his tirade.

'We're sorry, Sergeant,' Jum said. 'We raced back here as fast as we could.'

'Where were you?' asked Hill.

'We slept in, Sergeant,' mumbled Bob.

'Haven't got your mother here to wake you up, Buchannen?' Hill had been filled in on the previous day's events by Harold McErbain and he continued relentlessly, 'Well, Buchannen, I'm waiting. Where the hell were you? Where were you billeted?'

Bob, shifting his weight from one foot to the other, looked at Hill as embarrassment clouded his face. 'At a farmhouse, Sergeant.'

'Whose farmhouse, Buchannen?'

'It belongs to the lady who lives there, Sergeant.'

'Who is this lady, Buchannen?'

'Jeanne.'

'Jeanne who, Buchannen?'

'Jeanne Ricaud, Sergeant.'

Jum could see that Sergeant Hill was having trouble keeping a straight face. He winked at him and said, 'This poor, frightened girl was too scared to walk home on her own, so Gunner Buchannen offered to accompany her, for her protection, of course.'

'Well, Gunner Bevan, who was going to protect her from this oversexed young bloke here?' replied Charlie Hill.

By this time, word had spread amongst the men, and about twenty had quietly gathered outside the tent, listening.

Jum said, 'Well, Sergeant, as a matter of fact, the young lady in question had a friend who was also scared of the dark, so I offered to see her home to her cottage, too.'

'And to keep an eye on young Buchannen at the same time?'

'Yes, Sergeant,' replied Jum.

'Where did you sleep, Gunner Buchannen?'

An awkward silence followed, then Bob stammered, 'In a double bed, Sergeant.'

'And did the young lady become less frightened overnight?'

Bob Buchannen looked up and saw the laughter in Charlie Hill's face. A glance at Jum confirmed that he too was having trouble holding himself together.

'Well?' said Charlie Hill. 'Did she lose her timidness?'

Bob, now realising he'd been set up, smiled and said, 'She sure did, Sergeant, and she also said she'd like to lose it again tonight.'

Charlie Hill collapsed laughing into a chair, while Jum burst into hysterical giggling. The men crowded into the tent, laughing and slapping Bob on the back.

'Good boy, Bob!'

'Keep it up for Australia!'

'I wonder she didn't run when she saw that!'

'Ten-SHUN!' screamed Sergeant Hill. The men came to order as Lieutenant Colonel Tideswell entered the tent.

'What's going on here, Sergeant?' asked Tideswell.

Sergeant Hill, his face serious, replied, 'The men had such a great leave, sir, they came here to thank you personally.'

Tideswell grinned. 'Good, well done, men!' Then his tone changed. 'Whilst you are all here, I should let you know that the fun is over. We have some very serious business coming up. Dismiss the men, Sergeant.'

Sergeant Hill saluted, turned and said, 'You heard the CO.' He looked at his watch and said, '1230 hours, get fed and be on standby for orders. Dismissed!'

The men left the tent and headed off to eat lunch.

'What have we got, sir?' asked Sergeant Hill.

'Worrying news,' said Tideswell. 'Our intelligence reports massive German troop and artillery movements north and south of Roubaix, about 12 miles from here, heading west, straight towards us. Ypres looks like being the big test. We are to move forward to new positions immediately, dig in and make ready for a big offensive. HQs are calling up everyone they can – British, Canadian and Anzac divisions, in a big hurry. Also, HQ is predicting heavy rain, with snow in a week and extremely cold weather – the start of winter.'

The pair walked outside and examined the sky. A faint line of cloud was building to the north-west.

'That's where the weather will come from' said Tideswell, pointing towards Ypres. 'There'll be a meeting of all officers in HQ in fifteen minutes.'

'Yes, sir.' Sergeant Hill saluted.

In the mess tent, Jum and Bob moved to a table by themselves.

'Well, now, Bob, you can tell me. How was it?'

Bob, assuming a sudden worldly sophistication, waved his hand. 'Not too bad, I suppose!'

'Come off it, mate, I know it's your first time. Tell me!'

Bob's demeanour changed dramatically. In a hushed whisper, he said, 'I didn't know what to do! She got into bed, but I was too embarrassed to get undressed, so I left my underpants on!'

'Jesus, you must have looked like a sailboat with a bowsprit sticking out!' laughed Jum.

'Jeanne got my underpants off, and got on top of me.' A look of amazement returned to Bob's face as he remembered the night before. 'It was far better than all you blokes at the dam said it was.'

He suddenly realised how hungry he had become. They ate in silence, both lost in their memories of the previous evening. Bob looked up at Jum. 'She made a mistake, though. She thought I was someone else,' he said between mouthfuls.

'How come?' asked Jum, surprised.

'She kept calling out, "Robair! Robair!" I was almost waiting for some bloke to burst in!'

'She was calling your name, idiot!' laughed Jum. '"Robair" is Robert in French.'

'Oh,' said Bob. With a sheepish look, he changed the subject. 'What about you?'

'Nothing, mate. We both fell asleep,' said Jum, deadpan.

'That'd be right,' replied Bob, disbelieving.

Followed by Lieutenant Colonel Tideswell and Captain Conrick, Sergeant Hill walked into the mess tent.

'TENSHUN!' shouted Sergeant Hill.

The mess tent, three-quarters full with about forty men, stood and came to order.

'The CO wishes to speak to the mess tent.' Sergeant Hill stepped aside and acknowledged the colonel.

'Men, we've had a tough six months so far. Unfortunately, I can tell you it's going to get tougher in the coming months. The Boche are moving divisions of top-line troops from 12 miles east around Roubaix towards the north to Menin Road near Ypres, and south towards Beaumont, Bapaume and Albert. You all remember Sausage Valley, east of Pozières?' Many heads nodded in recollection.

'Our brigade will be moving north to stronger positions and higher ground. We'll be digging in under a most serious threat, the strongest threat of concentrated enemy offensive that we have so far encountered. We expect the Boche will take a short time to position themselves, a few weeks at most. It will give us time to prepare to a certain degree. We will move by battery, so our defences are not left open to attack.'

Tideswell paused. 'Thank you, men. I know you'll acquit yourselves well. Your battery captains have all the details. One more thing – winter is coming on fast, and it is incumbent upon all of you to look after yourselves. Guard against frostbite; keep well rugged up. We don't want unnecessary sickness to deplete our ranks.'

'Dismissed!' called Sergeant Hill.

Tideswell motioned Conrick and Hill over to him. 'I want to see you both in HQ, now if possible.' Both nodded and followed the colonel to the Headquarters tent.

Tideswell sat down and commenced.

'As we all know, Captain, you are to be my adjutant until further notice. No front-line artillery for you, yet. Another matter: I need an experienced officer, or a person who will make a good officer.'

'Someone from the ranks, sir?' asked Conrick.

'Yes, Terry. Who would you both suggest?'

Terry Conrick looked at Charlie Hill and both spoke in unison. 'Harold McErbain.'

Tideswell smiled. 'I wish you two would stop arguing!'

'We also need a corporal, now that Henry Larkin is no longer with us.'

'Jim Gillies for me,' said Conrick. Hill nodded.

Tideswell looked at Hill.

'Thank you, Sergeant, that will be all.' Hill rose and left.

'That leaves one more matter, Terry,' said Tideswell. 'How does "Major Conrick" sound?'

'Thank you, sir!' said Conrick, surprised.

'It's just come through. I took the opportunity just after you caught it at Pozières to recommend your promotion in my report to 2nd Division.'

'Thank you for your faith in me, sir,' said Conrick.

'We have some new targets for the next twenty-four hours. Division want to put a dent in the Boche advance. We will lay on a moderate barrage tonight, just to let them know we're still here.'

'Yes, sir.'

'Call past later and get the orders for the officers concerned. Thanks, Terry.'

Conrick walked away slowly, savouring the moment of his promotion. He saw Corporal McErbain approaching. 'Good afternoon, Lieutenant.'

'Charlie Hill wasn't joking then?' grinned McErbain.

'No, Harold. You'll leave for England tomorrow for a four-week intensive course at Larkhill, the British artillery school in Wiltshire.'

'I'm excited, sir,' said McErbain. 'I just hope I do well.'

'You will, Harold.'

'And now we need a driver and another corporal, Major Conrick.'

Conrick spun to face McErbain. 'How the hell did you know?'

'Rumours and half-truths are what an army marches on, sir, not their stomachs. The men have known for weeks about your promotion.'

McErbain and Conrick walked slowly and companionably back to their tents.

NOVEMBER 1916

BRIGADE DIARY

15.10.16 At the Railway Embankment near Ypres. 14th Battery go to centre group.

The 14th Battery had moved with the 105th Howitzer to new positions south-east of Ypres. The light rain became a heavy, drenching downpour – icy cold and often turning to sleet. The ground had been churned to deep mud, making moving into battle positions slow and difficult.

The 5th Division, Australian Infantry, had been attacking German lines near Fleurbaix–Fromelles in October 1916. A month later, Australian troops of the 1st, 2nd, 4th and 5th Divisions learnt with dismay that they were being returned to the Somme, as part of General Haig's plan to break the impasse.

The heavy rain had made accurate artillery fire impossible. The German force, a mile east of the 14th Battery position, had dug in substantially at their second line of defence, the Railway Embankment. The 5th Brigade Artillery waited cautiously for the enemy to show its hand. Both the Allied and German commanders were reluctant to begin operations. The fast-approaching winter was not the time to begin offensives: it was the time to consolidate, recondition equipment and, most importantly, rest the men.

The 14th Battery began firing on suspected German trench mortar emplacements. For two hours, there was no retaliation from the enemy line, until mid-morning, when the German mortars suddenly commenced a ferocious reply. Their fierce barrage resulted in many direct hits, with five men of the 14th Battery killed and fifteen injured.

Under light cover, Jum turned to Jim Gillies. 'Well, we know what these bastards are up to now, Gill.'

The barrage ceased as abruptly as it had begun. Sergeant Hill ran from his outpost to No. 1 Gun.

'What do you think? Any ideas, boys?' he asked.

As if in answer, the first gas shell landed nearby, exploding into a dense white cloud of phosgene. It was quickly followed by a barrage of shells that fell with deadly accuracy within the battery positions.

'For Christ's sake!' Sergeant Hill, tears streaming down his face, yelled at Jum. 'Get back to HQ and get a heap of gas masks, quick as you can!'

Jum sprinted for the horses tethered near the outpost. He slipped astride the first pony he came to, then booted it forward as the downpour continued. The heavy, malevolent gas mist curled in and around the positions of both batteries and headed slowly west towards Headquarters.

Once he reached the timber track, Jum moved the pony into a careful canter, making ground quickly as Headquarters came into view through the rain. He rode directly to the stores area and called out, 'Where the fuck are you all?'

'Right here next to you!' replied the stores sergeant, then, 'Jesus, they're using gas shell, right?'

Jum nodded and said urgently, 'Quick, get me two bags of masks, sling them on the horse. I've got to get back!'

'You can't see,' said the sergeant.

'The bloody horse can, I hope,' replied Jum.

Four men were hurriedly filling two large hessian bags with gas masks. The sergeant called to another man who was bringing up more masks, 'Drop that, get to the CO at Headquarters and let him know 14th and 15th Batteries are under severe gas attack. Hurry!'

The private ran from the tent. The men swung the bags onto the horse as Jum remounted.

'You all right, mate?' inquired the sergeant.

'I'll be fine, the horse knows the way,' said Jum. He gently kicked the horse in the direction of the gun positions.

The rain hammered down, filling the multitude of shell holes. The pony carefully picked its way, avoiding the holes and staying on firm ground. Jum could hear the 18-pounders quite clearly above the rain. He estimated that he still had a few hundred yards to go before he reached the positions. But about 100 yards further on, Jum encountered the phosgene gas cloud moving westwards. At the same moment, a German 77-millimetre shrapnel shell detonated just a yard in front of the pony's forelegs.

The shrapnel did the job it was designed to do. Pieces of metal as large as a man's fist ripped off the pony's forelegs, while the base plate – the largest piece of shrapnel – rocketed through the pony's chest and heart, killing the beast instantly. A smaller piece, deflected by the edge of the saddle, ripped through Jum's hat, laying open a yawning wound in the side of his scalp. As the pony collapsed, Jum was thrown forward, landing awkwardly on his head and shoulder. Knocked unconscious by the impact, he lay still. Blood flowed from the gash in his head. The gas enveloped the remains of the pony and Jum's lifeless form. The rain continued, and a river of blood flowed from the carcass of the pony into a much smaller stream threading its way from Jum's head.

Sergeant Hill ran to the No. 1 Gun position.

'Bob!' he called. 'Get moving, see what the bloody hell is holding Jum up!' Bob, also blinded by the gas, stumbled to the second tethered pony, which was coughing and sneezing, attempting to break away from its halter. Once astride, Bob wheeled his mount towards the track. No sooner was he over the back breast of the positions than he saw the still form of the pony with Jum's prone figure in front.

Bob leapt from his mount, turned Jum over and raised his head from the pool of blood.

'Jum! Jum!' he shouted, shaking the unconscious figure as the blood flowed over his hands and cape. Laying Jum back down, Bob sprinted back to the battery command post and screamed for help. Wagga and Ron ran after Bob as he returned to where Jum lay. Sensing trouble, Gillies retrieved a stretcher and headed for the scene. He took a quick look, felt a soft pulse in Jum's neck and yelled, 'He's still alive, but only just. He's lost a lot of blood. We have to get him back to the CCS in a big hurry!'

Ron grabbed the pony, which was patiently standing nearby. 'I'll get a wagon!' he yelled, leaping astride. With no consideration for himself or his horse, he booted the animal into a wild gallop, clearing shell holes on the way.

Bob and Wagga gently placed Jum on the stretcher. They glanced at each other, then lifted the stretcher and set off at a steady jog for the casualty clearing station.

Wagga was 6 feet 3 inches of hard muscle. Years in the saddle had filled out and toughened both the brothers from Wagga Wagga. Bob, now also over 6 feet tall, had developed a similar build. Six months of punishing physical exertion, pushing and pulling the 18-pounder guns and hoisting thousands of rounds of ammunition, had strengthened their physiques further. Although Jum weighed only 145 pounds, after 400 yards Wagga and Bob were gasping for breath as they moved through the gas fog. Setting the stretcher down, they caught their breath, then took off again. They continued for 800 yards, their arms and legs turning to lead as they fought exhaustion and cramp.

Ron appeared out of the gloom, driving a horse and wagon. He jerked the wagon to a standstill, and the pony panted. An orderly leapt down, ran to Jum's side and inspected the head wound, then quickly applied a tight bandage. Willing hands swiftly lifted Jum into the wagon, which Ron had already turned around. Then, showing greater care than he had on their journey out, Ron drove the wagon back to the CCS.

At the clearing station, Dr Stanley Davies looked up at the faces around him. Bob held the oil lamp. 'Keep your fingers crossed,' said the doctor. 'He's lost a massive amount of blood.' He had quickly and expertly repaired the gash in Jum's head with some twenty sutures, and the bleeding had stopped. The orderly bathed Jum's eyes in saline to reduce the effects of the gas as the doctor turned to Bob and the Wagga boys and said, 'I'd be doing the same for your eyes, too, if I were you.'

He turned to another orderly.

'I expect we'll have a heap more of the men suffering from gas here shortly. We don't have enough room for that many. Go to HQ and speak to the CO. We're going to need space there to handle the gas cases.'

The three gunners had been coughing spasmodically, bringing up yellow spittle from their inflamed lungs.

'You three – go and bathe your eyes, then I want you to sit or lie quietly.' The men nodded.

Jum had not stirred.

'Don't worry, Bob,' said Wagga. 'He's one tough bastard.'

Bob could not be reassured, although he knew more than most how tough Jum was.

An hour passed. The men were still coughing, often violently. Bob had hardly taken his eyes from Jum's face. Then Jum moved his head. The faintest sound came from his lips as his eyes fluttered open.

The doctor moved quickly to his side. 'Steady, don't move. You're lucky to be alive. Just lie quietly.'

Captain Jenkins pushed the tent flap aside as he entered the CCS.

'How is he?' he asked the doctor.

'He's doing well, Padre, considering. But if one of those men hadn't ridden like crazy to get a wagon, and the other two run with him on a stretcher, he wouldn't have made it. His blood loss was too great. Another three or four minutes of that sort of bleeding, and it would have been all over.'

'They're a close bunch in the 14th Battery,' said Jenkins, 'protective of each other. It's been their strength as a unit.'

The doctor nodded, then moved away and started preparing for the expected influx of gas victims.

Some hours later, Conrick addressed Tideswell. 'This has knocked our strength badly, sir,' he said. Twenty-three men from the 14th Battery had suffered severe gas inhalation and another fifteen had minor respiratory problems.

'What's the situation, Terry?' asked Tideswell wearily.

'Well, thirty or so, including Bevan, will be sent to Boulogne General Hospital for four to six weeks. The others will be rested off-duty for a couple of weeks. Billets will have to be arranged for them around Zillebeke,' said Conrick.

They heard raised voices outside the Headquarters tent. Conrick quickly moved to the annexe at the entrance. A mounted runner had slid to a stop a few yards away, and a corporal was attempting to hold the excited pony.

The drenched runner gasped, 'Bad news from the 105th Battery, sir!'

'Inside, come inside!' ordered Conrick.

'What's your report, Private?' asked Tideswell.

'I've just come from the 105th, sir. They copped about four direct hits.' The runner was trembling with exertion and shock. 'Five men killed and about fifteen casualties, sir, with two 4.5-inch Howitzers completely destroyed.'

'Names, man, I want names!' barked Tideswell.

'Major Dawson got shrapnel in his arm, but he's on his feet, sir, still in control.'

Tideswell looked at Conrick. 'Thank God we haven't lost Freddie Dawson!'

'Four OR's killed in No. 2 Gun position,' the runner continued, 'and one in No. 3 Gun position. The casualties are all shrapnel wounds, sir; some are walking, others are down. We have them under makeshift cover – some sheets of iron, sir,' he explained.

'Get around to the wagon lines and organise three wagons, see the stores sergeant. Away you go!' The runner dashed from the tent.

'The Boche are getting some good intelligence,' said Tideswell. 'It's uncanny how accurate they've become.'

'Yes, sir,' replied Conrick. 'In this blasted rain, too. I'll draw up a request for replacements, sir. The brigade will now be down by' – he checked his notes – 'some seventy-five men, about 12 per cent.'

'And also two 4.5 Howies, Terry,' added Tideswell.

Along with about thirty other soldiers suffering from severe gas poisoning, Jum was waiting in Zillebeke for the motorised bus to transport them to Ypres railhead, a journey that would take two hours. They had already spent an hour on the wagon between the CCS and Zillebeke.

Bob was standing next to Jum, who was now shakily sitting up. The men were still hawking and coughing continuously from the effects of the gas.

'Time to go, boys. The bus is here,' said the corporal.

The patients boarded the bus and settled in for the 20-mile ride to Armentières railhead, where they were to board a train for

Boulogne. The troop train, fully loaded with wounded soldiers suffering a vast array of injuries, steamed its way towards Boulogne, south of Calais on the Pas de Calais, 70 miles from Armentières. The desolate landscape of the front line – where hardly a tree, building or road remained intact – changed subtly as they progressed. Gradually, green fields appeared, along with forests and small villages that dotted the gently rolling hills.

Once at the Australian General Hospital in Boulogne, Bob and Jum managed to secure adjacent beds. The walking wounded used the mess hall at the rear of the ward area for meals and relaxation.

The weather, sunny but cold with winter approaching, continued to hold. A light breeze off the Strait of Dover had Jum and Bob thinking of the smell of salt spray along the beachfront in eastern Sydney. They soon settled into the hospital routine, and after an easy week, most of the men showed marked signs of improvement.

DECEMBER 1916

9.12.16 Cabled home for some cash.

Bob and the remainder of the artillerymen at the hospital in Boulogne returned to Armentières. Their lungs had almost recovered from the effects of the gas. But Jum had not fared so well. Recurring headaches had prevented him from returning to his unit.

One morning, a nurse changing Jum's bedding noticed discoloured blood on his pillow. A subsequent examination revealed a shard of shrapnel lodged in his head; in the flurry at CCS, it had been missed.

Once the shrapnel had been removed, the headaches disappeared, and Jum was well on the way to a complete recovery.

The 5th Field Artillery Brigade had been relieved whilst Jum was in hospital. The brigade had left Zillebeke for the village of Papot, where the men were treated to hot showers and clean clothing. The unbelievable comfort of lice-free clothes meant the men were able to enjoy days of sound sleep and recuperation. Forty horses and mules were moved to pastured rest areas, where many animals were recovering from wounds and injuries sustained over the previous three months. Jum returned in good health.

The brigade senior officers kept the men active. Rugby and league football games were quickly organised, with various teams slogging it out every afternoon.

Flurries of light snow heralded another winter. There were severe frosts every morning, and puddles froze to thick ice during the night. New horses were issued to the brigade, which was ordered to advance to Oesthove Farm, 2 miles north of Armentières.

There, the 5th Field Artillery Brigade relieved the 7th Field Artillery Brigade, which had been severely tested over the previous four weeks, suffering intensive enemy shelling for days on end.

The men were lucky enough to secure excellent billets in farmhouses in an area that was free from the deep mud and destroyed roads endured by the brigade for the past eight months. The gun positions here were well-maintained, with firm roads leading to Brigade Headquarters, Armentières and Steenvorde.

The ten days of rest, bathing, football and clean clothes came to an abrupt end on the night of 20 December 1916. Using 77-millimetre guns and heavier artillery, including 210 Howitzers, the enemy kept the brigade under constant heavy barrage for two days. It was a sobering prelude to Christmas, but Jum was determined the men would celebrate.

'You want to what?' exclaimed Major Terry Conrick.

'Since I'm on light duties, sir, I thought I could go to Armentières and line up food and drink for a bit of a Christmas party,' said Jum.

'What do you propose to use for money?'

'I've collected from the men. We have about £25.'

'That won't feed and water seventy men!' said Conrick.

'We'll have to make do, sir,' said Jum.

'Wait here a moment,' said Conrick.

As Conrick entered the tent, Lieutenant Colonel Tideswell – as usual poring over maps on his trestle desk – did not look up.

'Sir, the men of the 14th Battery have put together some money for a Christmas party. Is that all right with you?'

Tideswell raised a tired face. 'Yes, that's fine, Terry. It will give them a good break.' He produced a key and continued, 'Division HQ have sent £200 and various comforts from the Red Cross for Christmas. I suppose if we give the four batteries £50 each, they can do what they like with it.'

'Sounds great, sir. I'll let Gunner Bevan know.'

'How is Bevan, by the way?' asked the colonel.

'Very lucky, sir. That piece of shrapnel that sliced his head – well, an inch closer and it would have been curtains. As it is, he's close to fully recovered.'

'Well, here's the £50, Terry,' Tideswell said, as he re-locked the drawer. 'The paymaster will need to change it to francs.'

Conrick took the money, thanked Tideswell and moved outside, where Jum stood waiting.

'The CO says he thinks a further £50 will help the party no end.'

Jum's face broke into a grin. 'Great!' he said, 'We'll make it a party to remember!'

Swirling flakes of snow made visibility difficult as the wagon trundled along the pitted road. Jum sat hunched in the driver's seat, his greatcoat turned up at the neck and his slouch hat pulled down tightly over the lumpy scar that ran up his scalp behind his left ear.

He often fingered the scar, now grown over with hair, and marvelled at how close his escape had been. Twice now Bob had been instrumental in saving his life, first in the trench at Fleurbaix and then at Zillebeke. He smiled wrily, thinking of how he'd promised Maude Buchannen he'd protect Bob. The promise had been reversed.

The battered outskirts of Armentières appeared ahead. Destroyed buildings – the result of eighteen months of intense shelling – looked sad and resigned under their light covering of snow. There was no sign of movement on the lonely streets.

Jum made his way to a charcuterie. The proprietors, an elderly couple, agreed in broken English to Jum's list of provisions. There was some haggling over price, but eventually everyone was satisfied.

Jum climbed aboard the dray, gave the pony a slap with the reins and trotted towards the brigade camp. At the Headquarters tent, he reported to Major Conrick. Facing Conrick, his back to Jum, was a lieutenant who looked familiar.

Conrick smiled at Jum. 'Someone here you know, Jum.'

The lieutenant turned, his face split with a wide grin. 'G'day, Jum!'

'Bloody hell, it's Harold!' yelled Jum, leaping forward to give him a hearty slap on the back. 'Jesus, sorry, Lieutenant,' he said as he stepped back and saluted.

'Cut the bullshit, Jum. How are you now?'

Conrick had told McErbain about Jum's recent wounding and the gassing of the 14th Battery.

'I'm well, the odd headache, but no problems, really.' Jum turned to Conrick. 'Is Harold staying with us, sir?

'Sure is. As of today, he's the GPO of the 14th Battery.'

'The old team back in business, eh?' Jum said, delighted.

The men fell to small talk, mainly about the coming Christmas party, which was shaping up as a major event.

BRIGADE DIARY

25.12.16 Xmas Day.
14th Battery men have obtained a large
tarpaulin which they placed over an old,
shelled barn. An open fire and much food and
drink turned into great merriment.

Christmas Day, 1916, dawned to a continual fall of light snow, building on the mantle of white that had fallen overnight.

There was little artillery activity, and when the time came, Lieutenant McErbain despatched a mounted runner to stand down the gun detachments. A crowd of hungry, excited men converged on the bombed barn, the venue for the Christmas festivities.

It was strangely quiet.

'It's eerie,' remarked a corporal from No. 3 Gun. 'Hardly a sound, not a rifle shot, nothing. We even heard a few birds calling in that copse of trees earlier.'

'Let's hope it stays that way,' said one of the men.

And stay that way it did. A mounted runner at the front line was ready to despatch information at the first sign of any German activity but, happily, his vigilance was not rewarded.

Lieutenant McErbain called the eighty or so men to attention as Lieutenant Colonel Tideswell entered the barn.

'At ease, men,' called an exhausted Tideswell, 'and a very merry Christmas to you all.'

Major Terry Conrick tapped a glass with his knife. Instant silence followed.

'Men,' said Conrick, 'please be upstanding and charge your glasses.' Conrick raised his glass to King and Country.

The assembled throng repeated the toast.

Padre Jenkins then said a brief grace. 'Here we are gathered to celebrate this most wonderful day, the birth of Jesus Christ. It would have been most enjoyable, of course, to do so with our families and loved ones at home; but that is not to be. We are here to carry out and complete the task before us – securing peace at all costs. There will be no peace without sacrifice. We have all experienced that, and will continue to experience the loss of many of our friends.'

Most of the company lowered their heads during the padre's prayer, but Bob, Jum, Ron and at least half a dozen others stared straight ahead. Jum noticed with some surprise that Jim Gillies had his head bowed and his eyes closed.

'But today,' continued the padre, 'may we be truly thankful that we are here, together, protected from the elements, thanks to Jum, Bob and the Wagga boys.'

Handclaps and whistles followed.

The men attacked the table with gusto, washing down the delicious food with beaujolais and Belgian beer.

Tideswell had eaten well, and the colour had returned to his face. He leant over to Conrick and said over the uproar, 'I think I'll just slip away, Terry. I've work to do.' Conrick moved to rise, but Tideswell shook his head. 'Don't disturb the fun, Terry. They've earned it.' He left the barn unnoticed.

Two hours later, Wagga stood unsteadily. 'Hey, Jum, one of our boys is standing guard at the positions. What say I take him some lunch?'

'Great idea, Wagga,' said Jum. 'I'll help you get the food together.' They found an empty ammunition box and filled it with enough food and drink to satisfy at least ten hungry men.

Wagga drove the dray towards the front line, east of Oesthove Farm. The stillness and quiet were broken only by his drunken yells of enthusiasm.

The lone sentry sat by the outpost with his mount nearby, dejectedly peering towards the German line some 1,800 yards to the north-east. At the sound of Wagga's approach, he dropped to the snow, cocked his rifle and nervously looked around, trying to ascertain where the noise was coming from. Then the dray hurtled into view and Wagga slammed it to a halt.

'Here you go, mate – come and get some Christmas tucker into you!'

Once he was over his initial amazement, the sentry began to demolish the food and drink. Chatty with the alcohol, Wagga helped him.

Back at the barn, the party had become boisterous. The officers had left earlier, and men from the other batteries and the 105th had arrived, drawn by the noise and singing. There was still an abundance of food on the table.

The party continued until well into Christmas night, with many of the men content to sleep where they lay in the warmth of the barn.

Dawn brought thunder and heavy falls of snow, awakening the men from a deep slumber and bringing them back into the real world of hangovers and headaches. On this cold Boxing Day, German artillery could be heard laying on an initial barrage around 0630 hours.

The men stumbled hurriedly back to their billets and tents to prepare for the offensive.

Wagga and the sentry, asleep in the outpost, were awakened by the German shells. They hastily returned the horse and dray to Oesthove Farm Headquarters. Conrick stepped from the Headquarters tent.

'What's happening, Wagga?'

'They're laying on a few .77s, sir, just to let us know Christmas is over,' answered Wagga grimly.

'All right, then, clean up and get some food. Meeting here at 0700. Spread the word,' barked Conrick.

'Yes, sir,' replied Wagga, feeling more than a little queasy.

The assembled men of the battery waited glumly in the lightly falling snow as Conrick and McErbain addressed them.

'Half battery until further notice,' said Conrick. 'No. 1 Gun and No. 3 Gun. Numbers 2 and 4 back here in reserve.'

The men moved off. Christmas, with its stolen cheer and goodwill, was over.

JANUARY 1917

The Great Somme Offensive of 1916 had seen Allied and German troops lose their lives by the tens of thousands in the ferocious attack and defence of areas around Albert, Pozières, Bapaume and Lagnicourt.

Sapignes had fallen to the Germans, as had Bucquoy and Vaux. It was depressingly clear that the Germans were gaining control over much of the area. The Allies returned to this crucible of death early in 1917.

Unusual reports were received from various front-line battalion night patrols, who relayed the information that some front-line enemy trenches were empty, while others were manned only by a single machine gun emplacement.

The High Command set aside many of these reports as unfounded or lacking in veracity. It was inconceivable that the German Command would consider withdrawal, considering the frightful loss of men and equipment that had been the cost of holding the front-line areas gained in 1916.

But unbeknownst to the Allied Command, the enemy had formulated a systematic and orderly plan of withdrawal. The Germans knew that the intense effort required to hold the Somme area in 1916 could not be maintained in 1917.

Late in 1916, the German Command had poured men and equipment into the construction of what became known as the Hindenburg Line. From Passchendaele in Belgium past Saint-Quentin, east of Amiens, this defensive line stretched over 300 miles.

Since September 1916, Belgian, British and French prisoners, along with German civilians and soldiers, had been digging and pouring reinforced concrete into a trench system far superior to any of the existing front defensive lines.

Concrete dugouts 20 feet deep and 200 yards of barbed wire had the German Command confident of repelling the most intense of any future Allied attacks. The Hindenburg Line, Germany had decided, was the unchallengeable final salient that would repel the Allied offensive. The Germans thought their submarine force, which was about to commence activity in the English Channel, could destroy supply lines of men and equipment from England. The Hindenburg Line would then become the final bastion of the 1917 German offensive.

In northern France, the new year began with desultory artillery action and freezing temperatures. The men continually swabbed their equipment with kerosene to prevent the breech mechanisms from locking solid. Despite the numbing cold, they preferred the frozen ground and ice to the foul, clogging mud they had experienced all summer during the Somme campaign.

When the German front line became ominously quiet, the men knew something was up. Lieutenant Colonel Tideswell could not enlighten his officers. 'Divisional HQ are not saying anything of note, but there are reports of German trenches being found empty and abandoned. It seems almost unbelievable, considering the men and equipment lost over the summer. For either side to relinquish even a yard or two of ground gained would be inexplicable.'

Major Freddie Dawson said, 'Could it be that the Boche is retiring to regroup?'

Tideswell stroked his chin. 'Don't know, Freddie. HQ don't know either. It's a mystery. But one thing Intelligence is sure of is that we will see a massive, all-out German assault this year, concentrating on the Somme area. We've been ordered back to the village of Grevilliers, west of Bapaume and very close to the German front line. We'll be able to move men and equipment about much more easily in this big freeze than a few months ago. We're being relieved here by the 7th FAB in two weeks' time. In the meantime, I suggest some leave would improve the men's spirits no end.'

Conrick turned to McErbain. 'We might as well get some of the men out of the line immediately. What say we furlough the four No. 1 detachments of the battery? Keep the No. 2 in reserve and then rotate?

'I'll get onto it immediately, sir.'

Jim Gillies sat down in the mess tent. Both battery detachments were enjoying their midday lunch. 'Seems we've all been good little gunners,' he said. A few questioning faces looked up. He grinned. 'Leave passes – Armentières, here we come!' The men cheered.

Jum and Bob glanced at each other. 'Zillebeke, here we come,' said Bob.

The wagonload of happy men moved along the Armentières road from Oesthove Farm. Splintered trees stood out starkly in a landscape of gigantic shell craters that stretched endlessly in all directions, covered by a thick layer of snow. The men alighted at Armentières railhead. Many were bent on securing rail passes to Boulogne or Calais. But Jum and Bob prevailed on the driver to head south-east to Zillebeke after Armentières.

They jumped off at the cottages. With a farewell wave, the driver headed back towards Headquarters at Oesthove Farm.

Light snow was still falling as the pair made their way to Anna's front door, which was already opening to them. Anna stood in the doorway with an astonished smile on her face. Jeanne was in the hallway behind her. After excited greetings, the four decided to visit Zillebeke.

They quickly covered the short distance in Jeanne's horse and cart, and made their way to the café where they had eaten the evening they met. They ordered fresh bread, cheese and a bottle of beaujolais. Comfortable in the dim, smoky interior, the two couples were finishing their light meal when Jum said, 'What about going to Ypres for a couple of days?' The girls looked at each other, smiled and agreed. They returned to the cottages to pack before meeting Jum and Bob at the cold bus terminus in town.

In Ypres, Jeanne and Anna knew of a cheap but clean *pension*.

'*Bonsoir, mesdemoiselles*,' said the rotund concierge behind the desk. The others waited while Anna negotiated with the concierge in French, handed over money and received the keys.

'Two rooms for two nights,' she said. 'He said the bathroom and toilet are down the hall, and breakfast is from 7 till 9.' The concierge ushered them up the stairs to their rooms on the first floor.

Jum and Bob entered one room, where a fire had been laid in the grate. Jum lit the kindling, then turned to Bob, saying, 'Better go and light the girls' fire, Bob.'

Bob knocked and waited. Anna opened the door about 2 inches. 'And what do you want, *Monsieur*?'

Bob blushed and stammered, 'Jum said I should come and light your fire.' Anna turned to Jeanne and repeated what Bob had said. Bob could hear them giggling.

'Come on, Anna,' he pleaded. 'Let me in!' The door opened, and he saw shadows from the fire flickering across the room.

'We have our fire, Robert,' said Jeanne, 'but you can stay and light mine!'

Anna made for the door. 'I must make sure my Jum is all right.' She checked her watch. 'Two hours. That will be 5 o'clock.' Jeanne nodded. Anna quietly shut the door behind her.

Anna and Jum were at ease with each other. Their lovemaking had been considerate. They talked now about the war, the destruction of France, and the future.

'Would you stay in France, my Jum?'

'I don't know, Anna,' said Jum. 'I've got no great memories to keep me here – apart from you, of course,' he added with a smile. 'We're heading down there in a few days,' he said, more sombrely.

'To the Somme?'

'That's what we hear.'

'Is that where the most Germans are now?'

Jum turned and smiled. 'When we were there six months ago, I thought the whole bloody German Army was in front of us. They fought like maniacs, and we defended like maniacs.' His tone changed. 'And for what? A few greasy yards of mud, worthless destroyed land, not a tree or a building left standing. What a bloody waste. And the men. I feel guilty being here with you with so many under the snow, thousands and thousands of young blokes like me who never had a chance.'

Anna's arms were around Jum's tense body, and she talked softly into his ear. 'We have these moments, my Jum, and we may not have them again. We must live for our time together. Our time is precious.'

WENTWORTH SHIRE COUNCIL LIBRARY

'I don't want to go back there,' he almost moaned. 'I want to live. I want a wife, like you. I want children. I want this to be over.'

Anna clutched Jum tightly. 'It will be over soon, Jum, and we will be together. Keep this in your mind and your heart.'

'Why don't we leave here now, Anna?' said Jum. 'We could go west to Boulogne – you speak Flemish. I could work.'

Anna put her hand on Jum's mouth. 'No, no, my Jum! You would never forgive yourself. Your friends, what would they say?'

Jum closed his eyes. He had known the answer before Anna had spoken.

'Just be careful and come back to me,' she pleaded.

'I will, I will.' He buried his face in her shoulder.

'Come, now, my Jum, it is time for us to eat.'

Jum got up and knocked lightly on the adjoining wall of the two rooms. A knock came back in reply. They quickly dressed and the four made their way to a nearby *estaminet*.

Meanwhile, Wagga and Ron were sitting back, quietly smoking and enjoying the train ride to Ypres, when a large figure in khaki entered from the next carriage, carrying a small haversack.

As he reached the seats of the artillerymen, he nodded and asked. 'May I?'

'Sure, sure, sit down,' called Ron.

'A. J. Casey, 3rd Australian Pioneers.' The large soldier extended his hand in greeting and smiled. 'Just call me AJ. You two boys artillery?'

Ron and Wagga nodded. 'We're with the 5th Brigade.'

'You fellers helped us out at Morlancourt last year?'

'Sure did!' they replied in unison.

'Yes! You were in the middle of A Company 3rd Pioneers.' He grinned. 'Gave the German bastards something that night they won't forget!'

'Are we still holding the area we took that night?' asked Ron.

'We are,' answered AJ. 'Morlancourt to Sausage Gully. I remember two of your boys who were helping us in the trench we were attacking. Bloody hell, I came round a trench corner, your two blokes were there with three dead Germans. The older one had me in his sights straight off. The younger boy was on the

128

ground holding his rifle. I near pissed myself. Thought I was going to wear one of our own bullets!'

Ron and Wagga looked at each other.

'That was Jum Bevan and Bob Buchannen,' said Ron. 'and it was the first time either of them had killed anyone. Bob had just shot a sixteen-year-old boy.'

AJ slowly nodded. 'The first few are the hardest,' he replied. 'They all seem too young.'

'What brings you to this neck of the woods?' asked Ron.

'We've been carrying out some urgent road repairs around Albert and the Ancre River. Looks like that road's going to be used a lot in the coming months,' replied AJ.

'That fits with what we know,' agreed Ron. 'We're off to Albert and the Somme in a couple of weeks. Our brigade is, anyway.'

'Where you going now?'

'Just a couple of days off in Ypres,' said Wagga.

'I'm the same – three days' furlough, and then back to Pozières.'

Sergeant Alan John Casey was pleasant company, but his easy attitude was contradicted by the expression in his eyes. The face smiled; the eyes did not. He was a hardened, disciplined soldier, inured to the atrocities he had witnessed and been a part of.

'If there's trouble, he's the one I want at my back,' thought Ron.

As the train came into Ypres Station, the three soldiers retrieved their knapsacks from the overhead racks and moved to the carriage's exit doors.

Fierce flurries of snow greeted them as they moved to the main thoroughfare in town – rue de Gambetta.

'A drink first, boys?' asked Casey.

'You betcha!' Ron opened the door to the *estaminet* and moved towards the bar.

'Well, bugger me!' he said, as he spied Jum and Bob seated with two girls at a long wooden table.

'Room for us, Jum?' called Ron.

Jum and Bob waved the newcomers to seats beside them, and there were handshakes all round.

'Remember Sergeant Casey here?' said Ron, putting his hand on AJ's shoulder.

Jum searched AJ's face, then snapped his fingers.

'Sausage Gully, the Somme, 3rd Pioneers,' he grinned. 'You came along in the trench.'

Casey smiled. 'You had me in your sights and I thought, "Shit, I'm gone!" You and young Bob here did a great job on the Boche that night.' Then, sensing Bob's discomfort, he changed the subject. 'Anyway, what are you two beautiful girls doing with these bloody artillerymen? You should get some infantry boys. They're much more fun.'

Drinks were ordered, then Casey said, 'I have to get a bed for the night.'

Ron and Wagga agreed. Jum held up a hand.

'Let Anna go to our *pension*. We're the only ones there, and she'll do the best deal.' Anna jumped up and Jum pressed francs into her hand.

'One room for you three boys?' she asked. All three nodded.

'Who goes into the big bed?' she asked, winking at Jum.

'I'm not sleeping with you, Ron,' laughed Wagga. 'You snore and fart all night.'

'I'll take the single, to stop the argument,' said Casey.

Anna disappeared into the gloom. When she returned, the seven of them ordered their meals. The war had entered its third year and food was now very basic.

A piano sat in the corner, and the proprietor told Jum he was happy for him to use it. The five boys crowded around the keyboard whilst the girls sat and chatted.

'What say we start with "Mademoiselle"?' said Jum. He thumped out the opening chords and began to sing.

Mademoiselle from Armentières, parlez-vous,
The maid she went a milking, boys, parlez-vous.
She pulled its tail instead of its tit
And all she got was a bucket of shit.
Inky, pinky, parlez-vous.

The four boys had taken up the tune with great gusto and sang heartily for another four verses. More drinks were followed by more singing, including a soft, melancholy song by Anna with Jum idling along in support. Wagga insisted on singing 'When the Dog

Sits on the Tucker Box'. Eventually, the group made their way to the *pension*.

Snoring could soon be heard, with the girls quite content to burrow into their respective beds. By breakfast next morning, AJ and the Wagga boys had decided to travel to Steenvorde for two nights before returning to Ypres, and thence back to Oesthove Farm.

'We're due back at Oesthove Farm at 1600 today, mate,' Bob said to Jum.

'I think there's a bus at midday that's supposed to get to Zillebeke about 1330, allowing for a few stops,' said Jum.

Anna joined in. 'We can get you to Oesthove by 3 pm easily.'

Jum, Anna, Bob and Jeanne arrived at the bus terminus at 11.45. Entering the office, Jum approached the short, bald attendant at the counter. 'Four for Zillebeke, please,' he said, digging into his pocket.

The man shook his head and spoke in a flurry of French, waving his hands. Jum turned to Anna. 'Is there a problem?'

'The motor bus has broken down,' she said. 'He says it is the gear box or something.'

Jum looked at his watch, slightly agitated. 'What time's the next bus?' he asked. Anna spoke to the attendant for some minutes.

'It is not good, my Jum. The other two buses have been taken by the British Army. They are moving soldiers from the Messines area to Ypres, then going back to Messines for more men. He thinks we will be very lucky to get transport to Zillebeke today. Maybe late in the afternoon.'

'What's the trouble, mate?' asked Bob, who had been totally engrossed with Jeanne.

'No bus or transport to Zillebeke today. Means we're AWL from 1600 hours,' grunted an annoyed Jum.

'Shit! We'll be in trouble,' said Bob.

The snow had become a cascade of white. It built up on the steps to the terminus and on the roadside, deepening by the minute. The two couples sat hunched in the freezing shelter, waiting impatiently. Occasionally they would walk about, slapping their arms against their chilled bodies, trying to generate a little warmth. The hours slipped by, but there was no omnibus, no telegraph, no word.

'We could always march there, Jum,' ventured Bob.

The girls quickly shook their heads.

'It is very dangerous. If you are lost out there, you will die from the cold. You would not be found until spring,' said Anna firmly.

'Same as a Boche bullet,' muttered Bob.

Jum turned to Bob. 'It's 15 miles to Armentières, and another 3 miles to Oesthove Farm. We could do it, but the bloody snow is 2 feet deep. The girls are right: if we got off the track, we could disappear in a shell hole and not be seen again.'

Finally, they all trudged back to the *pension* and arranged for a further night's accommodation.

By morning, the snowstorm had moved south, leaving a carpet of white 3 feet thick over the entire countryside. Jum wondered if this was nature's way of covering the ugliness that man had left in his wake.

The news was better at the terminus. Anna relayed the information she had gleaned from the attendant. 'We may be lucky, my Jum – a motor truck is on its way here with some men and then going back to Oesthove Farm with other men.'

'What about you girls?' inquired Jum. Anna smiled and said, 'I have a friend here who will give us beds for as long as we want.'

Thirty minutes passed, with Jum and Bob looking anxiously for the truck. Jum suddenly stood up. 'I think I hear it!' Slowly making its way along the snow-covered road, the army vehicle finally slowed to a stop outside the terminus. The driver went to the rear, and unloosened the rear canvas canopy. Eight British soldiers carrying equipment jumped to the ground. Jum approached the driver, a British Army corporal.

'Can we get a lift to Oesthove Farm, mate? We're AWL and in deep shit,' he said.

The driver smiled and indicated the rear of the truck. 'In there, OK? We leave in two minutes.'

The boys ran to the girls, hurriedly embraced them and ran for the truck. The driver, now waiting at the vehicle's rear, watched the goodbyes.

'AWL?' he said to Jum, as he and Bob climbed into the truck. 'Mate, I'd be AWL for fucking years if I was you!' Jum and Bob grinned as the driver clipped the canvas shut. The motor truck took off into the snow, away from Ypres and on to Oesthove Farm.

Lieutenant Colonel Robbie Tideswell was furious. 'Lieutenant McErbain, I don't care what excuse the men have, they are some twenty hours AWL. I want them here now!' Around twenty men were late returning to camp. Coupled with heavy storms, this meant that the brigade was now two days behind its scheduled departure.

The twenty men of the brigade stood silently as Tideswell tongue-lashed them. 'Not only that,' he said, 'the men you were all supposed to relieve yesterday now have two days' less leave than you enjoyed. You've all had five days. They will only get three!' He turned to McErbain. 'They are all fined two weeks' pay. Now get them out of here!'

McErbain marched the men out of the Headquarters tent. 'You heard the CO. All of you, hotfoot it to your battery positions and relieve the men doing your bloody work. Go!' he screamed.

'Jesus, Jum, lucky we got that bloody lift,' panted Bob, as they ran to their tent.

'Are you in, Padre?'

The padre was in his tent, about to begin a letter to his sister Adele. He raised his head in response. 'Yes, certainly.'

Harold McErbain stepped into the tent, and the padre rose and extended his hand.

'Good morning, Harold, how nice to see you. Please sit down.'

McErbain sat carefully on the small stool beside the padre's bed. Jenkins waited while McErbain appeared to gather his thoughts.

'I have a small personal problem that I would like to discuss with you. That is,' he added hastily, 'if you're not too busy.'

Jenkins smiled. 'Not at all, Harold. That's why I'm here, you know.'

McErbain drew a letter from his pocket.

'I've just received this from my wife in Sydney.' He hesitated. 'I should explain from the beginning, shouldn't I?'

'That may help, Harold. All in your own good time.'

McErbain took a deep breath. 'I once told Jum Bevan that the reason I enlisted was that I felt it was wrong for one country to attack another without just cause, and I felt guilty because I wasn't helping fight that. That was certainly part of it. But the other thing was that my marriage had struck trouble.

'I was working six days a week at the dam, and I'd often stay there on Sundays too, to catch up on work that was behind schedule. One Saturday, I changed my mind and decided to go home after I'd told Lucy – my wife – I'd be staying on.' His voice hardened. 'When I got home, the lights were out. I switched on the lights and then I heard the back door slam. I asked Lucy what had been going on, and she started to cry.

'I grabbed her and shook her by the arms, and she said, "You were never here, I got so lonely. I thought you didn't love me anymore!" I was mad as all hell. I only saw her one more time before I enlisted, and then only to see my son.'

The padre interrupted gently, 'What did your Lucy have to say then?'

'She said she'd made a dreadful mistake and asked me to forgive her. But I was in no mood to forgive anyone.' After a pause, he continued, 'I've sent her and my son most of my wages to make sure they're well provided for.'

'Well?' said the Padre. 'What is the position now?'

'Lucy has sent this letter, begging me to forgive her and return to our marriage and family.'

'What have you decided to do?'

'I don't know, Padre. That's why I'm here with you now.'

The padre stood up. 'Let's walk, Harold, and talk.'

They left the tent and walked slowly up the rise away from the camp.

'Do you still love your wife, Harold?'

'I don't know how to answer that, Padre.' They had breasted the rise. A few hundred yards away a burial party was toiling away, slowly but surely extending the graveyard.

The padre pointed to the rows of crosses. 'Harold, those men had no chance to forgive anybody. I'm not saying forgiveness comes easily, especially when one has been deeply wounded; when trust has been abused and deceit has crept into a union. But, as our good Lord has shown us, there must be forgiveness, or hate will eat away at us and erode our ability to be compassionate and merciful.'

McErbain listened silently.

'The act of forgiveness is a wonderful thing,' continued the padre, 'a great test of character, but it must be unconditional, with no strings attached; otherwise it is not genuine forgiveness, and it will fail.'

'I'll be honest, Padre. I don't know that my character is strong enough.'

'I can only advise, Harold. The decision is up to you.'

The men made their way back to camp and stopped at Jenkins's billet.

'Thank you, Padre, I'll consider what you've said.'

The men shook hands and Padre Jenkins moved into his small tent. He knelt and prayed that Harold McErbain would find it in his heart to forgive his wife's indiscretion.

February 1917

The 5th Field Artillery Brigade had successfully moved close to Grevilliers, west of Pozières, to support the 15th and 8th Australian Infantry Brigades in the proposed attack on Grevilliers and Bapaume, both still held by the German regiments. Haig was headstrong in his desire to attack the German forces again at the Somme, and refused to be swayed from his views on how the war should be won, regardless of the horrendous losses of Allied troops. He would brook no interference from Neville, the French Commander who wished to wait until America could enter the war.

Allied Command feared a German retreat would lure the Allies too far forward. It was thought that the enemy would then launch a massive counterattack. This fear had kept the Allies advancing nervously, making less progress than they would otherwise have done.

Darkness was an hour away as the 14th Battery continued laying a soft barrage on the village of Grevilliers. Lieutenant McErbain was studying the barrage effect through binoculars from the outpost, and failed to observe the stealthy enemy movement to the north-east of his position.

He turned to Corporal Gillies.

'I expect we'll be standing down soon, Jim.'

Gillies nodded in agreement. 'Light's fading, sir.'

'Jim, for Christ's sake, cut the "sir"!' exclaimed McErbain. 'We worked together on the bloody Cordeaux Dam, remember?'

'I suppose it's automatic, Harold. I see the pips on the shoulder and I say, "sir".' He grinned. Then his expression changed. 'Bloody hell, here's a mounted runner and coming fast.' He pointed to the north. The rider was approaching at a full gallop. Not dismounting, the runner gasped out his message, while the pony pranced about.

'German infantry, hundreds of them, heading this way from the north. They're only 1,000 yards away!'

'Understood!' called McErbain, and the runner galloped off towards Brigade Headquarters some 2,000 yards west.

'You go to 1 and 2 Guns, I'll get to 3 and 4!' yelled McErbain, as he ran along the base of the parapet.

McErbain had tried to explain to Lieutenant Colonel Tideswell that he considered the 14th too close to the front line for safe operation. Tideswell had dismissed his concerns, saying, 'Harold, it's a fact that the Germans are about to retreat. There's every indication from our patrol reports that they are moving. If so, we need to be as close as possible to give our infantry support. If not, the Germans could re-attack, the infantry would be cut to pieces and any ground gained by the advance would be lost. You must stay in that position, we have no option.'

Yelling to No. 3 and No. 4 Guns to load up with small arms, he turned and sprinted back to his outpost. As he ran, his worst fears were realised. A line of German infantry in advance formation was moving rapidly toward his battery emplacement. Sprinting towards No. 2 Gun, he screamed, 'Here they come, 300 yards out!'

The guns were silent as the detachments feverishly loaded their Lee Enfield .303s. The German line kept advancing. 'Grenade!' yelled Wagga, as a German stick grenade landed in the area forward of the 18-pounder. The entire detachment of eight men flung themselves to the ground, their arms covering their heads in anticipation of the blast. The grenade exploded with a deafening roar, the shrapnel ricocheting off the metal plates of the 18-pounder.

The detachment was lucky – the plates saved their lives. Not so lucky was the padre, who some hours earlier had decided to hitch a ride with an ammunition wagon to the gun positions. As he climbed down from the wagon at No. 1 Gun, ricocheting shrapnel hit his right arm and right cheek.

He staggered into the position. All eight gunners were either unconscious or badly dazed. The first injured gunner he noticed was Jim Gillies, blood flowing from his badly gashed head. He fell on his knees and placed Jim Gillies's bleeding head on his thigh. With his left hand, he applied pressure to Gillies's gaping head wound; his right arm hung uselessly by his side. He was unaware of the three German infantrymen clambering over the front of the parapet.

Two of the three, with bayonets fixed and rifles lowered to cover any movement, were now quickly assessing the situation. Muffled shouts, screams and shots filled the air as the other positions became scenes of hand-to-hand combat.

The third German, a Prussian captain with his revolver drawn, stepped towards them. In heavily accented English, the captain addressed the padre. 'What have we here? Are the English so short of men, they use priests as infantry? In any case,' he continued, 'we do not take prisoners, especially injured ones.'

He slowly raised his Steyr 9-millimetre revolver to the padre's temple.

Badly dazed by the grenade, Jum had heard enough of the conversation to understand what was about to happen. Lying still, face down, he was close enough to the German officer to touch the heel of his boot. He leapt upwards, crashing into the officer's back and smashing him into the steel wheel of the 18-pounder. The bullet whizzed harmlessly past the padre's head into the sandbagged wall.

Jum frantically grabbed the Steyr from the earth floor, rolled over and fired at the nearest German infantryman, who doubled up as the 9-millimetre slug slammed into his stomach.

The other German infantryman jumped at the sound of the revolver, spinning around in panic. He quickly dropped his rifle and raised his hands as Jum aimed the Steyr. Jum, keeping an eye on the surrendering German, moved back to the stunned officer. He jammed the revolver under his jaw. 'Kill my padre, would you, you mongrel bastard? See how you like this.'

A large fist clamped over Jum's hand, forcing the muzzle away from the Prussian's face. 'Easy, Jum, easy!' Sergeant AJ Casey carefully removed the Steyr from Jum's fingers, then instantly covered the enemy officer.

'This bastard was going to kill our padre!' yelled Jum as he smashed his fist into the German's mouth. The punch slammed the officer's head into the steel rim of the 18-pounder wheel, and he fell back unconscious.

'Mate, we don't want to kill this piece of shit yet,' said AJ. 'We'll get plenty of info from him before that.' The pair looked around the position. Two other Australian Pioneers had control of the surrendered German.

Jum was amazed that none of the detachment had died in the blast. Padre Jenkins had slumped back, semiconscious from his wounds. Men were shaking their heads and rising unsteadily to their feet. Wagga cradled Jim Gillies in his arms. Sergeant Alan Casey and his three men stood at the parapet, carefully watching for any further attacks by German infantry.

'Where'd you come from, AJ?' asked Jum.

'We'd been sent out for a night patrol and just happened to come across you buggers in this shit fight,' he replied. 'The other detachments look like they're on top of it.'

Jum carefully raised his head and glanced through the gloom to No. 2 Gun. The shooting and yelling had stopped; the khaki-clad figures were in control. 'We'll wait while you get sorted out,' called Casey.

'We need to get Gill and the padre back to the CCS in a hurry,' said Jum. 'We'll be OK, AJ, and thanks a heap – we were in trouble there.'

Jum hoisted the padre onto his broad shoulders and made his way to the rear parapet of the position. Wagga had lifted the now unconscious Gillies and was a few paces behind Jum.

The rattle of a German Maxim machine gun came from 300 yards out. A sweep of bullets blasted the parapet top of the No. 1 position. Jum fell heavily, a bullet in his thigh.

'Get that bastard!' yelled Casey. 'Watch for the muzzle flash!'

Wagga gently laid Jim Gillies down. He jumped to the lifting handle at the rear of the 18-pounder, calling loudly as he moved. 'Quick, Ron! Here, give us a hand!'

Ron Roberts reached Wagga. With a superhuman effort, Wagga raised the rear shaft and swung the gun barrel to point at the machine gun, still firing in bursts. Putting his shoulder under the lifting handle, he grunted under the strain. He raised the dead weight of the steel gun as Ron quickly slammed an empty ammunition box under the recoil arm to prop it up. Wagga released the arm onto the box.

'Range, Ron, range!' yelled Wagga as he dragged open the breech.

Ron, his eye to the rangefinder, wound the wheel down. 'Range on!' he yelled, as Wagga slid the shell into the breech and snapped the lanyard. With a thunderous roar, the gun fired. Earth, mud, metal debris and human parts erupted in a cataclysmic blast.

'Reload!' screamed Ron. Wagga already had the breech open. The mud erupted again. Bob began feeding shells to Wagga.

AJ Casey and his infantrymen stopped firing their .303s and watched, open-mouthed, as the two brothers and Bob lashed the area with six high-explosive shells in forty seconds.

Ron held up his hand. Both he and Wagga were panting hard.

'I think they're done, Wagga,' said Ron. Bob stood with a live shell ready.

'Fucking done, all right!' said Sergeant Casey. He surveyed the 30-yard smoking crater where the machine gun and its detachment of four had been only moments before. 'Glad I'm here, not there!' he muttered.

'Jum!' yelled Wagga, as he ran towards Jum, who was lying across the parapet. The padre had slipped from Jum's shoulders as the machine gun burst had sprayed across, hitting Jum's right leg with two rounds. Jum lay motionless, his face twisted in agony.

The clean-up of the injured men took two hours. The casualties and dead were moved back to the CCS, with fresh detachments of gunners now at standby in the positions.

But there was no further machine gun or rifle fire from the attacking German force. The offensive had been repelled. Eighty or so German prisoners had been taken, and a rough body count established that there were forty-five dead German troops. Five gunners had lost their lives, and some fifteen men had been injured.

On the crude operating table, Jum Bevan had the second bullet removed from his thigh.

'He has a bone fragment chipped from his femur,' muttered Captain Stanley Davies, as he carefully sutured the neat scalpel incision. 'He'll be going to the Australian General Hospital at Sandgate or Perham Downs with this injury.' He addressed the assisting orderly. 'How is the padre?'

'He's doing well. We removed the three pieces of shrapnel from his arm, and his cheek is all neatly sewn up. We gave him a draught, and he's sound asleep.'

Jim Gillies slowly moved his head to obtain a view through the tent flap. A single oil lamp hung from the tent's centre pole, casting a dim light and throwing dull shadows on the tent sides. Gingerly, he felt his head. His only recollection of the battle was the warning yell and the bounce of the German grenade.

Some ten other still forms lay beside each other on the tent floor. With his lamp raised, a medical orderly inspected the injured men under his care. When Gillies moved, the orderly knelt beside him. 'How goes it, mate?' he inquired.

'What happened?' asked Gillies.

'You No. 1 Gun detachment?' Gillies nodded. 'You caught a grenade in your position,' said the orderly. 'How you all survived, we'll never know. You got fifteen sutures in your head gash, you lost some blood, but you're all right.'

'Who else is here?'

'Jum Bevan – he caught a machine gun burst as he was carrying the padre out of the position, got two in his right thigh. And of course the padre was clobbered.'

'What?'

'Stay down, stay down, he's fine. That's him sleeping in the corner there. He caught some small pieces in his right arm, and had his cheek opened up, but he's all right. Tell me, Gunner, what the bloody hell was a padre doing in the gun position, anyway?'

'He's always doing it,' said Gillies with a wry smile. 'I think he must be a frustrated gunner or something.'

The orderly rose, checked the other injured and moved from the tent.

Jim Gillies lay back. Aided by the pain-killing draught he had received earlier, sleep quickly overtook him.

Hours before, as the stretcher bearers finalised the removal of the dead and injured, Bob sat on the edge of the gun position. He had wanted to be allowed to accompany Jum back to the CCS, but McErbain was firm. 'No, Bob,' he repeated. 'Jum's doing well. You'd only get in the way of the medical staff.'

Wagga sat beside Bob and placed an arm on his shoulder. 'He'll be fine, Bob. As I've said before, that Jum's a tough bastard.'

'I know, Wagga, but he always seems to be getting whacked.'

'How the hell are you going to explain the padre's wounds?' Ron Roberts asked McErbain. As temporary battery captain, it was McErbain's task to write the daily reports detailing injuries and deaths.

'It won't be easy, Ron. You know Tideswell warned Conrick that he didn't want to have to explain a chaplain's death to Command. But we can't tie him up. They won't court-martial him. I don't know how they'll resolve it.' Then he added, 'We won't need to worry about him for a couple of months anyway – he'll be on rest and recuperation for some time.'

The German captain walked behind his corporal, carefully picking his way between shell craters, mud, destroyed artillery, human remains and large bloated horse carcasses half-immersed in sludge. Directly behind, Sergeant Alan Casey kept a watchful eye on the two prisoners.

The scared young corporal's eyes darted in all directions. He seemed to expect to be attacked or shot at any moment. The arrogant captain looked sullenly at the ground as the trio neared Headquarters.

The captain slowed deliberately and Casey slammed him in the back with his rifle butt. 'Come on, you square-headed bastard, keep moving! *Schnell! Schnell!*'

The German turned. 'I speak excellent English. Please do not address me in German.'

'If you don't move, I'll blow your fucking head off! Do you understand that language?' said Casey, slipping the safety catch on the .303 rifle.

The sergeant standing guard outside the Headquarters tent asked, 'What have we here, AJ?'

'A couple for interrogation – the Boche captain may have something,' replied Casey.

They entered the dim tent, which was a hive of activity. An infantry major of the 2nd Division came forward. The corporal was taken outside to a newly erected wire compound.

'Where did you capture these two, Sergeant?' asked the major.

'They attacked the 14th Battery after tossing a grenade into the No. 1 Gun position. We three 3rd Pioneers happened to be on patrol, saw that we were needed and jumped in. The square head speaks English!'

The Prussian captain drew himself to attention. 'I will give my name, serial number, rank and unit.'

Casey's large hand clamped on the German's neck. 'Speak when you're spoken to, Boche, and you'll tell the major whatever he wants to know.'

'My name is Carl Ernst Junge, Serial Number 765422, Captain, 4th Division, Prussian Guard.'

'Prussian Guard, eh!' said the major. 'Interesting!'

'May I leave now, sir?' asked Casey. 'My men are waiting.'

'Of course, Sergeant,' said the major as he showed Casey to the tent flap. 'We don't get many Prussian Guard prisoners,' he added, more quietly. 'He's a real prize. They're usually full of information, but it's hard to get them to talk.'

'I'm sure you'll manage, sir,' said Casey, saluting smartly and setting off back to his men.

The major called to the sergeant at the tent flap, 'Sergeant, put this bloke in the compound. We need a couple of staff officers to be present at his interrogation.'

Standing in the compound with forty or so other prisoners, Junge's eyes took in everything. He gestured almost imperceptibly to the corporal taken prisoner with him at the gun position. The young man walked casually over to him.

'I am going to escape from here,' Captain Junge whispered in German. 'I will need your help.'

'Yes, Captain, if I can be of assistance.'

The men stopped speaking as an officer passed by.

'Hi, Charlie,' the officer greeted the sentry.

'How are ya, sir?'

'Fine. All good here?'

'Yeah, no trouble.'

The officer moved into the Headquarters tent.

'That private did not even salute his officer!' the German corporal said.

'You know what would happen in our army?' the captain asked. The corporal nodded. He knew only too well the result of insubordination.

'After dark,' the captain continued, 'I'll move to the back of the wire. You engage the guard – ask him for a cigarette. I'll get under the wire. It has been put up in a hurry, and it won't hold.'

Darkness closed in quickly after 1730. At a nod from the captain, the corporal moved to the gate. By hand signals, he made his desire for a cigarette plain.

'Fuck off, mate,' said the Australian sentry. 'I've only got two left.'

The German pleaded by gesture.

'Oh, all right. Only one, though.'

Meanwhile, the captain, taking advantage of the situation, lay on his back, while two other prisoners squatted in front. Two of the captured Germans had spent some hours unobtrusively digging with their boots at the base of the wire. The captain strained the wire up and slithered through the small opening. He had taken care during the afternoon to smear mud over his regimental flashes and had also removed his captain's ranking. He hoped that, since it was dark, the uniform would pass at a distance.

He had carefully observed the mounted runners coming and going during the afternoon: how they dismounted, hitched the reins and how long they were inside. Although his pocket compass had been taken, he knew the topography to the north-east like the back of his hand. Escape depended entirely upon where the infantry was currently positioned. Of further concern – should he get that far – was the reception awaiting him when he approached his own front line.

He rolled and stood, his hands in pockets. He attempted to imitate the rolling gait of the Australians he had studied all afternoon.

Captain Junge could not believe his luck. Hung around one of the hitched ponies' saddles was a slouch hat. He quickly mounted the pony, jamming the hat down on his head and securing the chin strap under his jaw.

He resisted the desperate urge to gallop headlong away and allowed the pony to canter slowly in the direction of Beugny and

Morchies to the north-east. What could be more normal than a mounted runner cantering towards the front line, slouch hat barely discernible on the moonless night?

He acknowledged a few waves from groups of infantry with a raised right hand. As he approached what he judged to be the front line, he slowed his mount to a trot. One mistake here would cost him his life.

He glanced to either side. Troops asleep in shell holes, large craters and defiles did not stir. The road to Morchies was now little more than a rough track. He trotted carefully, avoiding the large holes.

He approached a sentry, who turned, casually watching him draw near.

'Where are you off to, mate?'

With his hand appearing to adjust his chin strap, Junge called out, his voice muffled, 'HQ outpost.'

'Go down to the right, about 200 yards. You'll see the sentry.'

Junge waved as the sentry turned away. His heart hammering, he spun the pony to the left, kicking it in the ribs. The animal flattened its ears, breaking into a full gallop.

The sentry turned and called, 'Not out there, you stupid bastard to your right!'

Junge, riding low over the horse's neck, did not look back.

The sentry, in disbelief, unslung his rifle. 'What the bloody hell!'

Horse and rider disappeared into the darkness. Junge continued for half a mile, slowing to a canter. A bullet whined past him to his left, another thudded into a tree stump, and a third slammed into an earth mound.

He quickly dismounted, slapping the pony on the rump. He moved towards the German line cautiously. He knew the front line German sentries would fire at anything that moved, except for their own returning evening patrols. He had no alternative but to wait until morning or join up with a night patrol. He hid himself in a small clump of bushes.

He heard the patrol before he saw it. '*Ich bin Deutsch! Ich bin Deutsch!*' he called quietly. He stood, raising his arms and repeating, '*Ich bin Deutsch.*' Deathly silence followed, and he felt the hair on the back of his neck rise.

Then a quiet, authoritative voice asked, in German, 'What is your unit?'

'4th Division, Prussian Guard,' he replied, also in German, his body flooded with relief. The shadowy figures came into view. 'Thank God I found you! I have just escaped from the English.'

'Was that you on the horse?'

'Yes, I commandeered one of their ponies.'

The patrol accompanied him towards the German line.

LATE FEBRUARY 1917

The German submarines in the English Channel were wreaking havoc. In the third week of April 1917, fifty-five British merchant ships were sunk, severely affecting supplies of men, arms, food and ammunition to France. Still, the port of Le Havre was crowded.

The Hospital Ship *St David* sat low in the water, full to the gunwales with injured men. The hawser lines, dropped one by one, were hastily hauled aboard by waiting seamen. The *St David*, freed of the last hawser, gently edged away from the wharf.

Easing along at two knots, the *Saxone* slowly edged her way into the space left. The ships operated a busy shuttle service, taking injured men out and bringing restless, eager new infantry in. With hundreds of injured and mutilated men bound for long hospitalisation, slow, lingering death or a mindless, blank existence due to mental damage, the ships were kept extremely busy.

Jum Bevan was aboard the *St David*, bound for Perham Downs in Wiltshire. Padre Jenkins's destination was Worgret Hill, where injured men who were considered likely to recover fully were hospitalised.

At Southampton dock, Jum was still stretcher-bound. His injuries, though healing well, had caused his leg to stiffen and become immobile.

He felt guilty leaving the men of his battery behind to deal with the enemy onslaught, but thought, 'I'm useless as I am, and I feel I've earned a damned good rest.'

Padre Jenkins and Jum sat together as they awaited transfer. Jum lit a cigarette. Jenkins broke the silence. 'I don't know how to say this, Jum, but I owe you my life. Thank you.'

Jum blushed. 'Come on, Padre. Anyone would have done the same thing.'

'No, Jum, not everyone would have done what you did. Sergeant Casey told me the whole story.'

Jum looked up at the high timber ceiling. Pigeons fluttered everywhere, trying to land amongst the rafters. He cast his mind back to the gun position.

'Well, Padre, that German mongrel was about to shoot you like a sick dog. He would have made sure he killed all of us in the position.'

'Yes, I thought I was gone when I saw the look on his face. Anyway, Sergeant Casey is writing a report on your actions, and he'll forward it to Lieutenant Colonel Tideswell for his consideration.'

Two stretcher bearers approached. The leading one called out, 'You Gunner Bevan?'

'That's me,' replied Jum, as Claude Jenkins rose and moved aside.

'Sorry, mate,' said the second bearer. 'Have you finished here?' He'd noticed the padre's white collar.

'Just thanking this man for saving my life,' smiled Jenkins to the bearer.

Jum, reddening with embarrassment, muttered, 'It was nothing.'

'Saved your life, eh?' grinned the stretcher bearer.

'One-way ticket to heaven, mate, I reckon,' chirped the other bearer, 'saving a padre!'

'Right, Padre, Gunner Bevan is off to Perham Downs. Where're you heading?'

'I'm for Worgret Hill, I think,' replied Jenkins.

The bearer looked at his list. 'We have a couple for Worgret Hill. You might as well come with us. I'll check with the boss.'

The bearers carried Jum on the stretcher while Jenkins walked alongside, moving towards a large motor lorry that had been converted to an ambulance vehicle.

After loading Jum into the rear, the bearer spoke to a transport sergeant.

'I know you're going to Perham Downs and Worgret Hill, but the padre is a captain; he has an ambulance to himself,' explained the sergeant wearily. The injured were arriving in greater numbers, and his transports were unable to cope with the ever-increasing demand.

Jenkins, overhearing the discussion, asked, 'Are you short of vehicles, Sergeant?'

'Padre, we're desperate. It's got so bad the walking wounded may have to go by train,' the sergeant replied.

'Find me a seat in the back of that truck, then. Gunner Bevan is from my brigade. I'll be happy to travel with him.'

The sergeant needed no second bidding. 'Get the padre aboard, with a good seat,' he instructed the bearer.

The warm spring weather was a far cry from the mud and rain of northern France. The ambulance toiled on its way to Salisbury, providing the patients with an uneventful ride. A wide, curved gravel driveway welcomed the casualties at Perham Downs Hospital. The administration offices were directly behind the oval lawn and gardens, with wards throughout the three-storey Victorian building. The sentry on the main gate was jovial.

'All right, Corporal, you know where to go. Glad to see you brought some good weather!'

A matron emerged from the main entrance as the corporal opened the rear flap of the ambulance. Handing the matron his schedule, the corporal waited. 'What have we here, driver?' an officious voice demanded.

The corporal turned, saluting as he did so. He knew what was coming. The last person he wished to encounter was Subaltern, 2nd Lieutenant Chesterton.

Six weeks' training had done little to improve Chesterton's knowledge of the army, weapons, the enemy or any other matters of importance to a young army Officer. What he did understand was the 'us and them' mentality, carried over from his public school days and two unhappy years at Oxford. Being aware that a single pip on each shoulder had the power to make ordinary soldiers jump to attention leant an otherwise timid person a modicum of confidence. With his swagger stick clutched under his left armpit, he leant forward, peering into the darkness of the ambulance.

'We have some stretcher cases, sir,' said the young matron.

'Yes, Matron, I can see that,' scowled the lieutenant. Claude Jenkins, stiff from the two-hour ride from the Southampton docks, was stretching as he moved to the rear of the lorry.

'Why do we have walking patients taking up valuable space in a stretcher ambulance?' the lieutenant asked the corporal driver. He turned and addressed Jenkins as he dismounted. 'Explain yourself, Private. Why are you in this ambulance?'

Claude Jenkins's benign smile faded.

'I was travelling with my friend, who was badly machine-gunned, to keep him company.'

'Balderdash, you had no right to travel in this ambulance!'

'Excuse me, sir,' piped up the corporal.

'Speak when spoken to,' the 2nd lieutenant barked at the driver.

He turned again to Jenkins. 'I asked you a question, Private. Who gave you the right to travel in this ambulance?' He turned and snatched the clipboard, with the corporal's orders attached, from the nervous matron. 'I might have known, bloody insolent Awestralians,' and turned back to Jenkins, who had now alighted from the rear of the lorry.

Jenkins had heard enough. 'TENSHUN!' he screamed in the 2nd lieutenant's face.

The lieutenant, taken aback, dropped his swagger stick.

'I am Captain Claude Jenkins, 5th Field Artillery Brigade, 2nd Division, Australian Imperial Force. Now you salute me, you humbug, or I'll have you court-martialled so quickly, your pants will drop off!'

The lieutenant made a flustered salute.

'Take me to your commanding officer at once,' commanded Jenkins. 'Matron, will you arrange movement of these injured men, please. I'll return soon.' Jenkins seemed to have grown 3 inches taller as he strode off, the 2nd lieutenant unhappily trying to keep pace with him.

The corporal turned to the laughing audience in the ambulance. 'Who the hell is that fireball?'

'That's our brigade padre, Captain Jenkins,' said Jum.

The driver shook his head. 'No one, but no one, speaks to Chesterton like that. His uncle is a brigadier, boss of one of our regiments.'

'The padre's been wounded twice in action,' said Jum. 'I don't think a pipsqueak like that's going to worry him.'

The HQ door opened and the orderly captain of Perham Downs strode through, accompanying Jenkins.

'Give these men immediate treatment, Matron,' said the captain, 'We must get them out of this hot sun. You,' he pointed to the corporal driver, 'on the double, round up orderlies to get these men inside – move!' The corporal ran to the nearest ward.

The captain turned to Claude Jenkins and said, 'Is there anything else I can do, Captain?'

'Thank you, no,' said the padre. 'It is a pleasure, though, to be helped by polite people.'

The English captain took Jenkins by his left arm and steered him towards a waiting staff car. 'My driver will take you directly to Worgret Hill, Captain.'

But the padre excused himself briefly and walked over to Jum, now lying on the portico out of the sun. Jum sat up and smiled as Jenkins held out his hand.

'Thanks, Jum. I'll never forget what you did.'

They shook hands, and Jenkins walked back to the staff car, which disappeared down the gravel drive towards Worgret Hill Command Depot.

A week passed, and Jum improved each day. Food and proper care paid large dividends. Despite the pain, Jum forced himself to walk. A naturally fit, restless man, inactivity depressed him. The cool walks through the leafy forests that bordered the road uphill from Tidworth soon rendered Jum's limp barely noticeable.

He was concerned that no word had arrived from Bob. He felt a great sense of relief when the corporal driver he'd met on the first day handed him the envelope containing Bob's hastily written note. It assured him that all the Brigade men were well and healthy.

Bob also mentioned that the talk was that a few of the brigade were to be sent to England for training on the new Mark IV 18-pounder. Jum wondered what changes had been made to the gun. He guessed that the recoil mechanism had been redesigned, to make the weapon more tractable and easier to use.

While Jum had been worried about Bob, he still hadn't informed his own family of his health or whereabouts. Bob felt more like family to him now, as did the men of his detachment.

He only contacted his real family in Australia occasionally, when he needed a quick fiver.

A couple of weeks later, Jum waited impatiently as the doctor twisted his leg, then made him squat and jump and stretch the injured leg in all directions.

'Well, my good man, it appears you have made a remarkable full recovery,' smiled the doctor. 'A few more days and we'll have you off the sick list, fighting fit again.' He smiled again as he moved to the next patient.

Jum was in two minds: he was delighted to be moving out of the hospital, but not too keen on returning to northern France. It seemed impossibly ironic that, just as he had recovered his health and spirits, he was to be returned to the nightmare of the Western Front.

A week after the scene between Claude Jenkins and Lieutenant Chesterton at Perham Downs Hospital, the latter's uncle, Brigadier Chesterton, and his adjutant, Captain Jonathon Smythe, were enjoying their afternoon tea and a chat.

'With respect, sir,' said Smythe, 'Bertie carried on like a twit that day. And the captain in HQ at Perham Downs saw the whole thing – he was watching from the window.'

'Well, there you have it, Jonathon,' said Chesterton. 'He's the product of a weak, ineffectual father – my brother was never a disciplinarian – and a monstrously demanding mother. The boy was never allowed to make a decision for himself. He was bullied at Old Cranleigh and a dismal failure at Oxford. But he did inherit his father's mathematical ability, if nothing else. His father is a professor, you know.'

'Have you ever thought that perhaps a challenge would do him good, sir?' asked Smythe.

'Do you have something in mind?'

'The artillery school at Larkhill is said to be first class. What about tossing the boy in the deep end? Could be the making of him.'

'I'll give it some thought,' said the brigadier, nodding slowly.

The following morning Brigadier Chesterton called Smythe into his office. 'Well, Smythe, I've taken your advice. I've spoken to Brigadier Holmes at Larkhill, and he's only too delighted to help out. Bertie moves in about three weeks, when the current school is completed. He'll start at the bottom.' He rose from his desk. 'I hope I've done the right thing.'

'I'm sure you have, sir,' said Smythe.

LATE MARCH 1917

The spring sun slid slowly behind the low cloud hanging over the green hills of the Wiltshire countryside. Nurses and orderlies hurried everywhere, trying desperately to keep up with the increasing stream of casualties from the Western Front.

Jum was bored. His injuries were now close to being healed, and the enforced inactivity of the hospital made him anxious.

The convalescent hospital at Perham Downs sat on a rise, 1 mile from Tidworth village. Jum had dressed and meandered away from the rear of the hospital building towards the high, wire perimeter fence surrounding the grounds. The gathering darkness ensured that he would not be seen. He found a loose area of wire along the fence and wriggled his way through.

He set off, moving away from the main gate and the sentry on duty. Strong vines wrapped around his ankles as he tried to move quietly. A few hundred yards from the entrance to the hospital, Jum emerged from the deep brush onto the road to Tidworth. He moved quickly towards the village, where he made his way to the Ram's Head Hotel on the main road. The bar was full of a range of people, including artillery instructors from nearby Larkhill Camp, service personnel from Perham Downs, locals and a few girls from the village.

Jum breasted the bar and ordered a pint from a pretty blonde barmaid. He anxiously searched the crowd, but saw no familiar face that could confirm his AWL from the hospital. He faded back into the general hubbub.

The open fire in the lounge countered the chill of the approaching evening. Jum sat back on the leather sofa, relaxing as the beer took effect. He felt his leg where he had been hit by the machine gun burst. Though it was still a little tender, he seemed to have lost some feeling in his thigh around the scar. 'Hope it won't interfere with my diving,' he mused.

Deep in thought, he hadn't noticed the girl who had sat down next to him on the sofa.

'How are you, love?'

Jum turned and smiled. 'Not too bad, I suppose. Nearly good enough to get back to the line.'

'You on the Western Front?'

'Soon as my leg heals.'

'Oh, you got a "Blighty", did you?'

'Bit worse than a Blighty. Machine gun burst to my leg.' Jum smiled again. 'Care for a drink?'

The girl eyed Jum. 'I shouldn't, really. People round here talk about anything.'

'Half a pint of bitter?' Jum stood. His face creased in an inviting smile, his blue-grey eyes twinkled.

'Oh, all right then. They can think what they like.'

Back on the sofa with drinks in hand, Jum and the girl talked quietly.

'My boyfriend's somewhere on the Somme, I think. He's not really my boyfriend, though, just a friend,' she said quickly.

'He'll be seeing some tough action over there at the moment,' said Jum.

'My name's Sally, Sal to my friends.'

'Just call me Jum,' he answered with a crooked smile. 'You live around here, Sal?'

'About half a mile back up the east end of the village with my mum and dad and the family.'

Sally was attractive in a plain kind of way and had an air of uncomplicated ease.

'I work up at Perham Downs Hospital,' she added. 'I'm an assistant cook.'

Jum paled, then relaxed. 'I'm in the hospital at the moment.'

'Shouldn't you be in bed?' Sally said, a mischievous look in her eye. 'It's after lights out.'

'I snuck out for a few beers,' said Jum, 'and lucky me, I met you!'

Sally laughed. 'Don't get caught. They say if you're good enough to drink at the local, you're good enough for the front line.'

'Good enough for anything, I reckon.'

Later in the evening, most of the locals had left the hotel. Just a handful of servicemen remained at the bar. Jum spoke to Sally.

'I wonder if I can get a bed here tonight? I don't feel like tramping up to Perham Downs in this.' Jum pointed to the window. The rain was sheeting down in great wind-blown squalls from the west.

Sally stood. 'I'll ask Liz at the bar.'

Jum watched as Sally spoke to the barmaid. She walked back to him.

'You're lucky, they have a cancellation.'

Jum waved and nodded to the blonde behind the bar. With his spirits up, the next words rolled off his tongue.

'Well, maybe I'm your saviour – you can't be expected to walk home in this. I'll sleep on the floor, you can have the bed.'

Sally looked at Jum, then stood abruptly and walked back to Liz at the bar, returning after a few moments. 'It's all arranged. I often stay here in town with Lizzie. She'll cover for me tonight, and you certainly won't be sleeping on any floor.'

Sally and Jum made their way to the stair off the entrance, Liz slipping a key unobtrusively into Sally's hand as they passed.

The first-floor room faced the increasing storm from the west. It wasn't long before the storm outside paled into insignificance beside the tempest in progress in the room.

Liz had refused payment from Jum for the room. When he awoke, Sally had gone; the bed was quite cold. Although the rain had eased, dark threatening clouds still rolled in from the west. Jum set off briskly up the hill, away from Tidworth, towards Perham Downs.

He considered his course of action. Through the rear fence or through the front gate? The thought of battling his way through saturated undergrowth made his decision easy.

The sentry eyed him suspiciously as he marched smartly through the gate.

'Where'd you come from, soldier?' he asked abruptly.

Without breaking stride, Jum answered, 'Just back from my morning walk,' and kept going.

He slipped into his ward, sat on his bed and quickly removed his damp tunic.

'Jesus, mate, have you caused a bloody ruckus around here!' The patient in the next bed shook his head slowly. 'They searched for you for hours. You'd better get your story right.'

Half an hour passed. The orderly sergeant appeared and marched to Jum's bed.

'The wild duck has finally settled, eh?' he said sarcastically. 'Now that we have you back again, I suggest you get dressed very quickly and present yourself at the CO's office. NOW!'

Jum sat waiting outside the CO's office. Eventually the orderly sergeant came through the door.

'Come on, Bevan, on your feet, to attention!' The sergeant gestured to the door. 'Get in there! Quick march!' Once Jum was in the room, the sergeant snapped, 'Halt! Stand to attention!'

Lieutenant H. E. Shaw looked up from his desk. 'Absent without leave from 2130 hours on 28th March, 1917 to 0900 hours on 29th March, 1917,' he droned. He did not ask for any explanation. 'Awarded seven days confined to camp, and forfeiture of three days' pay under RW 2nd DAC Standing Orders. March the private out, Sergeant.'

April 1917

8.4.17 Perham Downs.
Received fiver from mother.

Jum Bevan sat quietly in the sun, as he had done for a few days. Corporal Rodney Smith, alighting from his motor lorry ambulance, waved as he approached. He had arrived at Perham Downs with a full load of injured men.

'How's the leg, Jum?' he asked as he sat down.

Jum smiled. 'Fully healed, says the doctor.'

'Well, back in action soon, I suppose, Jum?' ventured Rodney.

'I reckon so. I finished my seven days CC last week. I have five days furlough due. I should take it now, while I can.'

'Well, if your CC's over and you have a furlough due, my family doesn't live far from London. We could catch a train from Tidworth and be there in a couple of hours. Come and stay with us. We have a spare room. I lost my brother in France,' Rodney added. 'First Battle of Ypres, November, 1914 ... How old are you, Jum?'

'Twenty-four. Twenty-five in August.'

'You're the same age. Richard would have been twenty-five next month.'

'I'd love to spend a few days with your family,' said Jum. 'It'd be just the break I need.'

'Let's do it, then. Just let me know when. I can get leave easily.'

'Here you are, Gunner Bevan, your five-day pass. Report back here on the 20th of April at 1800 hours. Understand?' Jum nodded to the orderly sergeant as he tossed his bag onto his shoulder. The few civilian clothes Jum had purchased in Tidworth village had hardly made a dent in the wad of English pounds sitting snugly in his pocket.

Rodney Smith was waiting outside. He had organised a ride for Jum and himself to Tidworth railway station, where they would take the train to London. Settled into the leather of the second-class compartment, the boys chatted away, filling in time. 'Me and my mum and my sister Cissie live in Mostyn Road, in Brixton,' explained Rodney. 'We have a few hard-heads and tough boys in the neighbourhood, but I know them all. There'll be no trouble.'

Small, single-storey terraces lined either side of Mostyn Street, where a swinging sign marked the local tavern.

'That a pub, Rodney?' asked Jum.

'Sure is, Jum, the Stag's Head. We'll be going there soon as we drop our bags.'

Rodney turned the key and swung the door open. A grey-haired woman appeared in the hall and rushed to hug him.

'How are you, my boy?' she asked, her blue eyes lighting up.

'Fine, Mum. I've brought a friend home for a few days. Jum Bevan, my mum, Edie. Jum's Australian, in the artillery. Had a bad time in France. He was machine-gunned, but he's fine now.'

Edie Smith's face clouded at the mention of France, but she said to Jum, 'Welcome to our house. And please stay as long as you wish.'

'Thank you, ma'am,' answered Jum, as Edie led the way to the parlour.

'A cup of tea, boys?'

Rodney looked at Jum, and they both smiled.

'We thought we might go to the –'

'Stag's Head?' finished Edie. 'All right. Show Jum to Richard's room. Dinner's at 7.'

Walking to the hotel, Jum glanced at the young man beside him. 'No dad, Rodney?'

'No. He died when we were young. Worked the coal face until a collapse fixed him up. The insurance bought us this place and we had a little left over. So we moved from Manchester ten years ago. Mum worked hard for years as a cleaning lady, put us through school. Richard was a mechanic until he joined up. Of course, I followed, and now I'm a driver.'

As they walked into the Stag's Head, the smoke and the noise of voices engulfed them. Rodney nodded here and there as they approached the bar. 'Two pints of bitter, Charlie,' Rodney called to the barman. With beers in hand, a group quickly formed around Jum and Rodney, firing questions at them.

As a wounded front-line artilleryman, Jum was given hero status. The pints kept coming, until Jum said finally, 'Jesus, Rodney, no more or I'll be heaving all over your mother's table.'

The cool evening breeze was a welcome relief after the smoky atmosphere of the pub. As they approached the Smith household, a tall, slender girl waved to them. Rodney returned the wave as the girl broke into a run to greet them. 'It's Cissie, my sister.'

Rodney introduced the pair and said, 'Jum and I had a few pints at the Stag, lots of fun.'

'Where are you from, Jum?' asked Cissie.

'Just a colonial, Cissie, from Sydney, Australia.'

'Oh, you're in France, then?'

'No,' he said. 'I'm in Brixton.'

Cissie laughed. 'I asked for that.'

The three entered the terrace and Edie met them with a welcoming smile.

Later, after they'd finished off a tasty Irish stew, conversation turned to the Western Front.

The boys lit cigarettes, retiring to the modest parlour. The two women quickly put the kitchen in order and joined them.

'You got a room here for four weeks?' asked Jum light-heartedly.

'Oh, do stay!' said Cissie.

Cissie had an attractive face and fresh blue eyes. She had a no-nonsense air, but laughter came easily to her. Jum could see the strength in her face. She asked endless questions about Australia, and within an evening knew and understood much about Douglas Park, the Cordeaux Dam and the Sydney beaches.

Edie turned to Jum. 'How much longer, do you think, Jum?'

'Well, last year we belted each other and gained nothing. We're still in the same position. It looks to be the same in 1917.'

'I think I've had enough of the Western Front,' said Edie. 'Were you where I lost my boy, Richard?'

'Yes, Mrs Smith, I was at the Somme, Pozières and Ypres. We lost a lot of mates.'

Jum put a cigarette to his mouth, hands trembling as he attempted to strike the match.

Cissie moved over to Jum and took the matches from his shaking fingers. 'Here, let me.' So saying, she quickly slipped a cigarette into her own mouth, struck the match, and lit first her cigarette then Jum's, her hand firmly holding his.

'Cissie!' said her mother. 'Smoking!'

'Mum, I've been smoking for two years,' said Cissie offhandedly. 'You need something to relieve the boredom in the munitions factory.'

She smiled at Jum as she slowly released his hand.

'We make 'em, you fire 'em. I work a press that stamps out the percussion caps for shells and smaller arms,' she explained. 'You must use an awful lot because we make an awful lot. We have teams working twenty-four hours now. The machines don't stop, except for breakdown or maintenance.'

'Just keep making them, Cissie,' said Jum with a rueful smile. 'We'll take all you can produce.'

Cissie stood up. 'I'm off to bed,' she said. 'My shift starts at 7 am tomorrow.' She waved as she left the room.

Jum's instant of panic was over – Cissie lighting his cigarette had eased the moment. He could still feel the touch of her hand. He'd thought of Henry Larkin and the others who were never leaving France; he had had flashes of the night in Sausage Gully when two Germans died at his hands and Bob had killed the young German boy; he had seen Padre Jenkins with the revolver at his temple, eyes closed as he waited for certain death.

'Time for bed, Jum?' asked Rodney.

'Sure thing, mate, I'm buggered,' said Jum.

Jum undressed and sank into the clean, sweet-smelling sheets, luxuriating in the softness. He dreamt. A woman, smooth and sensuous, rubbed against him. Jum woke gasping.

'Ssh!' the voice whispered. 'You'll wake the neighbourhood! It's Cissie. Just relax and be quiet.'

Aroused but exhausted, Jum drifted back into half-sleep. The next thing he knew, early morning sun was filtering through his closed eyelids. He rolled over in the bed and rested on one elbow.

'Damn,' he thought, 'that was some dream!' He rose, washed and shaved in the bathroom, dressed casually and walked to the kitchen. Cissie and her mother were eating a simple breakfast.

'Did you sleep well, Jum?' asked Edie.

'Like a log, Mrs Smith, thanks to your food and soft bed.'

'You were tired, Jum,' smiled Cissie. 'But not that tired!' she added softly. Edie Smith had turned to the stove. Cissie stood and placed her hand on Jum's neck. The sensation of her touch went down to Jum's toes.

'Bloody hell, that was no dream!' he whispered. She bent over his shoulder and nibbled his ear. 'Next time, I want you awake.' She squeezed his neck, called goodbye to her mother and left. At the front door she turned, waved and was gone. Jum sat, his mind awhirl, his erection swelling at the memory of the previous night.

'More toast, Jum?' asked Edie.

'No thanks,' he said. 'I think I've had all I can handle for today.' He excused himself and slipped into the bedroom, attempting to hide the excitement of the previous evening's encounter with Cissie.

The following three days and nights were amongst the most enjoyable Jum had known. Cissie called in sick and spent the next day with Jum and Rodney. It was now safe to enjoy London once again. Although approximately 500 London civilians had been killed in Zeppelin raids during 1916, five of these airships had been shot down over England in September 1916. Following these losses, the Zeppelins had been withdrawn from a combat role.

They visited markets, shopped, talked and laughed, even enjoyed a makeshift picnic. Jum felt content and at ease. Friday arrived too quickly.

'When are you due back at Perham Downs, Jum?' Rodney asked. Cissie looked up anxiously.

'Today at 6,' Jum replied in a quiet voice. 'I think I'll be late, though.' He turned and smiled at Cissie. She slipped her hand under his arm and gently held his wrist.

'Don't go AWL again, mate. It's not worth it,' said Rodney.

'Twelve hours late will get me one week's pay and seven days confined to Barracks. It'll be worth it,' Jum said as he gently kissed Cissie's cheek.

Rodney frowned. He knew his sister, and he did not want her hurt. She had suffered enough when Richard had died. 'Fine, we'll get you on the train to Tidworth tomorrow morning, early, right?'

'Fourteen hours AWL, Gunner, explain yourself!' The captain on duty, the morning orderly officer, had a blinding hangover. The mess dinner the previous evening had degenerated into a port-drinking exercise that had only finished at three in the morning. And here was this blasted Australian artillery gunner late back from leave, mumbling some pathetic excuse. 'Go!' he said. 'Get out of my sight!'

The sergeant stopped Jum in the orderly room outer office. 'Lucky for you the captain's not too well this morning! Your orders have come through. You're going to Larkhill for an advanced course on the new 18-pounder in two weeks' time. Get your gear together – you go by motor truck in one hour. You're to report to Headquarters in London. You're on light duties for one week. Move!'

Jum grinned inwardly as he ran to his tent to collect his kit. No charges, and a five-day holiday.

The sergeant stood before the suffering captain. 'Here, take these, sir,' he said, holding out two large headache tablets and a glass of water. The captain accepted them gratefully.

'Thanks, sergeant. Who was that soldier just in here?'

'A Gunner Bevan, from 5th Brigade, Australian Artillery. He's had it tough this last year. Been gassed, wounded by shrapnel twice, caught a machine gun burst to his leg, saw action at the Somme, Pozières and Ypres. He's just arrived here from hospital.'

'The poor bastard,' said the captain, hangover momentarily forgotten. 'He's heading straight back into that dreadful mess. I'm glad I didn't take any action against him. The way this bloody war is going, not too many men will return from the Western Front.'

***22.4.17 Doing guard at HQ London and done it
in through belting a dago which cost me £2.0.0
or a month. Payed the fine.***

Carrying a number of recuperating soldiers, the lorry turned into
Horseferry Road, where one of the Australian Imperial Force HQs
in London was located. Six men alighted from the vehicle and
moved past the guard into the orderly room. The sergeant opened
the door to an inner office.

'Replacements are here, sir,' he called. The orderly officer
entered the room as the sergeant called the men to attention. The
officer addressed the men.

'You're here for a week on light duties. You'll be moving out
to your respective units after that week. Dismiss the men, Sergeant.'

The sergeant showed the men to the sleeping quarters. He spoke
offhandedly. 'Duty roster's on the noticeboard outside the orderly
office. Remember what duty you're on and don't be bloody late!'

The men ambled over to the noticeboard, and Jum noted that
he was on guard duty at 0700 hours the following morning.

Horseferry Road was quiet, damp and foggy at 0700 hours; it was
the start of another miserable day. 'What the bloody hell am
I doing here?' thought Jum, as he peered from his sentry box. He
had been warned that officers came and left the HQ in a steady
stream, and were all to be saluted. The guard was changed every
two hours and off-duty guards stayed in the guard house writing
letters, reading, smoking or playing cards.

Guard duty was boring, repetitive and uneventful. At 1900
hours, Jum was again in the sentry box. The few civilian passers-
by had shown little interest in the men on duty.

A swarthy, well-dressed man with two female escorts
approached. Jum eyed the three carefully. The male had a cigarette
holder in his mouth, and sported ornate rings on both hands.

The trio stopped opposite Jum, and the man proclaimed, 'Here
we have the pride of England, saving us from the German
invaders.' The girls giggled. Emboldened, he continued, 'Seen any
Germans here tonight, General?'

Jum was in no mood for this. It was bad enough standing outside in the cold, which worked its way up through his legs into his back. He spoke curtly. 'Move it on, mate. I don't need your crap.'

The man was slightly taller than Jum. He disentangled his arms from those of his companions.

'Come on, Alfredo, we'll be late for the restaurant,' said one.

'Yeah, move it, Alfredo,' said Jum. 'You and your floozies had best be going.'

Alfredo moved to stand in front of Jum. 'Maybe this little soldier will make me go.'

'Maybe he will,' said Jum, launching a snappy left at Alfredo's nose. Noses have a nasty habit of bleeding badly, especially when broken. Alfredo's was no exception. Blood flowed over his white shirt and well-cut suit as he screamed, 'Police! I'll get the police!'

'Get who you like, mate, and would you like another one to help you on your way?'

A knot of uniforms appeared from the guard house to observe the scene. Alfredo was gesticulating towards Jum and telling all and sundry about his assault by the guard while attempting to stem the blood flow from his squashed nose. Jum was escorted into the guard house, relieved of duty and confined to barracks.

Some time after mid-morning, the orderly sergeant yelled, 'Out here, Bevan, on the double!'

Jum was marched before the orderly officer. The captain was less than pleased by this assault on a civilian. 'What have you to say for yourself, Bevan?'

Jum stood stiffly to attention and did not answer at first. Then he said, 'Sir, blokes just like me are dying in France and killing Germans who say nothing, an enemy we don't even see. Now along comes this loudmouth egging me on. He's lucky that's all he got.'

The captain tapped his pen on the desk. 'You men coming out of the line cannot take matters into your own hands. I see you have a number of earlier charges against you.' He looked at the charge sheet. 'Fined £2 or one month confined to barracks. March him out, Sergeant.'

The week passed slowly. Jum watched for them each time he was on sentry duty, but Alfredo and his two girlfriends did not appear again.

165

MAY 1917

BRIGADE DIARY

*3.5.17 Barrage carried out on Hindenburg
Line, Bullecourt and Reincourt.*

Nothing had changed to any great degree on the Western Front.
The fighting had moved a few miles to the east, and the ravaged
land – stripped trees, destroyed villages, fields cluttered with shell
craters and rusting barbed wire – bore mute testimony to the
ruthless ferocity of the combatants.

Fighting had intensified at Grevilliers in early March 1917. The
Australian 4th Division was experiencing savage, hand-to-hand
combat in areas such as Le Barque and Sapignies. The Allied
advance in this area had been quite rapid, and more than 200
German prisoners had surrendered or been captured.

German front lines at Lagnicourt, Noreuil and Vaux, 3 miles
east of Bapaume, were now the target of heavy artillery barrages in
preparation for a large, concentrated attack by the 7th Australian
Infantry Brigade. Late in March, the advance had commenced. As
the 5th Field Artillery Brigade bombardment lifted, the 7th
Infantry attacked.

Extremely heavy close combat finally secured the villages. But
the German counterattack was swift and severe, with continuous
bombardment of the newly-won Australian front line at
Lagnicourt. The batteries returned fire, repelling the German
attack. Due to their determined fighting, Lagnicourt was retaken
and secured by the 7th Brigade.

The cost of this highly successful operation was many Australian casualties. Approximately 350 men were killed or injured.

At the end of March, regiments of the German Army – the 111/91st RIR and 1st RIR – stubbornly resisted the 7th Brigade along the Bullecourt Road near Lagnicourt. These and other German regiments were observed massing troops for a major counterattack. Constant and intense shelling was kept up on these areas until the enemy's planned attack was abandoned.

Orders were received at the end of May for the 5th Artillery Brigade to march to the town of Albert, about 30 miles south-west of Bapaume and Lagnicourt. During the move to Albert, empty German trains were reported entering the town of Queant, and departing loaded with German troops. Destination – the Hindenburg Line.

Throughout March and April, the enemy had initiated a carefully planned withdrawal to areas of the Hindenburg Line. Allied bombardment on the Hindenburg Line was carried out relentlessly day and night for long periods.

German Command had planned well. Their retirement was ordered and effective. To make matters worse, a large counterattack by the enemy had broken through the Australian right flank, threatening capture of the entire 1st Australian Divisional Artillery. The 5th Field Artillery Brigade engaged in heavy concentrated fire to repel this German advance but was unsuccessful. Waves of German troops now descended upon the Sunken Road and the village of Lagnicourt. Wild hand-to-hand combat ensued, with neither Allied nor German forces capitulating.

After twenty-four hours of this intense battle, German troops attacked the leading Allied outpost, forcing the Allied troops to retire. Determined to hold at any cost, Command brought in the 5th Brigade Artillery, who unleashed a savage wall of steel, forcing the German troops to call it a day.

The Allied troops then pushed the German infantry back towards the Sunken Road. After this battle, Allied intelligence reported a massive German build-up of infantry, a precursor to an imminent attack. But with two Allied brigades brought into action against the German build-up, the proposed attack by the enemy was abandoned.

After eighteen months of some of the heaviest duty against the German war machine on the Western Front, Lieutenant Colonel Tideswell's command of the 5th Field Artillery Brigade was coming to an end. His orders were to take him to the 2nd Division Headquarters. He was appointed to the rank of brigadier. Responsibility for his men would be a thing of the past. He would now have a coordinating position, ensuring smooth transition of men and equipment, whenever and wherever required.

Conrick stood with Tideswell outside the Headquarters tent.

'When do we get our new CO, Robbie?' asked Conrick.

'Anytime now, Terry. You're in charge, of course, until he arrives. As you know, I move out tomorrow at midday.'

'It's been a pleasure to work with you, Robbie,' said Conrick. 'I hope the next boss is half as good as you.'

Tideswell put his hand on Conrick's shoulder. 'We've been through some, this last eighteen months,' he smiled. 'Will the detachment from the brigade make it back from Larkhill before I leave?'

'I'm not sure, sir. I believe they're coming through 2nd DAC.'

'I hope so, Terry. They're a bunch of real artillerymen. Now, here are my last orders as CO. Pull the 14th out of the line – they hand their battery positions over to the 13th and 15th, making them eight-gun batteries for the moment. The 14th are to withdraw to the wagon lines for rest.'

Conrick saluted Tideswell, who finished, 'Look forward to having dinner with you tonight, Terry, to meet the new chief.' Conrick waved as he moved back to the orderly tent.

That evening, Lieutenant Colonel Tideswell introduced Major Conrick to the new commanding officer, Lieutenant Colonel Andrew Smith-Stevens. Smith-Stevens courteously accepted Conrick's greeting.

'What unit have you come from, sir?' asked Conrick.

'1 Anzac. Spent some time in Turkey. Pretty tough down there.'

'Yes, we heard, sir. Gallipoli's a byword here at the Front.' Conrick knew that Smith-Stevens, a highly respected artillery officer, had been moved to France because the artillery was lacking in ranking officers of his calibre and experience.

Two days later, Tideswell bade farewell to his brigade officers as he reluctantly prepared to leave and join the 2nd Division Headquarters, currently established south near Amiens.

The appalling conditions of the previous year's offensives had improved dramatically. The general area of the Somme had surprised everyone with a slight growth of greenery, a welcome change to the deep mud and continual rain of 1916.

Lieutenant Colonel Smith-Stevens sat at his desk, conversing with Major Conrick. 'I understand it was tough here at Pozières and Thiepval, Terry?'

'The 1st and 2nd Divisions had been holed up under bombardment for eight days, no food, water, ammo or medical supplies with the mud waist-deep and impassable. When our artillery arrived, we disrupted the Boche with our own bombardment. Then we had to clear the front-line trenches.' He paused, catching his breath. 'That was something else. Eight hundred or so dead, another 1,200 injured, with the remainder walking out deaf, ravenously hungry and thirsty, filthy and covered in the blood of their mates. And to top it all off, the rats! Anyway, the 800 are buried back there towards Pozières.'

'I saw that graveyard on my way in from Le Havre,' said Smith-Stevens.

'A lot of good men gave their lives in that little deal at Sausage Gully,' said Conrick. 'And what we gained, we've now lost. These Germans just keep coming. We're in for tough times ahead.'

'There are more than 800 in that graveyard.'

'Well, a few months have passed since then. Newfoundlanders, British and New Zealanders are there now. Also about 2,500 South Africans who fought at Thiepval and Beaumont Hamel.'

'Haig wants to attack Belgium,' said Smith-Stevens, 'drive the Boche back away from the Channel. He's mighty concerned about the submarine attacks. If they're unchecked, the Germans have free and easy use of the Belgian ports, and they're decimating supply and transport ships. He's also concerned about the potential severe loss of troops in the Ypres area.'

'What a laugh!' broke in Conrick. '"The Butcher of the Somme." He's not well thought of in this area. Tens of thousands gave their lives uselessly for a few yards of stinking mud.

I've heard the men say things like, "Who's the Butcher going to carve up today?"'

Both men were briefly lost in their own thoughts.

Conrick broke the silence. 'Haig was still trying Boer War and Crimean tactics: attack at their strongest point. One thing he forgot, though – he wasn't fighting bloody Zulus with spears, he had Germans with Maxim machine guns cutting the troops to pieces. It was insane. I can't believe the men didn't riot or desert.'

After a moment, Conrick asked, 'Sir, when do we head east to Beugny?'

'Well, Terry, it's not far from here – only about 6 miles or so. I'd like to send you in charge of a team to reconnoitre for our gun emplacement areas. It looks to be an all-out effort this time. I think that maybe two days should be your ETD.'

'Thank you, sir. I'll submit six names for your consideration as my team.'

'Don't bother, Terry, just get your men together. I'll leave it to you.'

The 5th Field Artillery Brigade moved to Beugny. Wagonloads of men, ammunition and stores took a day to cover the 6-mile trek. Gun positions had been selected, with the 5th Field Artillery Brigade having a full complement of gun batteries. They were now a formidable artillery unit.

Bombardment of the Hindenburg Line – as well as the villages of Bullecourt and Riencourt, thought to be hiding German machine gun emplacements – was ordered. The artillery action started soon after the gun detachments had dug in.

8.5.17 Arrived Larkhill.

The main thoroughfare leading to Larkhill School of Artillery was rough and gravelled. From the rise, the Salisbury Plains stretched as far as the eye could see to the west, south and north. Smooth and undulating, the downs were covered in a rich blanket of green grass and shrubbery.

Jum studied the rolling hills. This was to be his home for the next three weeks. Light rain was falling, driven by the predominant south-west wind, directly off the Atlantic Ocean. The Wiltshire countryside was at its glistening best.

Larkhill had become a major artillery school and, since the beginning of 1916, a command depot that housed over 4,000 men. It was the training camp for the 5th Division, AIF, holding the 8th, 14th and 15th Training Battalions as well as the artillery.

The entrance to the camp was guarded by two cannon used in the Crimean and Boer wars. Their muzzles pointed ominously at any intruders brave enough to attempt unauthorised passage.

The orderly sergeant addressed the men standing before him. 'Welcome to Larkhill School of Artillery. You artillerymen are here for upgrading on the new model 18-pounder Mark IV.' He proceeded to read out the names of the waiting men. When he got to Jum, he said, 'You're 5th Field Artillery Brigade?'

'Yes, Sergeant, I've just come from Perham Downs.'

'We have a few more of your men arriving on Monday morning. The course starts Monday afternoon.'

Jum hung around the orderly room on Monday morning, eagerly awaiting the arrival of the others from the brigade. A covered motor truck rolled through the gates, past the sentinel cannons, and stopped in front of the orderly room.

Bob jumped from the truck and spied Jum. They greeted each other excitedly.

'Jesus, Jum, how are you?'

'I'm fine, back to my old self,' replied Jum. He looked at the others, still unloading from the truck. Ron Roberts, Wagga and Jim Gillies ambled over. Backs were slapped heartily all round. McErbain alighted from the front seat of the truck, made his way to the happy group and delightedly shook Jum's hand.

A loud voice brought sudden quiet. Standing on the verandah of the orderly room, a large, imposing sergeant major, complete with bristling red moustache, had barked out an order for attention. The men waited whilst the sergeant major spoke.

'Fall in here in your unit groups,' he barked again.

The men quickly formed ranks facing the verandah. The sergeant major turned and saluted an officer waiting in the doorway. An equally large lieutenant stepped forward and addressed the men. 'Welcome, men, to Larkhill School of Artillery. You are here for a specific purpose: to learn the new Mark IV. You will also become familiar with some new ammunition that is now in production. The course lasts three weeks. It is intense and demanding and will require your utmost attention.' He paused. 'The sergeant major will indicate where you are billeted. The first lecture is today, following lunch. Sar' Major, please take over.'

Following allocation to their tents, the men ate their midday meal. They were grouped according to their units, and each group was allocated a lecture room. The eighteen artillerymen from the 5th Field Artillery Brigade joined other men who had arrived for training. This lecture group, like the others, would remain together for the following three weeks.

The men sat quietly smoking and talking in the lecture room. The door was flung open and the sergeant major walked in. He slapped a handful of papers onto his desk. 'Who gave you lot permission to smoke?' he boomed.

'We grab one when we can, Sar' Major,' said Jum Bevan, in a seat close to the front.

'Not any more, you don't. You smoke when I tell you, *if* I tell you and not otherwise. Follow?' The sergeant major picked up a clipboard. 'Answer when I call your name. Gunner Bevan?'

'Here,' called Jum.

The sergeant major lowered the clipboard, glaring. '"Here, Sergeant Major" to you – understand? Gunner Buchannen?'

'I'm with him,' grinned Bob, pointing to Jum.

The sergeant major's face reddened.

Gunner Roberts joined the game. 'I'm with him too, Sar' Major,' he said, pointing to Jum. Wagga raised his hand. 'Count me in, with my brother that is, Sar' Major.' The remainder of the class hooted with laughter at the sight of the sergeant major about to suffer an apoplectic fit.

'So what have we here? A bunch of smart-arsed colonial convicts?'

'You a convict, Wagga?' asked Jum.

'No, but Granddad was.'

A gunner from 13th Battery piped up. 'My grandfather and grandmother were convicts, came out on the *Mary Kathleen* in 1824.'

Bob stood up and started walking around the room, dragging an imaginary ball and chain from his ankle. 'This is how my dad walks, he could never break the habit.' No one heard the knock on the door over the boisterous laughter.

McErbain entered the room, followed by a 2nd lieutenant wearing the uniform of the British infantry. The sergeant major screamed for attention and the men stood up silently.

'Good afternoon, Sar' Major,' said McErbain. The sergeant major saluted and stepped back. Jum nudged Bob as McErbain and the other officer, Subaltern Chesterton, sat to the side of the room away from the ORs.

'Continue please, Sar' Major,' said McErbain.

The sergeant major did a quick head count and announced, 'All present.' He extracted a large rolled sheet of cardboard from a tube and attached it to the blackboard directly behind him. Represented in great detail on the sheet was an image of the current 18-pounder QF gun of the British and Australian armies.

'This is the main field piece of the British Army,' he said, 'the 18-pounder quick-firing gun.'

'Looks a lot like one of Dad's tractors back on the farm,' said Wagga.

McErbain swung around. 'Pay attention, Wagga. Your life or your mate's life may depend on this one day.'

Chastened, the men gave their attention to the sergeant major, who gave them information on the weapon that most had missed in their early training.

Twilight had set in as the group sat outside their hut. McErbain joined them briefly.

'That officer today, Harold,' said Jum. 'Was that Chesterton?'

'It was. Do you know him?'

Well, the padre certainly does!' laughed Jum.

'Yes, I heard about that, when he mistook the padre for a private,' said McErbain. 'He actually seems a nice enough bloke, but a bit unsure of himself, I think.'

'Rod Smith, the corporal driver, said he had an uncle, a brigadier, in the infantry,' said Jum.

The conversation drifted, then the men slowly retired to their billets before attending more lectures the following day. Loading exercises and drilling with dummy shells had been programmed.

'What the hell are we doing with dud shells?' asked Wagga. The men at the table shook their heads.

'Beats me,' said Ron.

The men marched 200 yards to a position not dissimilar to the ones they were accustomed to constructing themselves. Within the position sat a gleaming 18-pounder gun. A shell-carrier limber stood nearby, loaded with the dummy shells. The position was replicated by two others, some 30 yards apart.

The large sergeant major with the bristling moustache addressed the men. 'Assemble yourselves around the position edge, men. You are about to witness the British method of artillery fire of the 18-pounder QF gun.' Eight British artillerymen in starched uniforms, brass gleaming, appeared at the position. 'Begin your demonstration, Sergeant,' barked the sergeant major.

The uniformed men moved snappily into the trench, assuming various positions in and around the gun. A sight-layer stood on the edge of the position while two men manned the ammunition cart and one sat in the range seat. Another man stood stiffly to attention, the firing lanyard in his hand, two stood ready to pass the shells, and the eighth gunner stood by in reserve. 'Commence firing!' shouted the sergeant.

The first shell was carried from the limber with a stiff, polished movement. The loader carefully slid the shell into the breech. The lock slammed shut, the lanyard-holder called 'Fire!' and snapped the lanyard to imitate firing. The breech re-opened, the spent shell sprung out and clanged to the ground, and the dogsbody retrieved the shell and neatly stacked it on the left parapet.

'There you have it,' said the sergeant major with satisfaction, 'the correct way to load and fire the 18-pounder gun.'

'One question, Sar' Major,' piped up Wagga. 'Those boys ever fire the real stuff at the front line?'

The moustache bristled with indignation, the eyes narrowed. 'For your information, Gunner, my men could take an 18-pounder apart in the dark and reassemble it blindfold. Their work rate is of the highest order and their drilling is unmatched.'

Wagga looked at Jum, then at McErbain. 'Sar' Major, have your men seen front-line action?' he asked again.

The sergeant major turned on Wagga, his voice sarcastic. 'Just because you bloody colonials fired a few shells in France doesn't make you the great experts. You're an untidy, rowdy, undisciplined lot.

'Look at you now,' he pointed to Bob, his shirt undone, hatless, lounging on the gun position edge. 'You're a disgrace. Tomorrow morning, we start where you people have never been – at the beginning.

'Report tomorrow morning, first lecture, in full battle order uniform. I want to see brass gleaming, boots and puttees polished and shining. I'll make soldiers of you if it's the last thing I do. Dismissed!'

Bob glared at Wagga. 'Jesus, Wagga, just look what you've done now!'

'Don't blame me, Bob. Your bloody shirt's undone and you're half asleep!' said Wagga.

'Well, boys,' laughed Jim Gillies, 'we all know now they haven't seen any action. They may be able to drill like buggery, but it'd be interesting to see them in the mud with the .77s, 5.9s and the occasional 150 Krupp dropping in to say hello.'

'Anyway, you blokes, time for lunch,' said Jum.

'Do we get to fire the Mark IV,' Ron wondered, 'or do we just get to look at it?'

'Oh, we'll get to fire it, all right,' replied Jum. 'They won't spend all this time and effort getting us here for a dry run.'

'That bloody Sar' Major doesn't like us too much, does he?' said Bob.

'Well,' said Jum, 'here we are, cheeky as hell, all you blokes giving him smart-arse comments. Yesterday in the lecture room, he was really pissed off. He's used to having ORs jump when he gives an order. You blokes don't jump, you just ask questions. We'll have to be careful though, or he could make our time here quite nasty.'

They walked grumbling to the mess hall.

Bertie Chesterton downed his lemon squash and turned to McErbain. They were seated at a small table not far from the bar.

'What say you to a drink, old boy?'

'Righto, Bertie,' said McErbain. 'Barman,' he called over his shoulder, 'two pints of bitter.'

'Yessir,' said the barman. 'Coming up!'

'I've never indulged in alcohol,' said Bertie.

'Well, Bertie, that's all about to change. If you're an officer in the artillery, you need to be able to sink a few big ones,' replied McErbain cheerfully.

Looking dubious, Bertie raised the pint of bitter and gulped a large mouthful. He gagged slightly, swallowed and then beamed and burped.

McErbain grinned, then asked, 'How are you finding the course so far?'

'I can't seem to get the hang of this artillery thing,' Chesterton confided.

'Did you study artillery at Officers' School?' asked Harold.

Chesterton shook his head. 'No, we just did basic infantry. Never touched on the other stuff – no time.'

'Would you like to learn about the 18-pounder and some of the heavier stuff later?' asked McErbain.

'I'm not too confident, Harold. I've never really succeeded at anything I've tried. The war gave me a commission, which made my family happy, so here I am in artillery. But I have a distinct feeling that Uncle Charles had something to do with me being transferred here.'

'Well, maybe we can make something of it,' replied Harold.

'What are you suggesting?'

'I have a man under my command who knows 18-pounders backwards. We could arrange for you to have a few sessions with him.'

'He's an OR then – a private?'

'Yes, Bertie, but early morning and after dark, no one will know. Want to try it?'

'Might as well. I've nothing to lose!'

Two days later, at 0500, three men stood in the gun position of the exercise 18-pounder.

'Gunner Bevan, this is Lieutenant Chesterton.'

Jum snapped to attention.

'Jum, no salutes. The lieutenant has not had the opportunity of intense study of the weapon that you have had. I suggested that perhaps you could help out with some first-hand information, bring him up to date.'

'Yes, sir.'

'I'll leave you both to it, then,' said McErbain, as he stepped out of the position.

Jum had not been keen to help Chesterton, remembering his arrogance as a subaltern at Perham Downs Hospital. But McErbain had spent an hour convincing Jum that helping him could pay dividends at a later date.

'He's insecure, Jum, and been sheltered all his life. We may be able to make something of him,' explained McErbain. 'Just describe how the 18-pounder works, its little moods, its good points, its bad points. And be patient with him, all right?'

Jum had reluctantly agreed.

'Lieutenant, sir,' said Jum.

'Please, in the circumstances, call me Bertie. If we meet outside of this gun position, I am Lieutenant Chesterton, understand?'

'Sure do, Bertie,' said Jum nonchalantly.

Jum sat on the recoil arm of the gun and addressed his pupil. 'This is the British Army artillery's 18-pounder QF gun, the most up-to-date field piece in the world today. It can be fired at a constant rate of sixteen to eighteen shells per minute, for extended periods – sometimes up to twenty plus rounds per minute, depending upon the detachment.'

Jum went on to describe in detail all aspects of the piece, often being asked pertinent questions by Chesterton.

'Time to go, sir,' said Jum finally. Chesterton looked at his watch, annoyed by the interruption.

'When can we continue?' he said.

'1700 hours here, sir?' asked Jum.

'Thank you, Gunner.'

'How'd he go, Jum?' asked McErbain.

'He's got a keen mind,' said Jum, who had been impressed by Chesterton's attention span. 'He really absorbs what you say.'

'Maybe because there are no distractions and smart arses putting him down all the time,' suggested McErbain.

'Anyway, we're on again tonight at 1700,' said Jum.

McErbain patted him on the shoulder. 'Keep up the good work, mate,' he said, as they set out for extended gunnery practice. Reviewing and studying the later version of the 18-pounder gun, with its greatly improved recoil system, would be the focus of the next few days.

Bertie Chesterton was excited. Not since his love affair with mathematics at public school had a subject caught his attention as keenly as the gun. He'd found that Gunner Bevan had a way of describing the most complicated aspects of the weapon in simple terms. A week passed, with Chesterton waking well before daylight each morning to revise the areas of the gun they had examined the previous day.

At the end of that week, Jum introduced Chesterton to the most sensitive and certainly the most important functions of the weapon – aiming and range. He drew a diagram in the sand with a twig.

'If that's the gun here, we have to determine the angle of the the barrel to put the shell on target,' he explained.

'That's easy, Jum,' said Chesterton. 'Do we know the distance from the gun to the target?'

'Yes,' said Jum.

'You know that this kind of mathematics is my area?' said Chesterton. Jum listened as Chesterton quickly outlined the formulae used to pinpoint elevation when distance and velocity were known.

Jum followed Chesterton's calculations with some awe. 'So let me get this clear, Bertie,' he said. 'If I give you distances in yards, and you know the velocity, you can work out a reasonably accurate elevation for the barrel pretty quickly.'

'Better than reasonably accurate, Jum. All we need to allow for is wind or differing elevation of gun in relation to target.' Chesterton smiled at Jum's surprise.

McErbain listened to Jum's recounting of their session with interest.

'I'd love to try him out on live firing, Harold,' said Jum.

'Well, you may get a chance,' said McErbain. 'The sar' major is still pissed off with you lot for having him on in that first lecture. He's planning to have a "shoot off" in a week, and I know he wants to beat the living daylights out of our best side. I saw his team practising two days ago, and they're very good. I'll keep you informed.'

'Thank you, sir,' Jum saluted smartly, aware of a group of three British officers approaching. 'Officers coming, Harold,' he muttered. McErbain turned to face the trio and saluted. The large brigadier returned the salute by casually touching the peak of his cap with his swagger stick.

The captain accompanying the brigadier smiled. 'Lieutenant McErbain, please meet Brigadier Chesterton,' he said formally. McErbain politely stepped forward and shook the brigadier's hand, noting that Bertie greatly resembled his uncle.

'Just wondering, Lieutenant,' said the brigadier, 'how my nephew is coming along. I hear that you've been helping him.'

'Yes, sir. The lieutenant has shown great application and I think he is doing well,' replied Harold. 'Gunner Bevan here, sir,' he said, nodding at Jum, 'has helped out a lot with the lieutenant. Before and after parades, unofficially, of course.'

Brigadier Chesterton moved around McErbain and stopped in front of Jum. He extended his hand. Jum nervously shook the brigadier's hand, meeting a surprisingly firm grip.

'It's my pleasure to meet you, Gunner,' said the brigadier. 'I respect soldiers of the line. You have most certainly been through it all and I wish you well.'

Jum stood stiffly to attention and said, 'Thank you, sir.'

Chesterton turned to McErbain. 'Keep up the good work, Lieutenant,' he said. Turning to Jum, he added, 'You, too, Gunner. I thank you for helping my nephew.' The trio of officers turned and marched off.

'Jesus, Harold, I was pissing my pants. I thought I was going to face a firing squad, or worse.'

'We must make sure that Bertie comes out on top,' said McErbain. 'Uncle knows what we're doing now.'

The next five days were spent in intensive training with the 18-pounder. All agreed the Mark IV was a superior weapon, with the savage recoil of the previous model now reduced to a small bump.

With two days remaining in the course, the men had virtually completed their training. They spent the second-last day familiarising themselves with the Percussion Fuse No. 106, the new secret method of shell detonation approved in March 1916. It was to be some time later, in 1917, before this innovation was used in live action.

The fuse detonated a shell instantly, before it entered the earth, unlike earlier variants that usually penetrated a foot or so underground before detonating. The advantage was twofold. The blast was much greater over a large area, causing an expansion of its killing range. And because the blast was above or at ground level, it caused much smaller craters in the fields, making it easier for advancing troops to manoeuvre.

At the end of this day, the red-moustached sergeant major addressed the entire group. 'Tomorrow is your final day at Larkhill. You Australians have done well, but tomorrow we will see just how well. At 1200 hours, three teams – one team of British gunners and two teams of Australians – will take part in a demonstration shoot-off using the 18-pounder. The contest will last sixty seconds, and firing rate and accuracy will decide the outcome.'

He spoke briefly to Brigadier Holmes, CO of Larkhill Artillery School, who had stepped forward. 'Men, one small matter: the losing two teams must buy beer for the winning team for two hours. Agreed?'

A spirited shout of assent greeted this announcement, and the men gathered around to discuss the contest.

McErbain spoke to the two lieutenants of 13th and 15th Batteries. They agreed that their men had nowhere near the experience of the 14th. It was quickly decided that team No. 1 would derive from the McErbain group and a composite team from the 13th and 15th would be team No. 2.

McErbain gathered his men together. 'Now, don't think this will be a walkover,' he warned. 'These Tommy bastards can really fire the 18-pounders. They're bloody experienced.' He turned to Jim Gillies. 'Well, Jim, who do you think for our team?'

'I'll go No. 1,' he said. 'Wagga and Ron, ammo and load, put Jum on the lanyard with Bob extra ammo.'

'That leaves us one short in the aim seat,' said Jum.

'I'm out,' said McErbain. 'I'm only allowed as observer.'

'I've got it!' said Jum. 'Bertie!'

'Bertie?' The men looked dubious.

'Yes, by Christ! He fired with us in that two-day live exercise and how good was he?' said Jum. 'He was working out the elevation in his head and he was spot on for the whole two days.'

'But that bloody sar' major will spot his uniform, and won't allow it,' replied McErbain.

'He's the same build as me,' said Jum. 'He'd fit into my working gear easily. With a hat on, nobody'll know the difference!'

'Of course,' said McErbain, 'he'd have to agree to our plan. I'll speak to him, but mum's the word, all right?'

'I don't know, Harold,' said Bertie. 'They could cashier me, jail me!'

'Nobody will know, Bertie; it'll be our secret. All you have to do is make sure your aim and range are correct.'

'That's the easy part, Harold. It would be a lark,' he mused, smiling.

The morning dawned clear and bright, with only a slight hint of breeze. Word had spread that the upstart Australians were about to be given a lesson in artillery management. As early as 1000 hours, many unofficial onlookers had gathered to witness the contest. A large number of villagers had also arrived from Tidworth, determined not to miss the action.

At 1130 hours, the British gun detachment marched from their barracks to their motorbus, and drove to the live range. At the firing range, the detachment leapt from their transport and fell in at close order, clean-shaven, shirts starched and ironed, boots polished. The detachment marched smartly to the first gun position. The sergeant major, moustache bristling more than ever, stood rigidly to attention.

In contrast, the two Australian gun detachments, dressed in their army regulation work fatigues, had meandered to their truck transport. At 1145 hours, their motor lorry arrived at the second position. The men clambered from the rear of the truck, then moved to the respective guns allocated to them.

'Bertie, keep your bloody hat on and for fuck's sake, slouch a little when you march,' muttered Jum.

The No. 1 Australian detachment immediately set to in the position, making sure all was in order. The British detachment was sitting to attention and had not moved since they had arrived.

The sergeant major had the three lieutenants from the three detachments before him.

'Now gentlemen, you all know the rules. There will be one round fired to register. At my whistle signal, commence firing at your individual targets. Points will be allocated for accuracy and number of rounds fired. All clear, gentlemen?'

'Yes, thank you, Sar' Major,' said McErbain. The lieutenants moved back to their detachments. McErbain beckoned to Jum. 'Jum, I've just been told in confidence that the British team have prior knowledge of the target distances. Our detachments were supposed to work that out themselves.'

'Sneaky bastards!' said Jum.

'The three targets differ in distance,' said Harold. 'I got the word from the barman, who knows one of the men setting the targets. Your target distance is shown as 2,000 yards, but its actual distance is 1,920 yards.'

Jum nodded and moved quickly to speak to Bertie, sitting in the range seat.

'Bertie, our range is 1,920 yards to target. Don't take any notice of the map distance.'

'But the map shows –'

'I know, mate,' laughed Jum. 'They're trying to pull a swifty on us.'

Chesterton made a quick recalculation on his notepad and adjusted the elevation to suit.

The sergeant major blew his whistle once – the sign for all detachments to fire one shell. Jum moved to Bertie and held his arm. 'Listen mate, let's play their game. Put your sighter down 10 yards. They'll think they have us.'

Chesterton nodded. 'Done, Jum – we're 10 yards down.'

The shells to be used were smoke for the registering shot, with non-explosive smoke shells for the contest. No. 1 detachment stripped to the waist.

'Fire!' screamed Jum as he snapped the lanyard. The two other detachments had fired a few seconds before. The British team scored a direct hit, right on target. The Australian No. 2 were 5 yards left, with No. 1 detachment correct on line, their shot falling – as anticipated – 10 yards under target. The British sergeant turned to the sergeant major, smiled and winked. With twenty seconds to the start, Jum turned to the detachment. In a voice filled with passion, he called out, 'Remember Sausage Gully, remember Fleurbaix, remember the Somme – let's give it to the bastards!'

Chesterton carefully adjusted his elevation and waited with bated breath for Jim Gillies's report on their first shot. Gillies had his binoculars trained on their target. McErbain had notepad and pencil ready to record direct hits or misses, as did the two other lieutenants.

The whistle shrilled. Ron caught the shell from Wagga and in one fluid motion, slammed and locked the shell into the breech. The lanyard jerked in Jum's hand. The beautiful weapon with virtually no recoil bucked ever so slightly. The empty case clanged on the floor of the position. 'Direct hit!' yelled Gillies, jubilant.

Wagga had the next shell in his hands as his brother Ron turned, took it and slid it rapidly into the open breech. The gun exploded. The team's experience was obvious to all watching. 'Direct hit, but left of centre,' yelled Gillies.

Chesterton, watching carefully, felt the slight breeze on his right cheek, and checked the impulse to re-align. His decision was rewarded. 'Direct hit!'

But the next round veered 3 yards left of target. 'Miss!' yelled Gillies, disappointed. Chesterton quickly realigned. With the breech slammed shut, the shell was on its way. 'Direct hit!' Time was now the main concern as the detachment laboured under the hot sun. 'Thirty seconds to go!' yelled McErbain.

A quick check showed eleven rounds fired – nine direct hits, two misses. 'The rest are for the padre!' yelled Bob. The tempo quickened. 'Direct hit! ... Miss! ... Direct hit!' Gillies shouted hoarsely.

Beads of perspiration appeared on the bodies of the shirtless men, their movements a fierce testament to hundreds of days of experience. The blast of the whistle brought a sudden stop to the ferocious sound of the three guns.

Bob leant on the wheel of the gun, panting and grinning broadly.

'Not bad, eh, Harold?' he asked. 'Yes! Nineteen direct hits, four misses,' read McErbain.

'Look out, Bertie!' warned Gillies. 'Sit down, here comes the sar' major.'

'What did you score, sir?' the sergeant major asked McErbain.

'Nineteen, Sar' Major.'

'Bad luck, sir,' said the sergeant major. 'The British have twenty.'

'How many misses, Sar' Major?'

'Three misses, Lieutenant.'

'That's great shooting, Sar' Major. So you got away twenty-three rounds?'

A scowl started to appear on the sergeant major's face.

'We fired twenty rounds – three misses, with seventeen direct hits, sir.'

'Sorry, I misunderstood, Sar' Major. We fired twenty-three rounds – nineteen direct hits, four misses. So deduct the misses, that gives the British a score of seventeen and the Australian No. 1 team a score of nineteen.'

The lieutenant in charge of the No. 2 detachment had arrived. 'How'd you do, Chicka?' asked McErbain.

'Looks like eighteen – one miss, seventeen direct hits, although it appears one shell clipped the edge of the target.'

'A hit is a hit, that right, Sar' Major?' asked McErbain. The sergeant major turned and walked off without answering.

'Bad loser, Harold?' asked the lieutenant.

'Bad loser,' said McErbain. 'The bastard cheated and still got beaten.'

Jum had joined the two officers near the position. After seeing the sergeant major's expression, Jum had correctly guessed the outcome. 'Pretty desperate to win,' he observed.

Brigadier Chesterton lowered his binoculars and turned to Captain Jonathon Smythe. 'I don't believe it!'

'What's that, sir?' said Smythe, stepping forward.

'Look at the No. 1 detachment and tell me what you see,' replied the brigadier. The men standing on an observation platform some 400 yards to the east had witnessed the contest at first hand.

'Bloody hell, it's your nephew!' said Smythe, as he turned to the brigadier. Smythe peered through the glasses again. 'He's wearing Australian work fatigues and has just taken off his bloody Australian slouch hat. Cheeky little bastard!' he muttered. He dropped the glasses and turned to Chesterton. 'Sorry sir, just a turn of phrase.'

But the brigadier was laughing. 'Jonathon, Bertie's never done anything like this before in his life. I can't believe it!'

The bar at the Ram's Head Hotel in Tidworth was filled to overflowing.

About thirty artillerymen, British and Australian, were downing pints with great enthusiasm. Earlier, the teams had gathered at the OR's mess in Larkhill, where the two losing teams had put money on the bar for the ensuing two hours of drinking. The winning team had drunk up the two hours' worth of free beer, but had no intention of going home yet.

'Your shout!' Bob yelled in Jum's ear.

Jum nodded and moved to the bar, carrying five empty pint mugs. He had to jostle his way through a knot of boisterous British artillerymen.

Reaching the bar, he found himself next to the sergeant major.

'What have we got here? The little Australian convict and his chain gang friends.'

'Our fathers might be convicts, but at least we're not fucking cheats,' said Jum.

'What do you mean by that?' said the sergeant major belligerently.

'You should know, you organised it. Your own men think you're such a shit, they gave you up.'

The sergeant major grabbed a handful of Jum's shirt-front. Men stepped back, forming a tight circle.

'You convict bastard!'

'My father may have been a convict,' Jum said, 'but you know the last thing he did before he left England for Australia? He fucked your mother.'

Anticipating the move, he ducked as the roundhouse swing whistled over his head. He lifted his left leg and stamped down hard on the sergeant major's instep with his steel-heeled army boot. The sergeant major gasped in pain and tried to grab his injured foot. Jum snapped a short, vicious left to the solar plexus. The sergeant major doubled over, unable to breathe.

Jum gently pushed him in the forehead, causing him to sink slowly to the floor, his back against the bar. He gulped, desperately trying to regain his breath.

The circle of men widened as three very large gunners in British uniform stepped forward.

Bob, as usual, had kept an eye on Jum. Sensing trouble, he had called, 'Let's go!' to the Roberts boys as the sergeant major grabbed Jum's shirt.

Jum faced the three very big English boys, warily eyeing them off. Wagga, Ron and Bob stepped up to flank him. Wagga moved forward.

'Bit lopsided boys, three to one. Mind if we even it up?'

There was silence, then one of the drunks at the bar bumped into the largest of the three English gunners, causing him to step forward to retain his balance. Inadvertently, he raised his left hand.

Wagga stepped inside, unleashing a huge left hook that was never going to miss. Pandemonium ensued. Within seconds, the bar was alive with writhing bodies hurling fists at each other. There were many near misses, lots of big misses and a few that found their target.

Bertie Chesterton sat blinking at the chaos. Not naturally a violent person, on a few occasions he had taken on the bullies at Old Cranleigh School. The results were highly predictable, until the gym master, sick of seeing Bertie with swollen eyes and a bloody nose, coerced him into the boxing ring, where he taught him a few of the finer points.

No contender for lightweight honours, he had nevertheless learnt enough to convince the school bullies that it was better to leave him alone. He realised Jum was receiving plenty of attention from two English gunners. Leaping from his seat, he ran hard and shoulder-charged the nearest assailant, who turned and threw a haymaker. Bertie ducked instinctively, then threw a hard, short right. Jum watched Bertie's punch connect with the gunner's jaw.

'Fucking beauty, Bertie!' screamed Jum as he tried desperately to remove the large arm trying to choke him to death.

Bertie grinned, but did not see the next big one coming his way. It connected with the side of his jaw and he slid to the floor unconscious.

Jum again performed the stamping trick with his left heel. His neck was immediately released. He jumped to Bertie's side and hauled him out of the melee.

McErbain had remained out of the action. He could see he was not needed. When it was obvious the Australians were in control, he leapt onto a chair. He held the whistle attached to his lanyard and blew a long, shrieking blast. About thirty dishevelled and bloodied men stopped and sucked in lungfuls of air. 'I've got 10 quid here for the bar,' McErbain announced, waving an English note. 'Let's have a drink!'

The scene transformed. Men who had been intent on killing each other now slapped each other on the back and laughed, moving rapidly towards the bar.

Jum had sat Bertie in a chair. As he came to, he attempted to jump up and back into the fray. Jum restrained him. 'It's all over, Bertie. I'll get you a drink.'

A large figure stood beside Jum. 'How is the little chap?' the sergeant major asked. Jum smiled as he accepted a pint from the outstretched hand.

'He's all right, caught one from behind,' answered Jum.

The two men eyed one another, then grasped each other's hands in a firm handshake.

'Fred Matthews.'

'I'm Jum Bevan. You're tough bastards, you Tommies.'

'You boys are not exactly retiring wallflowers yourselves,' observed Matthews. 'Look, I'm sorry about the convict business.'

'Don't mention it, Fred. I'm sure my dad never knew your mother, although your hair colour ...'

Fred erupted in loud laughter.

'And I don't blame you for the target business,' said Jum. 'We got an edge two days earlier with Bertie here.'

'What do you mean?' asked Matthews, as Jum pointed to Chesterton, who was draining his pint.

'Bertie was our aimer,' Jum grinned. 'I tell you what, Fred, this boy will become one great artilleryman. He's found his place. Aiming and range calculations are child's play to him.'

'I wouldn't've believed it,' said Matthews, surprised.

His beer finished, Chesterton's head lolled back. In a few seconds he was fast asleep.

'You've seen action, Fred. You know your way around 18-pounders,' Jum said.

Matthews pulled up his shirt, revealing a long, red, jagged scar. 'A bloody "whiz bang" got me in the first show at Ypres in 1915.'

'That must have been tough.'

'Tough!' exclaimed Matthews. 'The bastards ran all over us. They were superior in arms, equipment, officers and attitude. They were winning and couldn't be stopped.'

He took a long drink and looked at Jum. 'That's why I'm here. Lost half my stomach and a kidney. They won't let me back into action again. My sister's first boy bought it in the same campaign. Her younger son is a driver based at Perham Downs.'

'Rodney Smith?' said Jum.

'How the hell ...?'

'I stayed with your sister and Rodney and Cissie a month ago,' said Jum.

Matthews smiled. 'Watch out for that Cissie,' he said. 'She's a fast one.'

Jum flushed to his boots. 'Yes, she ... certainly is a lovely girl.'

The lorry ride back to Larkhill was leisurely. Draped between Jum and Fred Matthews was 2nd Lieutenant Bertie Chesterton. Back at the school, they laid him gently on his bed.

Bertie was convinced he was dead. Bright sunlight had been streaming onto his face for the past twenty minutes. He sat bolt upright. The sudden stab of pain across his forehead was horrific. He slowly moved to his bathroom and looked in the mirror. Two hellishly bloodshot eyes looked back at him. His jaw was monstrously swollen.

A knock on the door brought him out of the bathroom.

A Corporal stood to attention. 'Good morning, sir. Brigadier Chesterton wishes to see you in the Officers' Mess for breakfast.'

'When?' asked Bertie, wincing as he spoke.

'Right away, sir.'

Chesterton vaguely remembered the walk from the truck into the camp, the noise, singing and general skylarking by the inebriated artillerymen.

'Were you part of that group, Bertie?' asked the brigadier.

'I don't remember, sir.'

'Were you part of the group in the Ram's Head at Tidworth?'

'I suppose so.'

'Were you involved in the common brawl that occurred in the hotel?'

'I don't remember,' said Chesterton stubbornly, as he gently felt his jaw.

One of the other officers at the table gently cleared his throat. The brigadier continued. 'Were you involved in the Australian gun detachment that was successful in yesterday's contest? You realise that wearing another nation's uniform could have serious implications for a British soldier? Possibly a court-martial.'

He had had enough.

'Yes, sir,' he said. 'I wore the work fatigues of the Australian artillery. I was also part of that smashing gun detachment that thrashed the British yesterday. And I was in the brawl for about thirty seconds or so.'

Jonathon Smythe interrupted. 'How'd you go, Bertie?'

'I got one a beauty. There were two or three onto Jum Bevan, sir. I grabbed one and let him have it. His friend came from behind and caught me. And yes, I was in the group that walked through camp last night.'

He paused for breath. 'And just to get the record straight, sir, I was proud to be part of that Australian detachment. Those soldiers have been through the worst in France, and they're expert gunners. If we had a lot more of them, we'd beat these bloody Boche hands down.'

The CO leant forward in his chair. 'We have to investigate these incidents and consider your behaviour to ascertain whether any charges are to be laid against you. I think we can forget the part you took in the gun detachment, although you will get many credits for that performance. In the brawl in the Ram's Head, you obviously went to the aid of one of our colonial soldiers. Then there is the march through the camp. It appears that you, Lieutenant, were quite correctly attempting to restore order, but with little effect.'

The other officers nodded sagely.

'What we cannot overlook, Lieutenant, is the case of you coming to the Officers' Mess unshaven. As the CO of Larkhill artillery compound, I fine you sixpence and confine you to barracks for the next five minutes – all agreed?'

The other officers indicated that this was more than adequate.

Chesterton relaxed his shoulders. As the realisation sank in that nothing would come of the escapades of the last twenty-four hours, he began to smile.

The CO spoke again. 'One other thing, Lieutenant. Your progress in this course has been exemplary. Your written work shows your grasp of the 18-pounder gun to be concise and knowledgeable. I have suggested that you be enrolled in an advanced gunnery school for an intensive six-week course that will take you right through to the top level of our artillery regiments.

'I have also recommended your promotion to first lieutenant, as that is the minimum rank requirement for entry to the course.'

Chesterton could not believe his ears.

'This is a big chance for you, Bertie,' said the brigadier. 'I hope you make the most of it.'

His nephew jumped excitedly to his feet.

'Where are you going?' asked the brigadier.

'To tell Jum and the boys,' Chesterton shouted jubilantly as he flung himself through the door.

'He'll go a long way, Charles,' said the CO. 'His work was of the highest order.'

The motor lorry rumbled towards the sentry box at the entrance, loaded with men bound for Tidworth village. The men aboard were from the 5th Field Artillery Brigade, returning to Southampton. Sprinting furiously, Chesterton caught the driver's attention as he slowed the truck.

'What's wrong, mate?' Jum asked anxiously from the back of the truck.

'Nothing,' laughed Chesterton as he hauled himself onto the tailgate. 'They've put me into advanced artillery and given me one more of these,' as he tapped his shoulder.

'Bloody fantastic!' yelled Jum. 'I knew you could do it!'

The truck stopped at the sentry and boom gate.

'Thanks for everything, Jum. Thanks to all you boys!' called Chesterton as he jumped down.

The truck gathered speed, moving rapidly away from the figure standing in the middle of the road. Bertie Chesterton waved until it disappeared from view over the hill towards Tidworth.

JUNE 1917

20.6.17 Arrived Le Havre.

21.6.17 Arrived Rouen.

27.6.17 Back with unit.

Endless reams of paper work had completely consumed Brigadier Tideswell's time since he had arrived at 2nd Division Headquarters, but now, with a lull in troop movements, he had time to reflect. He had not realised the extent to which he would miss the front-line action.

A sergeant entered his office and handed him a sheaf of paper. 'Thank you, Sergeant,' said Tideswell, dropping it on his desk. He glanced at the top paper.

'Lieutenant Harold McErbain. Disembarked Le Havre 20th June, 1917. Reported for duty 22nd June, 1917, Longeau.'

Tideswell leafed through the papers, speaking the names aloud as he read. 'Bevan, Buchannen, Roberts, Roberts, Gillies. Sergeant!' he called loudly. 'Are these men in camp?'

'Yes, sir, arrived two hours ago.'

'Have them here as soon as possible.'

The sergeant rapped firmly on the door as he entered Tideswell's office five minutes later. 'The men you requested, sir.'

The men, led by Lieutenant McErbain, filed into the room and stood to attention. Brigadier Tideswell waited until the door had shut, then, grinning broadly, shook McErbain by the hand.

'Hello, sir,' smiled McErbain as Tideswell shook hands with the other five men.

'Damn! It's good to see some old faces,' Tideswell beamed. He motioned the men to sit as McErbain asked, 'What the hell are you doing here, sir?'

'The buggers have pensioned me off. They say I'm too valuable to be in the front line. Just have a look at what I'm doing, though – paper shuffling!' he said with disgust.

He changed the subject. 'How was the course?'

'Very interesting, sir,' replied McErbain. 'We won a shooting contest. Didn't make the Tommies very happy, but all turned out well at the finish. So, where's the action, sir?'

'Since you boys have been away, the Boche orchestrated a very clever retreat back some 15 miles to the Hindenburg Line. They dug in and have been constructing sophisticated concrete bunkers for months. We're in for a hard time digging them out. Anyway, back to business. You happy to return to 5th Brigade?'

McErbain nodded. 'Better being with people we know, sir.'

'Very well. Two days here gives you time for fresh kits and clothes.' Tideswell stood and bade them farewell.

The German Army withdrawal, codenamed 'Alberich', had been highly successful. The Hindenburg Line was designed to withstand the severest attack the English could mount. The Allied Command had set their sights on the Line as a major objective for capture in 1917.

The plan was to use the artillery 'creeping barrage' to allow infantry to advance behind the shellfire, without the harassment of German shelling. The manoeuvre had a good chance of success in dry weather, but was utterly hopeless in the wet.

The rain came in deluges, for days at a time. The deep mud they had experienced in the Somme in 1916 returned. Barrages, with high-explosive artillery shells, were a waste of time. Shells exploding 2 feet deep in mud did nothing except convert battlefields into crater-strewn areas that became impassable for troops, store wagons, equipment and artillery weapons. A few miles north, across the Canal du Nord towards Cambrai, men and horses were immobilised in the deep, oozing mud. Artillery pieces were abandoned as the steel-wheeled weapons sank until the barrels of the guns disappeared beneath the surface.

Following the successful attack on the Line east of Beugny, the 5th Field Artillery Brigade was ordered north to Spoilbank on the Ypres–Comines Canal, via Dickebush. The brigade had entrained west of Bapaume, en route to Dickebush. An unseasonable storm caught them unawares.

In sleet and rain, the troops began unloading equipment, stores, guns and ammunition from the train at Armentières station. The 10-mile march to Dickebush, through Messines, was looking difficult. Six-horse team wagons began transporting the brigade to Dickebush, pushing against heavy snow flurries. The road beyond Messines was snow-covered. Visibility was limited and progress slow.

The batteries approaching the town of Dickebush once again encountered odious, slimy mud.

Jum, riding the leading horse of the six-horse team, raised his hand to halt the wagon line. A sea of snow-puddled mud stretched as far as he could see. He slid from the lead horse and promptly sank to his knees in the mire. He struggled his way back to McErbain's wagon.

'I'll walk in front, try to find some passable ground,' said Jum, and floundered back to the lead horse. Grabbing the reins with one hand, he urged the team forward. The horses, as well as the men, were exhausted from the four-hour slog. Jum's foot slipped into a deep hole and he was immediately up to his armpits in mud. The two lead horses followed, the mud rising above their flanks.

He yelled in alarm to halt the convoy, as Bob and Wagga came forward. 'Come on, no time for skylarking, Jum,' laughed Wagga.

'For Christ's sake, get me out of this shit!' Jum, a man not easily scared, was scared now. The mud had now reached his neck and with each movement he sank a little deeper.

Bob hurriedly returned with a rope, looped at one end. He threw the rope to Jum, who quickly slipped the loop under his armpits.

Wagga and Bob heaved on the rope, but Jum did not budge. McErbain jumped from his wagon, unhitched the pony tied to the rear and led the horse forward. He and the horse added their efforts to the taut rope. Jum felt his shoulders tearing with the effort, then the mud suddenly let go. He was ejected from the glutinous hole as if shot from a cannon.

The three rescuers took one look and fell about laughing. A forlorn Jum stood naked from the waist down. Black mud covered his entire upper body, and his pale face peered from behind layers of sludge. Below were his white legs, topped by a small, cold penis hiding in pubic hair. Boots, puttees, trousers and underpants remained in the clutches of the quagmire.

It took the brigade two hours to locate the main track from which the convoy had lost its way. Unhitching the lead team from the 18-pounder was a devilish job. Jum, shivering uncontrollably, was wrapped in an army greatcoat.

A further six hours passed before the wagons entered the small village of Dickebush.

The brigade was grateful for their billets in a number of bombed out farmhouses, hay barns and milking sheds. Shelter had also been found for the horses, an unusual luxury. The horses were cleaned and combed by the troops. The men, weary and footsore, collapsed and slept deeply in utter exhaustion.

The brigade spent some days recovering from the debilitating march from Beugny while the weather improved and the unseasonable snow melted.

Lieutenant Colonel Smith-Stevens addressed his officers. 'We have been ordered into the line to positions at Fossewood, on the Ypres–Comines Canal. Battery COs will have their orders tomorrow morning, early.' Smith-Stevens studied the documents in his hand. 'We'll be supporting the 1st Division, who have as their objective the capture of the Ypres– Menin Road. The DAC Headquarters have ordered 8,000 rounds of 18-pounder shells and 4,000 4.5 Howitzer shells to be sent to Decauville Tramway, so the action will be hotting up. We'll be marching to the Fossewood positions, which will take two days.'

The No. 1 Gun detachment was completing the loading of equipment and stores. The group stood lazily in the warm sun, smoking and talking.

'Bloody hell, Jum!' said Bob. 'We'll be only a stone's throw from the girls at Zillebeke.'

'Don't get too excited, Bob,' Jum said. 'She may have somebody else by now.' He instantly regretted what he had said, seeing Bob's face fall. 'Come on, Bob, I'm only fooling. She'll be waiting for you.'

The loading completed, the brigade moved out. They arrived at Verbrandenmolen that afternoon, and camp was pitched in fine weather on firm ground. The following day, the brigade arrived at Fossewood, quickly setting up secure wagon lines and Headquarters areas 1,000 yards west of the battery gun emplacements, which were scheduled for completion in two days.

July to August 1917

Brigade Diary

20.7.17 Wagon lines at Dickebusch. Btys took up positions at Spoilbank, Ypres, Comiens Canal.

21.7.17 All Btys suffered heavy casualties.

The great bombardment announcing the Third Battle of Ypres began on 15 July 1917. More than 3,000 Allied artillery pieces were brought into action to commence the barrage.

After twelve days of continual shelling, day and night, the 49th German Reserve Division had been driven out of their front-line trenches. They were unable to recapture their lost lines, and their desperate counterattacks were constantly repelled.

During this violent offensive, the Australian artillery suffered badly, and there were many casualties. Their open position on the Ypres flats meant they were exposed to German artillery and vulnerable to German forward observation posts.

The Third Battle of Ypres differed greatly from the vast front-line artillery bombardments of 1916. Germany had produced more powerful heavy artillery with a longer range. The effectiveness of these weapons was devastating. Heavy artillery fire was concentrated on targets to the rear of the Allied force – Headquarters, roads, troop camps, railways and wagon lines. German long-range artillery was capable of accurately hurling shells in excess of 10 miles. Extremely heavy concentrations of German troops had been reported at the Hindenburg Line east of the Ypres–Menin Road.

Major Terry Conrick was agitated. He had spent the morning studying his terrain maps, especially the area due north of Fossewood, just across the border in Belgium. As McErbain peered over his shoulder, Conrick tapped the map with his forefinger.

'Here, Passchendaele, and further south to Broodseinde, Polygon Wood, Dairy Wood and Daisy Wood. The Boche has been heavily dug in in these areas for some time. Their wagon lines are extensive and good. Solid main roads are making it easy for large volumes of troops and ammunition to be moved very quickly.'

McErbain nodded. 'Yes, I see.'

'It seems obvious that we should be attempting to break the Hindenburg due east of Menin with a powerful salient thrust straight through their first and second trenches. This we would have to hold, and hold with strength, or the strategy will fail. The salient would completely sever their lifeline to Belgium. But the assault would have to be a surprise frontal attack – and we know what that means.'

'We do, indeed,' answered McErbain. 'Very heavy casualties in the line. Pozières all over again.'

'Anyway,' concluded Terry Conrick, 'it's not for us to make plans.' He smiled grimly. 'It's our job to carry them out.'

The 5th Field Artillery Brigade had completed their emplacements at Spoilbank on the Ypres–Comines Canal. No sooner had the brigade finalised their positions than the enemy artillery commenced their initial bombardment. German air reconnaissance had been accurate, pinpointing not only the brigade but also individual batteries and guns. The batteries of the 5th Field Artillery Brigade suffered heavy casualties in the artillery exchange.

Like all the men of the 5th, Jum was exhausted. The continuous bombardment had taken its toll. During a lull in the barrage, the No. 1 detachment was trying to relax in the sun.

'I'll be glad when this bloody July is over,' said Ron to no one in particular.

'Why?' asked Bob, and continued without waiting for an answer, 'September will be the same, so will October. Then the bloody rain will start. There'll be mud and more bloody mud ...'

'How many boys have we lost from the battery, Gill?' asked Jum.

'About thirty, I think.'

'Well, it's only a matter of time,' said Jum, bitterly. 'Don't worry about being happy or unhappy, Ron – it'll make no bloody difference.'

BRIGADE DIARY

31.7.17 Attack made, all objectives captured.
Bde limbered up and marched forward to new
positions at Fossewood.

31.8.17 1st Div Infantry taking very heavy
casualties. Fighting continued unabated for the
month of August.

Four weeks of non-stop fighting had drained the resilience of even the strongest troops.

It was impossible to maintain even basic cleanliness, and the condition of the troops had deteriorated badly. Trench foot, the most common complaint, occurred when the feet were immersed in mud or water for long periods. Extremely painful, it made the skin and tissue of the feet blacken and die. There was also a severe influenza epidemic. Large numbers of troops were treated at the Australian General Hospital in Boulogne. As replacement troops were scarce, heavy workloads weighed down the depleted battery numbers.

'Moving again?' exclaimed Wagga. 'We've only just finished digging this fuckin' hole!'

'We're much better going that way,' said McErbain pointing east, 'than this way.' He swung his arm around to the west.

'I suppose so, Harold,' said Wagga resignedly.

Digging an 18-pound field gun in and out was backbreaking work. This, coupled with the tension of battle and loss of sleep, left many of the troops short-tempered and aggressive.

The shell craters in the Ypres–Menin Road were deep and wide, and horse-drawn 18-pounder guns were cumbersome. It was hard work keeping the guns clear of the holes. Waist-deep mud only a yard from the road edge strained the already frayed nerves of the transport drivers as they toiled towards the village of Belleward.

McErbain emerged from the staff car at the entrance to the village. As the six-horse team towing the No. 1 Gun approached, McErbain stepped onto the wagon. 'Keep north through the village, Jum. There's a ridge about a mile north-east, can't miss it. Lake Belleward is at the bottom end of the ridge. I'll wait there for you.' McErbain jumped down and got back into the staff car, which was already moving forward. Muffled shellfire could be heard in the distance; it was coming from the ridge. Plumes of smoke rose from several areas of shell burst as the batteries approached their positions.

Conrick was standing with officers of the batteries on the plateau of Belleward Ridge. Below them, the muddied waters of Belleward Lake were testimony to the intense destruction wrought by two years of fierce battles.

The landscape that greeted the troops was barren, dark and muddy, punctuated with splintered tree trunks and the carcasses of wagons, half-submerged in mud. Empty concrete pillboxes, specifically designed to house teams of Maxim machine gun detachments, were showing the effects of heavy shelling. The Germans had retired from them to the Hindenburg Line.

Lieutenant Colonel Smith-Stevens had the attention of his officers. 'The 1st Division infantry, as we know, has suffered heavy casualties for the past two weeks. We are about to engage the Hindenburg Line to give them some relief. We are to lay on a continuous barrage, starting immediately. Before you leave, collect your information sheets on targets. Get set for some heavy work.'

The officers collected their orders and returned to their respective commands.

McErbain stood in the battery outpost. The troops had gathered around. 'Our objective is Anzac Ridge and Polygon Wood. HQ staff information shows German troop movement and established artillery. They'll be getting our full attention. Let's go! Four rounds per minute until further notice.'

The artillerymen went about their business in a workmanlike manner.

'Have you seen Padre Jenkins, Gill?' asked Jum.

Gillies nodded. 'Yeah, saw him back at Albert about a month ago. He asked after everyone.'

'Is he still with the 5th?'

'Yes – after he left Worgret Hospital, he was off for a long furlough in London, to stay with an old aunt he hadn't seen for years.'

'Has he recovered from the grenade blast?'

'Yes,' said Gillies, 'but he looks a bit like one of the Three Musketeers with that scar across his cheek.' The detachment laughed.

'He'll be a fire-eating preacher, now,' said Ron, 'with that battle scar. Nobody will want to argue with him!'

'You betcha,' said Bob. 'Yes, Padre! No, Padre! Anything you like, Padre!'

A German shell exploded 40 yards in front of the battery, and was followed by a string of successive blasts.

'Whizz bangs, Jum?' asked Wagga.

'I think so, Wagga,' said Jum, 'but they sound a bit different.'

Wagga watched the shells exploding nearby. 'I'll never complain to Harold again about digging in. These bastards are too close for comfort.'

A shrieking shell hurtled overhead, exploding loudly but harmlessly some 400 yards downhill towards Belleward Lake.

'Bloody hell,' said Wagga, 'wasn't that a 150?'

'Sure was, Wagga,' said Gillies. 'Keep your bloody head down.'

'That may have been a register, Gill,' said Jum.

Gillies nodded. 'Let's hope they didn't see where it landed.'

Strangely, the single shell was not followed by any further 150-millimetre Krupp specials.

Conrick sat quietly talking to McErbain. 'We can expect some of the British artillery here soon. They seem to have their act together and have something like four artillery brigades ready to move.'

'That's about eighty guns!' said McErbain. 'And six or so of the new 9-inch Howitzers are on the move, too.'

'That'll give the Boche something to think about,' mused Conrick. '2nd DAC are expecting to expend something like 4,000 shells per day when we get beefed up by the Tommies.'

'How the hell will they keep up the ammunition to the line?' asked McErbain.

'I believe about thirty new motorised trucks are about to replace the horse-drawn supply wagons.'

'That's a change for the better,' said McErbain emphatically.

Jum and Bob entered the mess tent and sat down. The other men at the table continued eating as the conversation moved to the upcoming offensive. 'We're on tomorrow, boys,' said a sombre McErbain. 'This'll be as tough as anything we've been through.'

The following morning Wagga looked north towards Passchendaele. As far as the eye could see, the Ypres flats were covered with Allied artillery pieces. Wagga turned to Jum. 'They look like a swarm of locusts, Jum. How many guns, do you think?'

Jum grimaced. 'In this sector, from Menin up to Passchendaele, I'd reckon nearly 3,000.'

'But that's 24,000 men for just one shift!'

'That's right. If you want the real figure, multiply the guns by thirty. That comes to 90,000 men in artillery alone in this area. What do you think, Gill?'

'We'll put together twenty divisions of infantry and you'll see maybe over 400,000 Allied troops waiting to tear the arse out of half a million German blokes over there,' he said, pointing east.

'What are we all doing here?' asked Bob.

'Beats me, Bob,' said Jum. 'Makes no sense at all. But we're here, so we'll make the best of it.'

Brigade Diary

7.9.17 2,000 18 pdr. rds and 1,000 4.5 How.
Ordered from DAHQ to be sent to Decauville
Tramway

The morning sun of late autumn had not yet appeared over the hills. Low-lying mist shrouded the bottom slopes and shallow gullies. A strange tension gripped the air as thousands of gun detachments waited for the gigantic battle to commence. It was 15 July 1917.

McErbain looked at his watch in the half-light. '0559 hours, one minute to go,' he said. The detachments looked towards McErbain in the outpost control. He raised his arm. Jum gripped the lanyard. McErbain's arm dropped.

Eighteen hundred 18-pounders, 600 Howitzers, with a hundred 60-pounder heavy artillery back 800 yards, opened fire simultaneously. It was later reported that the roar of the barrage was heard in Dover and Folkstone in south-eastern England.

Under the relentless onslaught, the Hindenburg Line was lost to view in a massive cloud of dust and debris. German infantry had expected a barrage, but could not have foreseen what was taking place. The German troops cowered in their deep trench system. Still the shells continued – hour after hour, without respite. Many German infantry, mostly young conscripts, were downing weapons and running away from the appalling deluge of death thundering onto their trench systems.

The German bombardment started some thirty minutes after that of the Allies. German heavy artillery once again harassed the rear of the Allied army, reaching back to Zillebeke, Armentières and even Ypres. The German Field Artillery also concentrated fire on the Allies' first line of artillery – the 18-pounders and 4.5 Howitzers.

The losses of men and equipment mounted. The artillery batteries that had been pinpointed by German aerial reconnaissance were targeted with great effect. The men's morale crumbled as the relentless barrage found target after target.

When relieved, each shift of men was happy to have survived. But back at their wagon lines, they were still under intense artillery attack. Sleep deprivation, a soldier's worst enemy, was having a profound effect on the strength of the men. The constant barrages kept the battalions awake and on edge even when the men were at rest. Mental weariness and physical exhaustion were debilitating the troops.

The 14th Battery was relieved at 0600 hours. But the rain that had swept across from the east for the previous five hours had made artillery operation virtually impossible. Traversing the 200 yards from the outpost station to No. 1 Gun became a hard slog through knee-deep mud.

Jum felt a bone-aching weariness. Any movement was an effort that sucked at his body's deepest reserve. The firing rate had reduced to one round every five minutes or so – a mere token, designed to annoy rather than attack the Boche. The enemy return fire was also desultory. Shells exploded deep in the sea of mud.

Gillies turned to Jum after glancing at his watch. 'Should be here soon, Jum.' Jum nodded as five figures appeared out of the sheeting rain. 'All yours, you blokes,' said a relieved Bob. Wearily, the detachment climbed from the position as the replacements moved in.

'One round every five minutes, Charlie,' said Gillies. Charlie nodded silently.

Waterproof capes were no match for the pelting rain. Streams of water relentlessly ran down their necks as the five men headed for the Headquarters area, billets and, they hoped, hot food.

Finally, after they had negotiated the vile mud, a wooden-planked track appeared. The detachment slowly trudged their way back to the rear lines some 500 yards west. The rain had eased slightly, allowing the men to catch glimpses of their tents in the distance.

Jum turned to Bob. 'You feel like some food or are you too buggered?'

Bob, his face shrouded by the rain, mumbled, 'I suppose I'm hungry.'

The group entered the mess tent. With plates of food in hand, the crowd moved slowly, waiting for a place to sit and eat.

Jum sank gratefully onto a bench seat just vacated by an equally exhausted group. 'Over here, you blokes,' he called.

There was little talk, as the men concentrated on satisfying their hunger. Jum stood up. 'Anyone for tea?' he asked. A couple of the men nodded. Jum moved to the large tea urn sitting near the tent entrance. As he waited in line, he glanced outside at the drenching downpour. Fifty yards away a lone driver sat atop his wagon. The rain had increased again in intensity.

Jum watched for a moment. 'You poor bastard,' he thought. He filled a pannikin with hot tea and draped a cape over his head, then walked over to the driver. 'Feel like some hot tea, mate?' he asked.

The driver turned and smiled. 'You bet! Can we get out of this bloody rain?'

'Sure, come over to the mess tent.' The pair made their way to the comfort of the tent. 'You look cold and hungry. Want some food?' said Jum.

'I'm that hungry I could eat a Chinaman's bum through a picket fence,' replied the driver.

Jum smiled as he held out his hand. 'Jum Bevan.'

'Ernie Buckleton, mate,' the driver replied as they shook hands.

They walked over to the food line and the corporal cook, disliked by most of the men in the brigade, glared at Jum as Ernie helped himself to the food. 'Who's your friend, Bevan?' he asked sarcastically.

'What's it to you, you fat slug, O'Brien?' Jum's anger rose quickly. It was not the first time they had exchanged words.

'I can't have just any bloke walking in here and getting fed. You should know better,' said the corporal.

'Ernie here is one of the blokes in the front line keeping the Boche away from the likes of you. He's been stuck in the rain and cold all day. Why don't you disappear and let the man enjoy his meal?' Jum and Ernie turned to join the remainder of the No. 2 detachment.

Jum introduced Ernie Buckleton to the crowd as they sat. 'He's a cranky bastard, that bloody cook,' said Jum.

Bob grinned. 'But he makes a great pony stew, Jum.'

Some of the men returned for second servings.

'What unit you in Ernie?' inquired Jum.

'1st Battalion, 1st Div.,' he answered.

'You a replacement in 1st Battalion?' asked Ron.

'No, mate, I joined up in August 1914. Been in since then.'

'You must have been one of the first,' said Bob.

'Regimental number 151,' said Ernie.

All eyes were on Ernie Buckleton. They knew now what this man had seen and been through.

'You from Sydney, Ernie?' asked Bob.

'Moorfield, though I spent a lot of time in the Randwick area.'

Jum looked up. 'My family live in Waverley, but I was working on the Cordeaux Dam, south-west of Sydney, with Bob here.'

'Did you work in Sydney, Ernie?' asked Wagga.

'Yeah, I'm a "penciller",' replied Ernie.

'A what?'

'A bookie's clerk. You've heard of horse racing, Wagga?' laughed Jum. Wagga's face lit up with understanding.

'I rode track work when I was a boy at Randwick,' said Ernie. 'Picked up a few quid, but always seemed to give it back to the bookies. So when my weight stopped me riding, I got a start with John Chalmers, a rails bookie at Randwick. I love horses, and I love being around them.'

'What made you join up, Ernie?' asked Gillies.

Ernie grinned. 'Same old question eh? Don't know, maybe getting bored with life in Sydney. Had nothing to keep me there, so I thought I'd give it a go.'

'Were you at Gallipoli?' asked Bob.

'No, I was stuck in Egypt. Maadi, Mex and Cairo. Fought the bloody Turks in the sand. Lots of fun – if you reckon fun is hot, sandy, thirsty work trying to kill those wild bastards. Left Cairo and ended up in hospital in Heliopolis for a few weeks ... with an infection.' He grinned sheepishly. 'Then straight into France. The Somme, Albert, Bapaume, the usual places.' Ernie had removed his cape. The men were relaxed, enjoying cigarettes.

Gillies nodded at Ernie's arm. 'You were a corporal once, I see.'

Ernie smiled. 'Until yesterday. I'd been at a pack saddlery school for a few weeks at a camp near Hazebrouck. We all got on the booze and stayed in town an extra night. I got busted to private yesterday.'

'Was it worth it?' asked Bob.

'She was beautiful,' grinned Ernie. He stood up. 'I'd best go and see if the road has been repaired yet. I'm trying to get to the wagon lines before dark.'

The rain had eased to a fine mist. Ernie Buckleton climbed onto his wagon, waved and moved off. 'See ya soon!' he called.

SEPTEMBER 1917

The Ypres–Menin Road offensive had been highly successful for the Allies. On the night of 16 September 1917, the 1st Australian Division relieved the 47th London Division on the edge of Glencorse Wood, with the 2nd Australian Division relieving on Westhoek Ridge, a few miles south-east of Zillebeke, on the edge of the Flanders fields.

The men stood ready. The guns were pointing north-east, ready to give artillery support to the advancing 1st and 2nd Divisions.

'Fire!' yelled Gillies.

The 18-pounder hurled the shell over the heads of the front-line infantry into the enemy trenches. But as dawn broke, the heavy enemy barrage on the 2nd Division resulted in many casualties.

Word of this travelled quickly to Rear Command and the Heavy Siege Batteries of the British artillery. They ordered an unrelenting bombardment on the German front line. The two Australian divisions on the left and the five British divisions on the right moved forward on an 11-mile front. Facing this enormous front line of Allied troops were the 121st German Division and, to their south, the Bavarian Ersatz Division.

The battle of 26 September went precisely according to the Allied plan. Advancing rapidly on the inside front, the Allied troops met only token resistance. Many Germans surrendered willingly when it became obvious they were fighting a lost cause. The enemy troops seemed dazed and bewildered by the ferocious intensity of the Allied artillery barrage.

As the infantry dug into their new ground – won at great cost to life – the artillery was ordered further eastwards to new positions.

Brigade Diary

26.9.17 Attack on Anzac Ridge and Polygon Wood. The Australian flag was erected on the 'Pill Box' christened Anzac.

Fierce attacks made by enemy. They could plainly see Passchendaele and Broodseinde Ridge are our main objectives.

Ernie Buckleton, corporal once again, glanced skywards. A grey, overcast sky deepened to a black, sinister horizon towards the east. The scene was horrific. Intense shelling by the enemy, coupled with unending downpours of sleeting rain, had once again turned the Menin Road into a muddy track. The ammunition convoy of motorised trucks battled its way north of Belleward towards Zonnebeke. A Pioneer captain halted the convoy east of Zonnebeke, speaking to the divisional artillery captain in the lead truck. 'It's no go past this point, Captain. The bloody Boche have blasted the crap out of the road to Broodseinde Ridge. I'm afraid you'll have to use pack mules from here.' It was fortunate that these small but powerful beasts were capable of carrying more dead weight than horses.

Swearing loudly, the captain stepped down from the truck. 'How far to Broodseinde Ridge?'

'About a mile. The action will start half a mile from here, believe me!'

It took the convoy two hours to unload their ammunition. The first team of ten men and twenty mules was loaded and set off towards Broodseinde Ridge. As the mud had become impassable, many mule teams had been brought to the forward area. The mules were the final solution to transporting ammunition to the front line. The Allied front line sat 700 yards to the south-west of the ridge. The German line was securely dug in, with their artillery half a mile back on the ridge, commanding a clear view west.

The intensity of the fighting at Broodseinde Ridge had badly depleted Allied ammunition. It was critical that the mule packs got through, for if the Germans took the incentive and launched an offensive, they could regain the ground gained by the Allies over the previous few weeks, and thousands of Allied troops would have died in vain.

Ernie Buckleton was now knee-deep in mud, which clung to his every step. He was grateful for the strength and power of his two mules. Laden as they were, they still muscled their way stubbornly through the mud, now up to their bellies. He gratefully hung on to the neck halter of his lead animal.

He passed a CCS, full to overflowing with dead and wounded Allied troops. A line of corpses 30 yards long lay behind the tent, and it was lengthening by the hour.

The Allied heavy siege shells were hurtling overhead, seeking the Hindenburg Line. Crackling small arms fire intensified as the pack mules neared the Allied front-line trench.

The screech of the German 150-millimetre mortar shell came too late to allow evasive action. The shell exploded in the midst of the pack team, with devastating effect. Equipment, men, mules and mud hurtled skywards. Other mortar shells came in quick succession.

Ernie Buckleton desperately tried to stand, but couldn't. 'I've bought it! Bloody hell!' he thought. He freed one arm and realised that he was alive, although his first mule was jammed on top of his body. The mule had taken the full impact of the explosion. While it had probably saved his life, it had also buried him deep in the mud. He finally extricated himself from under the carcass of the dead mule, only to be greeted by a horrifying sound.

A man's voice rose in an agonised scream for help, which quickly faded to loud moans. Ernie quickly surveyed the scene. Three mules were dead and one badly wounded, braying in agony. Three men were down, and the pack train was in chaos. One of the men lay very still; another, seeing Ernie, raised his arm. The third, a youngster of no more than eighteen, now screamed again as he lay in the deep mud. 'I want my mum! I want my mum!' he shrieked over and over. His leg was badly shattered, the femur broken and protruding through the leg of his tunic.

Bent double, Ernie ran to the still body. He looked down. 'You're going nowhere, mate, your war's over,' he mumbled, as he took in the man's mutilated upper body, lying in a pool of blood and water. He waved in response to the other injured soldier as he reached the young boy screaming for his mother. Another shell landed 20 feet from Ernie. The fierce explosion was muffled and contained by the mud.

'I'll get you to cover, Billy,' said Ernie, as calmly as possible. He wasn't feeling calm. His stomach churned at the sight of the injured and dead men and mules who had suffered the direct hit. He'd never get used to this.

Thirty feet back along the track, a fresh shell hole, still smoking, offered slight cover. He grasped the boy by his shoulders and began dragging him towards the crater. The boy screeched loudly with pain before he passed out. The sergeant in charge, badly shaken, had fought his way back through the mud.

'Bloody hell, Ernie, what a fucking mess!'

Ernie nodded and called over his shoulder. 'Keep going, Sarge, get your load to the line, quick as you can. I'll clean up here and catch up.'

The sergeant stumbled back to his load. The depleted mule convoy moved forward. Ernie carefully lifted the second injured man and stumbled awkwardly to the crater containing the unconscious boy. The soldier whispered as Ernie stepped into the shell hole, 'I think my arm's broken, Ernie.'

'I'll have a look soon as I get you down, mate.' He knelt carefully in the crater, gently placing the second man beside the still boy. 'Now, let's have a look,' he said. Tearing open the sleeve, he saw that the upper arm was a mangled mess of shattered bone and torn sinew. He quickly tore a strap from one of the dead mules, applying it to the upper arm as a tourniquet. The injured man fell slowly backwards.

'Thanks, mate,' he whispered, lapsing into unconsciousness.

'I'll be back soon,' said Ernie, as he moved from the trench.

He fought back a desperate urge to vomit as, on his knees, he struggled with the pack straps on the dead mules. The badly wounded mule had stopped braying, its eyes open and sightless as its carcass sank slowly into the deep mud.

Finally, exhausted, Ernie succeeded in transferring the packs to the mules that were still alive.

He dragged on the front mule, yelling to get the string of animals moving. 'Come on, you stubborn bastards, do you want to get us all bloody killed?' Once they were moving, Ernie grabbed the halter strap of the second tough little beast. The mud eased slightly and they slowly moved off. The sergeant, having delivered his load, had fought back to help Ernie to the line. 'Sarge, you get this stuff unloaded. I'll go back to the injured blokes in the shell hole,' said Ernie urgently. 'Hurry – it'll take two of us to get them to the CCS.'

The sergeant nodded as he led the team to the eagerly waiting men in the front trench. Crouching low, Ernie scurried the 300 hundred yards back to the shell hole where he had left the injured men.

'How the bloody hell can we move them?' he said aloud. He ran to a destroyed trench and jumped in. Grunting, he freed from the sucking mud a length of duckboard that was still in one piece. Throwing the duckboard clear, he leapt out as the sergeant reappeared.

'No time for stretchers, Sarge, we'll use this,' panted Ernie.

Another cluster of mortar bombs arrived, and again their blasts were contained by the deep mud. The two exhausted men slogged their way towards the CCS, where two orderlies took over. 'You blokes look buggered,' said one.

'There are still two more there,' said Ernie, gasping for breath. They made their way back to the other driver, who was unconscious in the shell hole. Returning twenty minutes later, they retrieved the body of the driver killed in the blast.

'How will they be, Doc?' asked Ernie, all his reserves spent, as he rested near the CCS tent.

'We'll set the boy's leg. I only hope that too much of that filthy mud hasn't got into his wound,' replied the doctor.

'What about the other one?'

'I'm afraid he'll lose his arm just below the shoulder, no chance of saving it. If we don't amputate, infection could set in and he'll die very quickly.'

After collecting the remaining mules, Ernie and the sergeant began the long trek back to the wagon lines, about a mile westward, towards Zonnebeke.

'You're a brave bastard, Ernie,' said the sergeant.

'Just did what I could, mate. That's all any of us can do.'

'I'm putting a report in to the battalion CO. Those two blokes owe you their lives.'

'No big deal, mate, part of the job.'

The pair silently trudged through the gathering darkness towards Zonnebeke village.

A number of weeks later, Harold McErbain said to Jum, 'I just read a report that Lieutenant Colonel Smith-Stevens had access to.'

'Somebody in the shit again?'

'No, far from it,' he replied. 'That mate of yours, Ernie Buckleton, was blasted by a heavy German barrage as they were taking ammunition to the front line at Broodseinde Ridge. The mule train got hit by German mortar fire. One bloke was killed, a couple badly wounded. Apparently Buckleton took over, got the wounded to safety through that awful bloody mud and mortar fire and delivered the ammo. He's been recommended for a Military Medal, and Brigadier General Bennett, CO of the 1st Division, has supported the recommendation.'

'Jesus!' said Jum. 'I knew he was a tough bastard, but that's something else.'

OCTOBER 1917

BRIGADE DIARY

26.9.17 Infantry attack made south west of Zonnebeke. Large massed parties of enemy fired on during the day.

'The 105th Howitzer Battery reported a plane with Allied colours, numbered C47, machine-gun attacking their position and shooting at pillboxes with tracer fire,' Lieutenant Colonel Smith-Stevens reported to his assembled officers. 'These German bastards will stop at nothing,' he continued, grim-faced. 'They were flying with our colours! We are to move a mile to the north, dig in, and register our 18-pounders on targets near Passchendaele. The entire brigade will dig in near Anzac Ridge. Clear?' The officers nodded. They all understood what was in store for them.

'Any good news, sir?' asked McErbain.

Three months in the field had again taken its toll. The Menin Road offensive, Polygon Wood, Broodseinde Ridge and finally Passchendaele had the troops exhausted, shell-shocked and on the verge of collapse. Later that week, the 5th Field Artillery Brigade was relieved in the field. A convoy of motor lorries transported about 800 men from Anzac Ridge to the Steenwerck area. A group was also billeted at Steenvorde, a nearby village.

The 14th Battery worked for two weeks repairing harness and equipment. New barrels were fitted to two of their 18-pounders. Horses were groomed and harnesses polished, fit for a regimental parade. But the work was not onerous and their billets at

Kruisstraat were sumptuous compared with the previous months of mud, rain and miserable cold.

As the men took a break, Jum glanced towards the road leading to Ypres. A continual line of infantry stretched for miles towards Zonnebeke.

'That must be 1st and 2nd Divisions coming out of the line,' Bob said. ''Bout time they had a furlough.'

'They've had it tougher than most for the past three months,' said Jum. He rose to his feet. 'Let's go see if Ernie Buckleton comes by.'

The five men walked up to the line of infantry wearily making their way west to Ypres. 'How far back is 1st Battalion?' asked Jum as a group trudged past. He received a vacant look. The next group was more accommodating. Two men paused to rest and converse. 'Yeah, they're not far back, about 500 yards or so.'

'There's Ernie!' said Jum, moving forward. 'Jesus, Ernie, you all right?' he said as he fell into step beside him.

'Tired mate, bloody tired,' replied Ernie. His face was drawn and grey.

'Can you drop off for a while?'

Ernie nodded. 'I'll tell the Sarge,' he said and stepped out of the column.

An infantryman wearing sergeant's stripes approached.

'Charlie, I'm off for a couple of hours with some mates here from artillery. Will you cover for me?'

'Sure, Ernie. It's only about 5 miles to the billet. See you soon.'

Ron took Ernie's pack and rifle. 'I'll drop this stuff into my tent. See you in the mess tent.'

Comfortably seated, with steaming mugs of hot tea, the men were silent. Ron sat down at the end of the makeshift table and smiled as he raised his cup of tea. 'Congratulations, Ernie, we heard about the medal.'

'How in hell do you blokes know?'

'One of our mates, Harold McErbain, got a field commission to lieutenant,' said Jum. 'He happened to see the report going through.'

'You buggers ever get on the receiving end of a barrage?' asked Ernie.

The group looked at each other and burst out laughing. 'Mate, we live with it every day,' said Bob.

'Feel like a drink, mate?' asked Jum.

'Try me!'

'Wagga, you know where the stash is.'

Wagga eagerly ran from the mess tent, returning in five minutes with a conspicuous lump under his greatcoat.

The group huddled together as Wagga brought out the bottle. 'This is special stuff, Ernie – half whisky, half jimjam juice. Take it easy.'

Ernie put the bottle to his mouth and gulped. His pallor was quickly replaced by a healthy glow as the liquid hit his empty stomach. Gasping, he turned to Jum. 'What the fuck, you trying to kill me?' he sputtered in a hoarse voice. The men grinned.

The bottle was passed around and its contents quickly disappeared.

Ron went outside. He noticed a loaded wagon approaching the officers' store. He ran back into the tent and got Jum's attention. 'The stores wagon is nearly at the officers' store,' he stage-whispered.

'Let's go!' said Jum. 'Come on, Ernie, you too.' The six men headed towards the approaching stores wagon.

'Bob, and you, Wagga, don't be silly, just make it look convincing,' said Jum.

'What are you blokes up to?' asked Ernie.

'Just stay close, Ernie. You'll see,' said Jum, mysteriously. 'You get the driver, Ron. Ernie, Jim and I will do the job.'

Wagga and Bob raised their voices as they neared the mess area.

Ron had moved to intercept the driver, who was heading for the rear of the stores tent. 'Want a hand, mate?'

'Nah,' said the driver. 'Thanks, anyway.'

The two voices, already raised in argument, became heated. Bob pushed Wagga forcefully onto his back. Wagga jumped up and the two men were hard at it, punching, shoving and yelling. Ron and the driver moved 20 yards closer to get a better view of the combatants.

'Get him, Wagga! Don't let that bastard get away with that,' called Ron.

A small knot of men formed and watched the fight closely.

'Come on, time to go,' said Jum. He slid up to the wagon and ripped open a cardboard carton in the middle of the packages.

Quickly extracting two bottles of whisky, he passed them to Gillies. Ernie grabbed another two bottles from Jum and rapidly moved away. Jum dropped two bottles into his greatcoat pockets, then slipped two more bottles under his arm. He quickly pushed the carton top back into place. Without glancing behind him, he, too, moved away from the wagon.

From the corner of his eye, Ron saw the job had been completed. He ran to the two fighting men.

'Come on, you two, break it up, break it up!' he yelled as he pushed between the two and held them apart. 'Now shake hands, you're both in the same bloody battery!' Reluctantly, Bob and Wagga shook hands.

Ron returned to the stores driver. 'There you are, three days away from the front line and they want to kill each other.'

The driver grinned, shook his head, and climbed back on his wagon. 'They need a night on the town to quieten them down,' he offered as he moved off.

Ten minutes later, the group met in the mess tent. Everyone was smiling, except Wagga. 'Bloody hell, Bob, you caught me with that left. I should've given you one back.' A red weal adorned his cheek.

'Don't worry, Wagga. All in a good cause,' said Jum, as he produced a bottle from under his coat. 'You're the guest, Ernie.'

Ernie raised the bottle to his lips, downing a couple of mouthfuls of the smooth Scotch. The bottle was passed around and quickly drained, and another took its place.

'Wagga, go and stash four bottles. No need to drink it all now,' said Jum. Wagga moved out of the tent. The noise level rose considerably as the number of empty bottles increased and the spirits of the men lightened. Men from the various batteries began arriving for their evening meal, with the boisterous party in the corner continuing.

Slurring his words slightly, Bob wagged an admonishing finger at Wagga. 'No, no, Wagga,' he said. 'Jum is the best horseman in this battery.'

'Well, if Ernie here used to ride track work,' Wagga replied, 'he might just give Jum a run for his money.'

Jum laughed, 'We'll never know. I'm not going out in that freezing cold for any bastard.' The good-natured argument continued as darkness closed in. A single kerosene lamp cast a dim light. Four bottles of Scotch had been drained.

McErbain moved to the table. 'What the bloody hell are you blokes doing?' he hissed. 'The whole camp knows you're on the piss. Get out of here or there may be trouble.'

At that moment, a figure filled the entrance to the mess tent. Captain Henry Chilcott was not in a reasonable mood. His nerves inevitably affected his digestion, and an hour earlier he had endured a raging bowel explosion that had left him sore and uncomfortable.

'Lieutenant,' he snapped at McErbain, 'these men appear to be intoxicated while on active duty.'

He turned to the group. 'On your feet,' he snarled. 'You are in the presence of an officer.'

The six men slowly rose to their feet. 'Take their names, Lieutenant. I will deal with this later.' He spun on his heel and headed for the entrance as fast as his chafed backside would allow.

'Get back to your tents and sleep it off,' advised McErbain. He squinted in the weak light of the lamp. 'Who the hell are you, soldier?' he asked Ernie Buckleton.

'Just one of the boys, sir,' said Jum.

Noting his shoulder flashes, McErbain exclaimed, 'Of course, you're Buckleton, 1st Battalion!'

'At your service, sir,' said Ernie with a half-hearted salute.

'Where the hell are you supposed to be, Ernie?' asked McErbain, suddenly seeing this little escapade getting out of hand.

'Just out of Ypres, sir,' said Jum.

'At a village called Vlamertinge,' added Ernie.

'Jum, go get a wagon and give Ernie here a lift to his camp, otherwise he won't make it,' said McErbain as he moved away, adding, 'Chilcott's a mean bastard, but I'll see what I can do.'

Lieutenant Colonel Smith-Stevens interrupted Chilcott. 'The men are not on active duty, Captain,' he said testily.

'With respect, sir, although on rest out of the line, they are still technically on active duty,' insisted Chilcott.

'Do it your way, Captain, but take it easy. Those men have been through a lot,' said Smith-Stevens.

The following morning, McErbain read the charge sheets.

First charge: Drunk and disorderly whilst on active duty.
Second charge: Stealing five bottles of whisky, property
of the Australian Imperial Force.

McErbain reluctantly wrote the six men's names in the spaces on the charge sheets.

Lieutenant Colonel Smith-Stevens studied the men before him.
'Where did you procure the alcohol?' he asked.
Jum stepped forward. 'We've had the whisky for some time, sir.'
'Mine came in a food parcel,' said Wagga.
'Don't talk rubbish, Gunner,' said Captain Chilcott.
Smith-Stevens sighed. 'You admit you had been drinking?'
'Yes, sir,' said Jum.
'I find you all guilty on the charge of drinking whilst on active duty.'
Chilcott piped up again. 'What have you to say about the five bottles of whisky missing from the officers' store, Driver Bevan?'
Looking directly at Smith-Stevens, Jum said in a level voice, 'I can honestly say, sir, that we are not guilty of stealing five bottles of whisky.'
Lieutenant Colonel Smith-Stevens wrote on the charge sheets:

On the first charge: Guilty. Fined one day's pay – 3/6.
On the second charge: Charge dismissed.

McErbain stepped up. 'About turn, march out.' As they marched out of the CO's office, the five men could hardly suppress their grins.
'Jum, you bugger, I kept my fingers crossed when you lied to the CO,' said Wagga.
'Now let's get one thing clear, Wagga,' said Jum. 'I did not lie. We didn't steal five bottles of whisky – we stole eight.'

NOVEMBER 1917 TO JANUARY 1918

BRIGADE DIARY

*6.11.17 Westhoek Ridge. Heavy rain
continuous making roads impassable. Btys
had to push forward into Hannebeke Valley
through mud waist deep.*

*Broodseinde Ridge captured, giving a
magnificent view of the enemy territory.
Zonnebeke heavily shelled. Visibility very
poor. Cannot see enemy lines. Many red green
and yellow flares from enemy trenches.*

*Westhoek being heavily shelled from Morslede.
Enemy still bombarding Westhoek and
Bellewarde Ridges.*

By the end of November 1917, winter had set in. Freezing winds
from the north brought widespread, heavy falls of snow that lay
6 inches deep.

The mess tent was cold, and the men were rugged up against
the chill. The few weeks of rest and inactivity had now become a
chore as the weather forestalled any outdoor activities.

Bob and Jum had been talking. 'Well, we're doing nothing.
Ask Harold,' said Bob.

'Ask Harold what?' said McErbain as he sat between them. Jum smiled as he turned to McErbain. 'Young Bob here hasn't seen his girlfriend Jeanne in months. She wouldn't know if he's dead or alive. You know she and Anna are in Zillebeke, about 15 miles south of here, toward Armentières?'

'Leave it with me,' said McErbain. 'I'll think of something.'

Some hours later, he left the Brigade Headquarters tent. He called to Ron, walking past to the wagon line.

'Hey, Ron! Get Bevan and Buchannen to report to me.'

'Yessir.'

Bob and Jum hurried to the Headquarters tent.

'Now, you two, you have to be back here tomorrow or my arse gets kicked. This despatch has to get to HQ at Armentières today, so off you go. Don't let me down.'

The two men ran towards the temporary stables. A corporal appeared. 'What are you two up to?'

'We need a rig. We're taking a despatch to HQ at Armentières,' answered Jum.

'Bullshit, the motor lorry takes it every afternoon to Armentières,' replied the corporal.

'Come on, mate, don't stuff us about,' said Bob. 'We've got orders to leave immediately.'

'Where's your requisition form?'

Jum produced the form, and the corporal examined it closely. 'A double rig. We'll be back in twenty minutes,' said Jum. The pair then ran to their billets to prepare for the chilly ride to Armentières and on to Zillebeke.

The horses trotted evenly along the narrow road. The track was well-worn by the heavy traffic continuously moving from Ypres to Menin and Zonnebeke village.

'How far to Armentières do you reckon, Jum?' asked Bob for the tenth time.

'Just over that hill, mate,' said Jum.

'Which hill?'

'That one, straight ahead.'

'Bugger you, you've said that about the last six hills we crossed.'

'I mean it this time,' said Jum.

The two-horse rig crested a slight rise and Armentières appeared in the distance. The Belgian town was devastated. The few buildings still standing showed the effects of three years of unrelenting bombardment. The once tree-lined streets that led to the town's main road were potholed and rutted. Even though the sun shone, a pall hung over the remains of the gutted town.

They went quickly to the Headquarters building in the town square. Bob held the rig whilst Jum ran to the entrance. A few moments later, he returned to Bob. 'We have to wait in case there's a reply.'

'Bloody hell!' said Bob.

A young captain, wearing the red braid of a staff officer, called to Jum. 'Over here, soldier!' Jum ran to the captain. 'No reply, soldier. You're free to return to your lines.'

Jum saluted and ran to the rig. 'Let's go!' He slapped the reins on the horses' rumps and they broke into a trot. The rig quickly moved east along the Menin Road to Zillebeke.

The cold was fierce. Bob was soon shivering in his greatcoat, slapping his thighs in an attempt to warm himself. Approaching the village of Zillebeke, both men anxiously noted the presence of Allied infantry, digging in and hurriedly unrolling large coils of barbed wire. Jum stopped the rig and approached a group by the side of the road. Bob followed.

'What's all this activity, mate?' Jum asked the corporal who appeared to be in charge.

'We're setting up the third defensive line,' he replied. 'The Boche are gearing up for their winter offensive, down south. The new defence system has three lines, about 2,000 yards apart.'

'Where's the front line then?'

'About 1,000 yards east of the village.' The corporal pointed to Zillebeke.

Startled, Jum turned to Bob. 'If the girls are still there, they'll be in the middle of this shit fight!'

'There are very few civilians in the village,' said the corporal. 'Most have gone to Steenvoorde or Hazebrouck to get away from the fighting.'

'We have friends in two small farmhouses about 600 yards past Zillebeke,' said Bob.

'Not any more, mate. There's no one in that area, no civilians anyway,' the corporal replied.

Bob felt a knot tighten in his stomach.

'Don't worry, Bob,' said Jum. 'We'll go to the village.'

The *estaminet* where they had originally met the girls was still open. Jum drove the rig past the *estaminet* to the post office. 'Maybe the postmaster will know something.'

They entered the small post office. '*Bonjour*,' said Jum, and in basic French, inquired after Anna and Jeanne. The old man shook his head and fluttered his hands, speaking rapidly. All they could make out was the word 'Armentières'.

Thanking the man, they left the building. 'The Allied front was only a few hundred yards away, so the girls up and left for Armentières,' said Jum.

Bob sat despondently on the public seat outside the building. 'I can't believe our luck. We were just *at* Armentières. All that bloody way and we missed them.'

'Can't be helped, Bob. We might as well head back to camp. We can't get to Armentières and back by tomorrow. Come on.' The pair climbed aboard the rig and made their way through the village back towards Ypres. 'You never know, Bob, we might get a week's furlough. We're due some time off.'

Back at camp, McErbain rose from his chair, surprised.'What happened? You're not due back until tomorrow afternoon.'

'Our girls have moved to Armentières. If only we'd known, we could have saved that bloody trip to Zillebeke,' said Jum ruefully.

McErbain smiled. 'Don't worry, the Boche are digging in for the winter, as are we. I think some long overdue leave may be forthcoming soon. Can't promise,' he added.

There was much activity in the camp. Jum noticed that four large huts were being erected for the 14th Battery. 'Looks like we're getting some reasonable shelter at last,' said Jum. Bob, too disappointed to speak, merely nodded his head. 'Come on, mate,' said Jum. 'Next leave we'll get to Armentières and visit that friend of the girls and chase them up.'

As they approached the huts, Jum noticed the distinctive shoulder flashes of the 3rd Pioneers. 'This is AJ's crowd,' said Jum. 'Wonder if he's here.'

A deep voice behind them called out, 'First I've got to save you from Fritz and now I've got to build bloody houses for you!' Jum turned. Sergeant Alan Casey was walking towards them.

'AJ!' yelled Bob and Jum as they shook hands with Casey.

'Where have you been, you old bastard?' laughed Jum.

'Up where you were, I suppose. Hellfire Corner, Passchendaele. We copped an aircraft bomb when we were planking a road out of Zonnebeke, but I survived.'

'Yeah, that was no bloody picnic. How long you here, AJ?' asked Jum.

'Soon as we finish your huts, we're off to Armentières for a week's rest.'

'We may be in line for a few days' rest ourselves,' said Bob.

'Say, whatever happened to those two girls you had in Ypres that night a year ago?'

Jum smiled as he put his arm around Bob's shoulder. 'We've just been chasing them in Zillebeke, but they've moved to Armentières.'

'Bad luck. They were beautiful,' smiled Casey.

21.12.17 *In action again.*

With Christmas fast approaching, Claude Jenkins reflected on the two years he had spent with the 5th Field Artillery Brigade. Everyone had thought the Third Ypres Offensive would end the war, but the Germans had drawn on hidden reserves. He cast his mind back to Pozières. After the offensive at Sausage Gully, he had spent weeks in the graveyard, praying at every cross for the men who had been hastily buried.

He gazed through the window at the silent, floating snowflakes. Was this God's way of covering the obscenity of the war?

Jenkins rested his head in his hands. His will and resolve were at their lowest ebb. He wondered how he could continue his work, saving the minds and souls of the men who now viewed the killing of other men so dispassionately.

The snow was now falling heavily. He left his hut and made his way to the mess tent, where the men of the 14th Battery were enjoying a steaming cup of cocoa.

Claude Jenkins smiled as the men waved and beckoned him over. He greeted them heartily.

With his chin in his hands, Bob was staring through the window at the snow. His mind was on Jeanne. He tried to imagine where she was and what she was doing.

'There's a rumour that a London furlough is half a chance,' said Gillies.

'Come on, Gill, don't bullshit us!' said Wagga. 'Sorry, Padre, I forgot you were here.'

Claude Jenkins merely smiled.

Jum looked at Bob. 'We may get to Armentières yet.'

Jum was blowing on his hands in No. 1 Gun position, but his hot breath did little to warm his numbed fingers.

Another German shell exploded behind the rear butt, muffled in the deep snow.

'These bastards won't let up,' he said. 'Don't they know it's Christmas Day?'

As if in answer, another four shells landed between No. 1 and No. 2 positions.

Gillies turned to Jum. 'We're copping about 60 rounds per hour.'

'Yeah, they must have got a wagonload of ammo for Christmas,' said Wagga.

The shelling continued until mid-afternoon.

New Year's Day dawned with a massive German bombardment on the front line. The beginning of 1918 was announced by a volley of 5.9's, 4.2's, 77-millimetre 'whizz bangs' and Minenwurfer trench mortars. Large black pockmarks appeared on the virginal snow-covered fields as the shelling intensified.

Despite the relentless barrages, the casualty list did not grow. The men were more concerned about keeping the bone-aching cold at bay than about death by shelling.

January 1918 drifted to an uneasy close with both sides content to fortify their own positions rather than battle the snow and mud for the few miserable yards of ground they might have gained.

FEBRUARY TO APRIL 1918

8.2.18 Spelling for Alquiness.

Jum and Bob walked slowly along the main street of Armentières, then turned into rue de Dunkerque. Standing in front of the door, Bob was too nervous to knock.

Jum pushed him aside and rapped firmly. The curtain was drawn aside and they heard an astonished squeal of delight. 'Anna, Anna, come quickly!'

The door opened. Jeanne, radiant and laughing, threw herself into Bob's arms. A tall woman, standing in the hallway, smiled at the joyful scene.

'*Pardon, Madame*,' said Anna. 'Please to meet Robert and Jum, our two friends we thought had been killed by the Germans.'

Madame Grigor moved forward. She was a woman of refined elegance. Jum gently took her outstretched hand, lightly kissing her fingers. 'My pleasure, *Madame*.'

'I see your friends have style, young ladies,' she remarked.

Bob gave his best smile, murmuring, '*Bonjour, Madame*.'

Madame Grigor sat watching and smiling as the four young people chatted and laughed. Anna snuggled up to Jum on the couch. She had drawn her feet up under her for warmth.

Monique Grigor thought back to nearly two years before, when she had first met Anna and Jeanne. She had been visiting a friend in Zillebeke in December 1915. At this time, the German army had control of areas in and around Ypres and Armentières, and she had been unsuccessful in her attempt to persuade her friend to move to Boulogne, away from the nightmare of the Western Front.

While waiting for the bus service from Zillebeke back to Ypres, she had seen Jeanne sobbing wretchedly, with Anna trying to comfort her, and had asked if she could help.

'Not unless you can bring her husband back,' Anna had said.

Madame Grigor's heart had gone out to the girls. The three had introduced themselves, and she had offered them the hospitality of her home in Armentières, should they ever need it.

She was startled out of her reverie by loud laughter.

'Madame's husband is a staff officer in General Joffre's Headquarters. Brigadier Grigor – that is him in the photograph.' Anna pointed. The framed print showed a handsome officer in full military uniform astride a magnificent horse.

'When was the photograph taken, *Madame*?' inquired Jum.

'In 1908. Paul, my husband, had just been promoted to captain. He was very proud.'

'How long since you've seen your husband?'

'Two years now, and I don't expect to see him for some time yet. He writes to me occasionally. His letters are full of the war – nothing else.'

Jum, understanding, nodded politely. 'We hear that General Joffre has been saying for months now that the German build-up at the Somme on the Hindenburg Line will be the strongest offensive of the entire war on the Western Front.'

'Yes, my understanding is that the worst of this war is yet to come. Of course, my husband does not put this in writing to me, but I read between the lines.'

'Well, there you have it, Bob,' said Jum. 'We're in for another year of mud.'

'Enough of this gloom,' said Madame, rising. 'I have to go shopping. Are you boys staying tonight? We have a number of spare rooms you can use.'

'If it is no trouble, *Madame*,' said Jeanne.

'Of course not. Please make yourself comfortable.'

Two hours later, having spotted her friend from the window, Anna stepped into the street to met Madame Grigor. 'Please, let me help you, *Madame*,' said Anna as she took packages from Madame Grigor's laden arms.

They went to the drawing room, where Jeanne, Bob and Jum stood before the fire.

'I'm sorry I was away a little longer than I expected to be,' said Madame.

Bob looked at Jum. 'We've been busy, *Madame*,' said Jum. 'So much to talk about.' The girls nodded in agreement.

'I'll get some coffee for us all,' said Madame, heading for the kitchen.

'I'll help.' Anna rose and followed Madame Grigor.

In the kitchen, Madame turned to Anna with a smile. 'I couldn't stay out any longer – I was freezing.'

Anna blushed. The older woman moved over to Anna and put her arms around her in a motherly, protective gesture. She spoke softly into Anna's dark hair. 'Enjoy the moment, Anna. Enjoy it while you can. We don't know from one day to the next what is going to happen.'

After coffee, the five decided to take an early evening walk through the town. The snow held off, although the sky was leaden, promising further bad weather.

Their walk took them past the railway station. A train stood at the platform. Behind the steaming engine, the five train carriages were filled with troops. Water and coal were being fed into the tender. Jum and Bob waved to the men and were acknowledged in return.

'Jum! Jum!' a voice yelled. Jum turned to see an infantryman hanging out a window in the second carriage.

'Bloody hell, that's Ernie Buckleton!' said Jum.

Jum and Bob sprinted onto the station towards the carriages as Ernie Buckleton jumped down onto the platform. Enthusiastic greetings followed.

'How long you here, mate?' asked Jum.

'About twenty minutes, I think. We're just taking on water and coal. We're going west to Calais. Got a month's furlough in London,' said Ernie.

'You lucky bastard,' laughed Bob.

'Come and meet the girls, Ernie.' Jum pulled Ernie towards the three women waiting at the station entrance.

'How the hell did you two ugly bastards meet three women like this?'

'Youth, good looks and money, Ernie,' said Bob, grinning.

For five minutes the group shuffled from foot to foot in an attempt to beat the cold. The attendant was swinging the water hose away from the tender as the driver made his way to the stationmaster's office.

Jum and Bob walked Ernie towards his carriage. With Ernie safely inside, the train jerked out of the station towards Steenvoorde, Saint-Omer and Calais.

Jum, Bob and the women hurried through the evening chill to Madame Grigor's home.

For the first night, the boys stayed in their room. On the second night, their self-imposed rule was thrown out the window. For four days and nights, the war on the Western Front faded from their minds. But the idyll ended all too soon.

'Come on, Bob,' said Jum. 'Time to go back to work.'

**5.3.18 In hospital with influenza,
7th Field Ambulance.**

14.4.18 Back with unit, Armentières/Somme.

Brigade Diary

**24.4.18 Intense bombardment of our line, 10
casualties. 4 killed and 4 wounded by direct
hit on our dugout. All communication lines
cut, our wireless failed to act. Bombardment
continued, intensifying all day. Heavy 'Yellow
Cross' gas, many casualties.**

Three weeks later, Bob and Jum were still recovering from a severe bout of influenza that had sped through the ranks of the brigade.

Despite ten days' recuperation in the 7th Field Hospital, Jum, Bob and the Wagga boys struggled with racking coughs. Their lungs were permanently damaged by the gas attacks they had suffered the year before, and the extreme cold only magnified their symptoms. But they struggled on.

The much anticipated German attack, part of an attempt to break through to Amiens, had begun, and German forces were threatening to overrun the city, much to the concern of General Haig. The action at Lavieville was intense, with heavy bombardment of the Allied forward lines by 4.2 and 5.9 German guns. Enemy balloons and aircraft kept up a continual presence, relaying vital Allied positions and strengths back to their Command.

Many thousands of crack German troopers, battle-hardened by the Russian offensive, had joined the Western Front. The revolt in Russia had resulted in the signing of an armistice between Germany and Russia, ending hostilities. These German troops were transferred to the Western Front, the launching pad of the main German attack.

The massive reinforcement of the German force in the Somme portended a grave future for the Allies, now desperately attempting to withstand the savage attack. The Somme areas, won and held with such ferocious fighting by the Allies, were once again being lost to the enemy.

The victorious German force now began to spread to the west and south-west. Péronne and Bapaume had fallen, followed by Albert and Morlancourt. The Germans, now seemingly invincible, marched on, capturing all before them.

With much of the Somme area lost again to the German forces, the final enemy advance commenced on Villers-Bretonneux on 30 March 1918. The German Command was desperate to break the Allied line before American troops arrived in France, so the fighting at Villers-Bretonneux – the gateway to Amiens from the east – was both fierce and unrelenting. The 35th Australian Battalion bore the brunt of the German advance. Attack after attack on the battalion resulted in high casualty rates for both German and Australian troops.

The German line advanced in great numbers from Marcelcave village towards the 35th Battalion. They were repelled by a deadly hail of Lewis gun and rifle fire, so accurate that the German line broke and ran. German officers regrouped their troops and again attacked. On three more occasions, the German advance was broken in the same manner, only for them to regroup and attack again.

Realising it was impossible to penetrate the Australian line, the enemy began concentrating the attack further south, where they succeeded at the line of the British 7th Buffs.

Quick discussions had the 7th Buffs regrouped and agreeing to stand by any attacking force of Anzacs. Here again, the German advance was halted.

In desperation, the enemy regrouped once more and advanced. A savage British artillery barrage accurately pinpointed this German advance. The British 7th Buffs became engaged in a fierce battle at close quarters with the enemy.

But north of the Roman Road, the advancing Germans were unstoppable. Unbeknownst to the 35th Battalion, which was still engaged by ferocious frontal and flank attacks by the enemy, the British 14th Division broke and retreated.

Lieutenant Thompson of the 35th Battalion ran as the Maxim machine gun fire kicked spurts of earth at his heels. He sprawled into the mud, glimpsing his second-last outpost 50 yards ahead. A brief lull in the fusillade had him on his feet and sprinting desperately to the post. He threw himself headlong into the shallow trench. The Vickers machine gun operator was sweeping the line of advancing Germans only a few hundred yards away.

'We must hold at all costs!' Thompson screamed as he leapt from the trench towards his furthest outpost.

As Lieutenant Thompson slid into the outpost, he heard the machine gun company captain scream, 'Withdraw! Withdraw!'

'What the bloody hell, I've just told them to hang on at all costs. I must get back and get them out of there.' The lieutenant sprinted back towards his left gun emplacement, yelling and waving. But 15 yards from the post, a burst of Maxim fire left him sprawled on the ground.

Lieutenant Thompson died instantly. His order to retreat died with him.

Unaware of the order, the four guns locked into a deadly fight with the Germans, who were advancing frontally and on either flank. The detachments were now subjected to fierce enfilading fire. A machine gun officer, Lieutenant Cecil Daniel Lockhart, yelled to his men, 'We're staying! Give it to these bastards!'

Lockhart saw with dismay that the final thirty rounds of ammunition were rapidly being used up. 'Run it right out, Charlie!' he screamed. The other three guns were out of ammunition, and their detachments were quickly retiring, their work done.

'Come on, Charlie, let's go!' yelled Lockhart, as the final round was fired.

They stood up. Sergeant Charlie Lawton was immediately hit by a burst of fire. He fell to the ground, critically wounded. Dazed and exhausted, Lockhart bent, grabbed Lawton and hoisted him to his shoulders.

Lawton gasped, 'Leave me, I'm gone.'

'I'm not leaving you here!' yelled Lockhart, as he ran towards the Allied line. He didn't realise that the German flanks had gone past his position and, in a tight pincer movement, now had them encircled.

He swerved and ran, with Lawton a crushing burden. Fierce fire came from all sides. Lieutenant Lockhart stumbled and fell, with Sergeant Lawton across his head and back. With lungs heaving, Lockhart called in a whisper, 'Charlie, stay still! Stay still!'

Sergeant Lawton had no choice. He had succumbed to his critical injuries.

The grey uniforms of the enemy moved slowly forward through the mud amongst the dead and injured. Occasionally a shot was fired to ensure no prisoners would be left alive. A heavy German trooper kicked the still body of Sergeant Lawton. '*Kaput!*'

Lieutenant Lockhart's turn arrived. A boot thudded heavily into his lower back, and he stifled a scream of pain. Again, the trooper grunted, '*Kaput.*' Lockhart stayed still. The German troops moved on, every now and then pausing to fire a round into the head of an Australian casualty.

As dusk settled, and the light faded, Lockhart slowly and carefully crawled his way to safety, back to the Allied front line.

MAY TO JUNE 1918

The mess tent was crowded with relaxing men. Jum grinned at Ernie Buckleton, who was on his way with a despatch to Command. 'Looks like the blokes are desperate to see who's the best rider out of us two, Ernie.'

'How much start do you want, Jum?'

Jum didn't reply, but sat contemplating the rolling, mud-covered hills. 'I've got an idea. Why don't we stage a race, you and me? We're about the same weight and height, so it'd be an even contest.'

And so 'The Great Race' was conceived.

An hour later, Jum and Ernie still sat in the 14th Battery mess tent, facing forty men.

'Are you two buggers serious?' asked Gillies.

'Bloody hell, Jum, that'll be dangerous,' said Wagga.

'Mate, we're in danger every bloody day. Let's have some fun for a change.'

It was agreed. Jum and Ernie Buckleton would race over an 800-yard course on two of the best ponies available, to decide the better rider. Jum and Ernie stood and shook hands in front of the men. The crowd began discussing the race with great enthusiasm.

There happened to be an 800-yard, relatively flat stretch, not far from the Headquarters wagon lines, that would be an ideal venue for the event.

The only problem was that this particular strip of sparsely grassed turf sat neatly in No Man's Land, between the front-line trenches of the Allied and German forces. A thousand yards separated the lines, which meant that the riders, if they were equidistant from each line, would be only 500 yards from the Germans.

'You two blokes are stark raving mad,' said an exasperated McErbain. 'You may think it will be a great afternoon's entertainment, but what do you reckon the bloody Boche will think?'

'Well, Harold, you know those sideshow shooting galleries, with the moving row of ducks ...'

As they sat alone later, Ernie said to Jum, 'We can really clean up big time with this. We'll set the odds and hold the book. It will be easy for us to get me up as the short-priced favourite, 2 to 1 on. You come home in the last 20 yards, and we win a pile of cash.'

'I don't know if I can trust you to let me win, Ernie.'

'Mate, if there's money involved, I can do anything.'

'What if the German bastards do take pot shots at us?'

'Every man for himself, straight for our lines and all bets off.'

Word spread quickly. The merits of both horsemen were appraised endlessly. 'The Great Race' was the topic of the moment, the war momentarily forgotten.

Three days later, McErbain asked, 'What are we holding, Ernie?'

Ernie looked up from his books. 'We have 145 quid on me at 2 to 1 on, and 60 quid on Jum at evens. So if Jum wins, we pay out 120, and pocket 45 bloody quid.'

'What if you win?

'We'll be in deep shit. But then, I won't win,' Ernie said calmly.

On the following morning, 'race day', the sun shone brightly in a clear sky. There had been no exchanges of artillery fire from the opposing batteries. The previous night, four Australians had carefully wormed their way to the centre of No Man's Land. The job completed, they moved noiselessly back to their lines. The race was scheduled for 1400 hours, when they calculated that the Germans would be dozing with full stomachs.

The Prussian captain had his field glasses to his eyes. '*Was ist das?*'

Three other pairs of eyes followed his pointing finger. In the centre of No Man's Land sat a sign facing their line – '*Anfang*'. They looked at each other. ' "Start"? Is this the beginning of a new offensive?'

Puzzled, the captain moved his glasses to the right. There was another, larger sign some distance away. He twirled the handle of his telephone.

A voice answered, '*Bitte?*'

'Kurt, what is on the sign in front of your company?'

'It says "*Schluss*". What do you make of it, Captain?'

'I don't know, Kurt. Be on the lookout for an attack.'

'*Verstehen, Kapitän.*'

The two sturdy ponies had been carefully selected and saddled. They waited patiently under shade near the front line. The entire 1st Battalion assembled as race time approached. Facing the men was a sign to their right, emblazoned with the single word 'Start' – the same sign that, on the German side, proclaimed '*Anfang*'. Further to the north, the larger sign announced 'Finish' to the Australian side, '*Schluss*' to the Germans.

Jum and Ernie mounted their ponies. They had agreed to canter quickly from the south to the 'Start' sign – a flying start.

Sitting low over their mounts' necks, the two riders appeared from the trench system. They rapidly approached the sign. Then, at full gallop with ears pinned back, both mounts flashed along the track.

The Prussian captain looked on, bewildered. His Maxim machine gunner jumped behind his gun. The captain laid a hand on the gunner's shoulder. 'Wait! Wait!'

The wind whistled as the two riders, up in the stirrups, drove their mounts forward. Pounding hooves rang out on the hardened ground. Jum's mount inched ahead. Ernie was content to sit his mount a long neck back. The cheering, yelling front line of the Australian battalion rose to their feet as the two horsemen thundered along. The German troops stood watching openmouthed in amazement and disbelief.

With 50 yards remaining, Jum led by a half-length. The bet was safe.

But a young German machine gunner close to the finish line, put on high alert by the captain, nervously squeezed his trigger, sending a burst just behind Ernie's mount. Ernie kicked the pony frantically into greater effort. He pulled up beside Jum, who screamed, 'The bet, the bloody bet!'

'Fuck the bet!' yelled Ernie.

As they flashed across the finish line together, another burst of Maxim fire kicked between the ponies' legs.

Veering left, both leapt their mounts across a shell crater, up the front mound of the Allied front line and, without easing pace, cleared the trench at full gallop, to the screaming cheers of the men below.

Sergeant Alan Casey, who was working on a road-building project in the area, had been seconded as the official judge. He lowered his glasses, a broad grin on his face.

'Who won? Who won?'

He held up his hands to quiet the mob. 'Would you believe it, you blokes – a bloody dead heat.'

The crowd erupted in boos and catcalls. He again held up his hands. 'Our rules state that in the event of a dead heat, all bets are returned.'

Back at the 14th Battery positions, Ernie and Jum had reined in their frothing mounts. Surrounded by a laughing mob, they dismounted.

'What happened, Ernie?' asked Jum.

'Didn't you see that German bastard nearly get me?' Ernie was white with shock.

'You're joking!' said Jum, 'I couldn't work out why you came at me like blazes on the post.'

AJ Casey stood outside the mess tent. As the crowd around him quietened, Casey said, 'Let's hear it for a gutsy ride by Jum and Ernie!' Screaming, stamping and yelling followed. 'As I said, a dead heat, all bets returned.'

Jum and Ernie grinned at each other. 'All that for nothing!' They laughed uproariously.

Later that afternoon, Lieutenant Colonel Smith-Stevens looked up as Major Conrick entered the Headquarters tent.

'What was all that commotion earlier, Terry?' he asked.

'Just a couple of runners testing two new ponies, sir. Nothing to be alarmed at.'

Bob and Jum lay on their bunks awaiting the call for rostered duty. That morning, after breakfast, Bob had received a letter.

'Guess what?' he said. Jum turned to look at him. 'Jeanne is pregnant.'

Jum sat bolt upright.'What! Are you sure?'

'She says so in this letter,' Bob replied.

There was silence as both men considered the news. Finally, Jum spoke. 'What the bloody hell will you do?'

Bob, grim-faced, rose from his bunk. 'I'm buggered if I know. I'm going to see the padre.'

After several hours of discussion, Bob was adamant. 'Padre, I'm only a young bloke, but I won't have a child of mine born out of wedlock. If I have to, I'll go AWL and get married in the post office.'

'Well, let's see what we can do,' said the padre.

Lieutenant Colonel Smith-Stevens was at a loss. 'What are we to do, Padre? If I allow this, I'll have every Tom, Dick and Harry rushing off to get married.'

'I was there when they met,' said the padre. 'She's a delightful young woman, and I believe there's a genuine bond between them. My opinion is that they should be permitted to formalise their union.'

'Very well, Padre, let me see what's in store for the next month. We'd have to limit the furlough to two days.'

'I'm sure that would be quite long enough, sir.'

Claude Jenkins returned to Bob's billet with the good news.

Jum stood there with his hands in pockets. 'We're all assuming that Jeanne wants to marry you, Bob. But what if she doesn't?'

Nervously, Bob tapped on the door of the villa on rue de Dunkerque. Madame Grigor greeted Bob and Jum and ushered them inside. Jeanne rushed into Bob's arms.

'Go on, Bob,' Jum said in Bob's ear. 'We rehearsed this all the way up from Albert.'

Bob, blushing nervously, took Jeanne's hand and walked with her down the hall to the front room. A few minutes later, they reappeared, smiling.

'Robert has asked me to marry him!'

The wedding day morning was cool and clear – perfect spring weather. An army truck trundled its way east from Ypres Railway

Station towards Zillebeke. Lieutenant McErbain sat beside Padre Jenkins. The six men in the rear were bumped and jostled as the driver fought to avoid the worst of the potholes.

'We won't be late, will we, Jum?' asked Bob again.

'No, Bob, I promise we won't be late.'

Bob looked at his watch anxiously.

'Only about 5 miles to go,' called Wagga from the back of the vehicle.

Jum turned to Ernie Buckleton. 'How was London?'

'I had a terrific time. Stayed for a week.'

'I still don't know how you wangled these two days off, Ernie,' said Jum.

'Easy, mate,' replied Ernie. He stretched and yawned. 'Your CO must be a good bloke.'

'No complaints so far,' said Ron.

'What reason did he give to let you all off?'

Gillies smiled. 'Compassionate leave, but Jum reckons it should be "passionate" leave.' There was laughter as Bob blushed.

The truck drew to a stop in Zillebeke village. The men clambered down from the rear as Padre Jenkins and McErbain alighted from the cabin.

McErbain looked at his watch. 1100 hours. 'Here tomorrow, same time, driver,' he directed.

'Sure thing, Lieutenant,' replied the driver, and swung the lorry in a circle back towards Ypres on the Menin Road.

The men clustered outside their favourite *estaminet* in the warm sun. Padre Jenkins addressed the group.

'I'm off to the church to see the pastor and make sure everything is ready. I'll see you back here about 1300 hours.' The padre turned and made his way across the cobbled road towards the church.

McErbain folded his arms. 'Now, you know I'm not a nark, but I don't want anybody pissed until after the ceremony. Have a couple of beers if you want, but don't be stupid.'

The church was hushed. Smiling at a very nervous Bob, Jeanne made her vows. Jum, the best man, glanced behind him. In the front pew sat Jim Gillies, Ron and Wagga, with Harold McErbain at the end. The aged postmaster had given away the bride; his wife smiled while dabbing her eyes with a handkerchief. Madame Grigor, looking exquisite, sat next to her.

Following the service, they headed to the *estaminet* across the road. The revelling continued for four hours, with Jum and the padre providing the music and Anna the vocal accompaniment.

The Wagga boys and Jim Gillies were determined to set records for the consumption of Belgian beer. Ernie Buckleton had sat quietly beside Jum for some time. He glanced at Madame Grigor. In the muted light, the flickering candle glow cast slight shadows, emphasising her high cheekbones and classic French nose. Judging by her flashing smile, she was enjoying herself enormously.

Ernie leant towards Jum. 'What's with the Madame?'

'You cheeky bastard,' said Jum. 'She's married, you know.'

'Yes, but where's her husband?'

'I think in Amiens. He's on Joffre's staff.'

'Well, he's not here, is he?'

'Don't get any ideas, Ernie,' Jum laughed. 'She's strictly top drawer material.'

Jum was deep in conversation with Harold McErbain and did not see Ernie stand and move across to Madame Grigor.

'*Madame?*'

She turned. 'Yes, young man?'

'I saw you sitting alone, and decided you needed some conversation,' he said boldly. 'I met you very briefly, once,' he continued, 'on the station at Armentières a couple of months ago.'

She frowned slightly. 'Of course, I remember – you came off the train.'

Ernie sipped his Belgian beer.

'Wasn't it a wonderful wedding?'

Ernie smiled. 'You are the most beautiful woman, not only in this room, but in all of Belgium.'

Madame Grigor raised her eyebrows. 'You're very flattering, but I must remind you that, not only am I a married woman, but I may be old enough to be your mother.'

Jum saw Madame Grigor looking straight ahead as Ernie spoke quietly in her ear. Ernie slowly rose. Madame Grigor did not move.

McErbain looked at Jum. 'Your mate Ernie is one game bastard. What d'you reckon he's up to?'

'I'm scared to even think about it.'

'He's putting the hard word on Madame Grigor,' said McErbain.

'Christ, no! Don't say that,' Jum laughed. 'How would I explain it to Anna and Jeanne? Although I suppose it would be nothing to him. He didn't win a Military Medal for being shy.'

Ernie sat down beside Jum, his back to Madame Grigor.

'Jum, where's she looking?'

Jum glanced at Madame Grigor.

'She's staring straight at the back of your head.'

'Is she smiling?' asked Ernie.

'No,' said Jum.

'Good!'

Ernie relaxed, downed his beer and smiled.

'What the hell did you say, Ernie? She's looking a bit pissed off.'

'Well, we talked a bit, then I gave her the "most beautiful woman in the world" line ...'

'And then?'

'She told me she was married and that she was old enough to be my mother.'

'Go on.'

'I said something like, "*Madame*, the decisions we make now may be entirely different to what we would do in a normal world. I could be dead tomorrow; we all could be. When an opportunity arises that offers a special experience, we should grasp it with both hands."' Ernie smiled again. 'That's it.'

'Well, you've got her thinking,' remarked Jum.

Ernie turned slowly and looked at Madame Grigor. She stared intently at him, the slightest smile playing on her lips.

By 9.30 pm, the party was slowing down. Bob and his new wife had retired. The men had moved two horses out of a rear stable to make room to sleep. They trooped noisily towards the rear yard where the stable and its piles of fresh, clean straw awaited them.

Ernie Buckleton had hung back in the alcove off the dining area. As Madame Grigor walked to her room along the hall, Ernie fell into step behind her. She stopped at her door and glanced back at Ernie as he passed her.

'Good night, Ernie.'

Then her voice stopped Ernie in his tracks. 'Ernie, I have trouble with my key. Will you help me?'

Ernie turned, his heart thumping hard in his chest, and casually walked back. Gently, he said, 'Here, let me.' The key turned easily. He swung the door wide. She slid past, brushing him softly.

'A small liqueur, perhaps, Ernie, before retiring?'

He nodded briefly, mumbling, 'Thank you.'

Madame Grigor closed the door and turned the key. She placed her wrap and purse on the table. She produced a decanter of liqueur brandy as Ernie carefully sat on the settee. The room was warmed by a glowing fire. She had slipped off her shoes and stood before him, offering a drink. His hand shook slightly as he took the crystal glass.

'You're shaking. It is cold in here, no?'

Ernie slowly shook his head.

She drained her glass and placed it on the small tray. Then she unbuttoned the back of her dress, slowly stepping out of the full-length garment. She bent over slowly as she removed her undergarments, beckoning Ernie with her full breasts. He reached up with both hands, cupping her warmth as she entwined her arms around his neck.

'Are you an opportunist, Ernie?'

He nodded dumbly.

'Well, I am feeling the cold. Let us not waste this opportunity,' she said lightly.

The half-light of dawn came creeping thief-like into the long hallway. Ernie Buckleton moved noiselessly into the hall, quietly closing the door behind him. With boots in hand, he tiptoed towards the stables at the rear. Carefully lying down in the warm straw, he noted the still figures whose stentorian snoring filled the stables with noise.

Jum rolled over. 'How was it?'

'Beyond description. I never thought I ...' He trailed off as words failed him.

Jeanne tried unsuccessfully to hold back her tears. The men were aboard the truck taking them back to Ypres, thence by train to

Bresle. Bob's face showed concern as he tried to comfort her. 'It won't be long, Jeanne. I'll be back soon.'

Anna and Madame Grigor stood beside Jeanne as Bob boarded the truck. Ernie held onto the tarpaulin cover near the tailgate. He looked at Monique Grigor, and she raised her hand in a soft gesture of farewell.

'I'll never see her again,' he thought, feeling an emptiness in the pit of his stomach. He raised his hand in response and stood immobile. The lorry wheeled across the square onto the Menin Road, then accelerated towards Ypres.

A few days after the wedding, the padre sought out Bob Buchannen in the tent lines. 'Are you there, Bob?'

Bob emerged. 'Sure, Padre, how can I help?'

The padre coughed, then said softly, 'I'm afraid it's bad news from home.'

Bob grabbed the padre by his arms. 'Is my mum all right?'

'Yes, yes, she's fine. It's your father. He was thrown from a horse on the farm, badly injured. I'm afraid he passed away.' The padre paused. 'Would you like to walk awhile? We can talk.'

Bob's face was hard. 'No thanks, Padre. I'm all right. My father and I were never close anyway. I only ever worry about mum.'

The lorry carrying ten men slammed to a halt outside the Brigade Headquarters at Pont-Noyelles, a small village 8 miles east of Amiens on the banks of the Hallue River. The men hastily jumped from the truck.

German shells were screeching into the Headquarters compound, exploding in great clouds of earth, causing men to scatter in all directions, anxious to find any cover from the bombardment.

Major Conrick ran from the Headquarters tent. 'Get under cover! Get under cover!' he yelled, as more shells began blasting the area. The men needed no second bidding. They ran to a small trench in the nearby tree line, where they watched the damage.

'Bloody hell!' called Wagga. 'The wagon line just got hit!'

They all looked towards the line. Horses lay dead or dying. Four or five bodies were also lying inert near the multitude of shell craters. As one, the men ran from the trench to their rescue.

'Where's the CCS, Jum?' panted Bob.

'Over behind HQ tent, but they're getting blasted too!'

Two of the five men were dead, the other three injured. A total of sixty-five horses lay dead.

Ron, Wagga and Bob, each carrying an injured man, made their way towards the CCS. Two soldiers in charge of the horses and donkeys climbed amongst the dead and dying beasts, every now and then putting a revolver to the head of those animals that would not survive their injuries. Sickened, Jum watched as he made his way through the barrage towards the CCS. The bombardment continued.

14.5.18 Now at gunpits, Ribemont, Somme as mounted runner.

The following morning, Major Conrick called to his sergeant, 'Charlie, find Jum Bevan and Jim Gillies. We need them for a week out of the line. We're short of good runners, and they're amongst our best.'

Sergeant Hill left Headquarters and moved quickly to the mess tent, which had miraculously escaped the heavy barrage. No. 1 Gun detachment had finished their morning meal after all-night duty beside the Hallue River.

'Jum and Gill, you two are out of the gun detachment for a week. We need specialised runners for HQ despatch work.'

Bob grabbed Jum's arm. 'Bloody hell, mate, be careful. The Boche snipers around here are good.'

'We'll be fine, Bob. Gill and I aren't about to become heroes. When do you want us, Charlie?' he asked.

'Get cleaned up and relax. We'll see you around 1300 at HQ.'

Gillies and Jum stood waiting outside Brigade Headquarters. The morning chill had been washed away by streaming sunlight.

Conrick appeared and smiled at the two. 'The Boche is digging in and bringing up supplies – men and artillery. We need to keep good communications open between the batteries and HQ. I'll be relying on you.'

The gully between Buire and Ribemont, about 8 miles east of Amiens, was normally a lush, richly wooded valley, but the foliage had been decimated by fighting. It lay near the banks of the Ancre River, a northern tributary of the Somme. The 5th Field Artillery Brigade had moved into the area, preparing positions in expectation of a large-scale German assault.

Jum, with Gillies, was standing beside the forward Command area. Enemy shelling had been desultory during the night. At 0100 hours, reliefs had taken over the guns of the 14th Battery.

The first German shell exploded nearby, ripping branches and growth from a copse of trees. Jum watched as a heavy white cloud rose from the impact area. He yelled, 'Jesus, Gill! The bastards are using gas!'

Lieutenant Harold McErbain appeared at the outpost entrance. Further shells were exploding throughout the area, and the low, dense gas cloud hung inert in the still air.

McErbain jumped from the dugout.

'On your horse, Jum! HQ must have this info straight away,' he shouted.

'See ya, Gill!' Jum called, as he leapt onto his pony.

Moving quickly to a fast gallop across the valley floor, Jum wasted no time in finding the track to HQ, about a mile towards Bresle.

Conrick completed writing the despatch as Jum waited.

Imperative Batteries stay in the line. Retaliatory barrages immediately to enemy front line of Infantry. German Infantry must be held at all costs as this may be start of large offensive.

Signed Conrick per Lieutenant Colonel Smith-Stevens.

'Happy with that, sir?' Conrick asked Smith-Stevens.

'Yes, Terry, get it going.'

Conrick handed the despatch to Jum. 'Be careful, Jum. We must keep communications open.'

Jum nodded, then ran to his waiting pony and was quickly away, back to the Ribemont Valley.

The low ground of the gun positions in the valley meant that the gas lay thick over the area. On reading the despatch, McErbain called the corporals from each gun to the outpost. He addressed them urgently. 'Orders are we are to lay it on thick, no rest. The Boche are preparing for a full frontal assault and must be contained. Do your best with the gas.'

The NCOs ran to their gun positions. The firing rate of the 18-pounders increased.

Disturbed by the men's activity, the gas roiled, wafted and lifted over their heads, and its effects were soon obvious. The men operated under extreme physical distress, with racking coughs and streaming eyes and noses. Because of an oversight by the supply group, gas masks had not been provided. Fortunately, the gas attacks had become less frequent.

After a brief respite in the late morning, the German gas attack intensified. Hour after hour, the men toiled relentlessly. Along with Gillies, Jum rode continuously between the forward gun positions and Headquarters. A number of the men had collapsed, physically incapable of continuing.

McErbain finished his despatch with difficulty. The gas had found its way into the outpost.

> Men at the end of their endurance. Cannot continue much longer.

As he signed the despatch, he could hardly see.

'Jum, HQ on the double!' Jum, his eyes also streaming, leapt onto the pony and sprinted towards Headquarters. His lungs, distressed by earlier gas damage, were now causing him severe discomfort. His breathing had shortened to gasps; he was afraid to inhale fully as pain wrenched at his chest. The pony stretched out, happy to be fleeing the debilitating white cloud.

Conrick read the missive and said to Smith-Stevens, 'Three hours, sir. I think we should get them out.'

'Yes, Terry – we've just received a report from 2nd Division that the brigade bombardment stalled the Boche assault. Aircraft reports have indicated the German infantry is retiring back to their front line. I think 14th and 15th batteries should be relieved immediately.'

Jum returned to the outpost of the 14th Battery as quickly as possible. 'Stand down. Thank bloody hell!' a relieved McErbain muttered to himself. After giving the order, he turned to Jum. 'How are you, Jum?'

'Bloody awful – I can't see!'

The gas shelling had stopped thirty minutes before, and slowly the gas drifted away from the positions. Many of the gun detachments had suffered badly. Two empty wagons transported the casualties back to the CCS.

'How many, Terry?' asked Smith-Stevens.

'At final count, about fifty men copped the gas, and about ten will need hospitalisation. Luckily, Boulogne American Hospital is well-equipped to handle gas victims. I'm worried about Bevan and Gillies, though – they were gassed in October 1916, and I'm afraid this will damage their lungs even more.'

JULY 1918

Boulogne American Hospital
recovering from gas.

Jum sat on the edge of the hospital bed as the doctor ran the stethoscope over his back.

'Big, deep breaths, please.' Jum inhaled. The burning sensation in his lungs was now only slight.

The doctor turned to the sister. 'He's not quite 100 per cent, but close. Unfortunately, we need beds,' he added, as he moved out of Jum's hearing.

'There's another train load of casualties arriving tomorrow from Villers-Bretonneux and Warfusee,' said the overworked sister. 'We don't have near enough beds.'

'Don't worry, Sister, I'll clear out as many as I can.'

That afternoon Jum sat by his bed. 'Well,' he mused, 'back into the shit fight again.' He decided Boulogne-sur-Mer must be worth a quiet excursion.

The wardman was emphatic. 'Don't go! First, you'll not get a pass; second, the MPs in this town are vicious; and third, you're leaving tomorrow morning anyway.'

Jum grinned. 'Just the odds I need to make it interesting.'

'Well, if you're going to go,' said the wardman quietly, 'there's a place on the river called "The Duck's Bill". The MPs never go there, only blokes like us.'

That evening Jum started off at Le Bec de Canard, but found it very quiet, with only a few locals. Closer to town he found an *estaminet* full of servicemen of various nations, laughing and drinking with a number of attractive girls. Jum soon attached himself to a small group of Australian 1st Division men. As the night progressed, Jum considered the possibilities, but none of the girls caught his eye. A week in hospital, alcohol-free, had lowered his resistance and he was soon light-headed and ready to leave.

13.7.18 Left Australian General Base Depot boob to be escorted up the line.

Entrained at Boulogne for Amiens.

The early summer sun struggled through the high, barred window of the cell. Lying asleep on his side, Jum was snoring loudly. An army prison cell's hard bunk was like a feather bed to the men of the Western Front.

He rolled over and opened one eye. 'Christ!' he thought. 'How in hell did I end up in the boob?'

The night slowly drifted back into focus.

The Military Police sergeant had been aggressive. 'Where's your pass, you smart-arsed bastard?'

Jum, his right arm locked up his back, was in no position to argue.

'I'm on my way back to the hospital. I'm late!'

The three police were in no mood to listen to the pleadings of a drunken private out on the town.

'What's your unit?' asked the corporal.

'If you bastards spent a little time in the front line, you'd know where we all come from.'

The corporal smashed a fist into Jum's ribs. He winced and doubled over in pain. The corporal grinned. 'Come on, you weak bastard. You're supposed to be made of sterner stuff. Show us how good you are!'

The three Military Police, though tall and strong, were not hardened as the front-line men were. Jum had had enough. He rolled sideways, slipping his right arm free.

'How good am I?' he cried. 'Cop this, you bastard!' He smashed a right hook into the corporal's mouth.

The corporal went down, minus his two front teeth. Jum spun around. The sergeant was not quite quick enough to dodge the boot to his shin and screamed in agony. The other MP got Jum in a headlock from behind. Jum dropped to his knees, springing up again as the MP hurtled over his head.

Two more MPs appeared, and at last Jum was subdued.

'Where are the others?' asked one of the newcomers.

'It's just him,' grunted the sergeant, whose shin was bleeding badly.

'This little jerk! You've got to be joking.'

The newcomer, grinning at the carnage, did not see the savage straight left that put him out of contention. He slumped to the ground.

'Right, you've proved you're tough,' said the sergeant, 'but you're in big trouble. I suggest you quieten down right now.'

Jum stood with his hands by his sides, breathing heavily. 'I was on my way back to the base hospital.'

'That's of no interest to us. No leave pass, you're in deep shit.'

The rattle of the mess plate against the barred door brought Jum back to the present. A plate of unappetising food was pushed under the door by the prison guard, who made no comment.

At 1000 hours, Jum was led from his cell and marched across a courtyard into a large building housing the general staff. He was taken into an anteroom where clerks sat typing.

'Wait here.'

Two of the three Military Police who had arrested Jum the evening before entered the outer office. Jum noted with satisfaction the cuts and bruises adorning their features. He also sported evidence of an active night, with a swollen cheek and a cut to the forehead.

The office door opened and a sergeant spoke to the two MPs. 'Bring the prisoner in.'

The MPs marched into the office, with Jum between them. The three men faced the CO of the Australian General Base Depot.

The sergeant read from a charge sheet. 'No. 10235 Driver Bevan, 5th FAB. Offences against Base Standing Orders. First offence: In town without a pass contrary to B.S.O. 27/3. Second offence: Absent 6 pm to 12.30 am on 4.7.18. Third offence: Out of bounds contrary to B.S.O. 25. Fourth offence: Violently resisting arrest.'

The sergeant faced the Lieutenant Colonel, snapped to attention and placed the charge sheet before him.

'What have you to say, Driver Bevan?'

'Sir, I was on my way back to camp, but got caught up with some friends.'

The CO nodded to the Sergeant. 'That will be all for the arresting officers, Sergeant.' The two MPs left the room.

Jum waited as the CO read through his 'Casualty and Statement of Services Record'.

'I see you've been in France for two-and-a-half years. You have numerous charges listed against you; but you've also been wounded on a number of occasions.' He paused. 'Any one of these charges is serious. Together they require a substantial award against you.'

The slightest of smiles could be seen in the CO's eyes. 'Why the hell, soldier, did you take on three big MPs?'

Jum looked straight over the CO's head. 'Sir, one was holding me, and the other one punched me in the ribs and called me a weak bastard. I don't like being called that, sir, and I don't like being punched for no reason. So I let 'em have it.'

The CO wrote for a moment and then read aloud, '"Award: Fined 28 days forfeit pay." Driver Bevan, I have no option but to have you escorted to Boulogne train station, boarded and despatched back to your unit.'

The CO stood. 'Attend to it, Sergeant.'

As Jum turned to leave, the CO spoke again. 'One other thing, Bevan. If you ever take on three MPs again, make sure you have a mate or two handy.'

Padre Jenkins carefully made his way down the gangplank of the *Saxone*. His final destination, Amiens, was many hours away. The train transport from Boulogne-sur-Mer was due to leave at 11.45 am. He would need to hurry to make the connection.

A three-week furlough in London had brought colour back to his cheeks and a lightness to his step. He climbed into the truck transport, speaking to the driver. 'I'm on the 11.45 train to Amiens, driver. I hope we can make it on time.'

The driver smiled. 'The twenty blokes in the back would be quite happy for us to miss the connection. They're in no hurry to get back to the front line.'

The padre entered Boulogne station, picking his way amongst the men and equipment. He spied Jum further down the station and waved as he stepped around the mass of men on the crowded platform. Smiling, he reached Jum with an outstretched hand.

An MP stepped in. 'You know this bloke, Padre?'

'Certainly, he's in my unit. What is your concern with him?'

'I'm here to ensure the prisoner leaves on this train.'

'Prisoner? What are you talking about?'

'It doesn't matter, Padre. I'll explain,' said Jum.

The padre eyed the MP. 'I relieve you of your duty, Corporal. I'll ensure Driver Bevan boards the train with me, as we're both returning to our unit at Amiens.'

The MP hesitated, then shrugged his shoulders. 'Fine by me, Captain,' he said as he walked away.

Jum smiled. 'Thanks, Padre.'

The padre took him by the arm. 'Tell me about it later. Let's try and get a seat.'

The pair boarded the train. Jum bustled his way through and with some heavy elbowing secured two seats next to the window. They sat down, relieved. At least they would not be jammed in the aisle for hours with packs, equipment and stale, sweating bodies.

The train slowly travelled east through the busy marshalling yards, the wheels clicketty-clacking across points and side lines. Once clear of Boulogne, the train steamed in a more south-easterly direction, towards Paris. The pair were silent as all around them servicemen sat immersed in their own thoughts. Resigned, drawn faces showed the strain as they drew ever closer to bullets, bombs, shells and death. One group played cards. Some read, and many slept.

After some time, the padre turned to Jum. 'What happened?'

Jum felt his swollen jaw. 'Wrong time, wrong place, I suppose. I decided to look the town over before we got shipped out. Had a few beers and decided it was time to go home. I went down a side street and there were three damn MPs waiting. I tried to talk my way out, but no go. This big mongrel corporal belted me in the ribs while his offsider held me.'

The padre nodded. 'So you up and got stuck into them?'

'Yeah. Fixed a few up and got 28 days no pay for my trouble.'

The padre thought for a moment. 'What are you going to do when this is all over?'

Jum smiled. 'Kill a few citizens, maybe.' He laughed as he went on, 'Don't know, Padre, I'm not allowing myself the luxury of thinking that way. I'll try and get a job, I reckon.'

'Do you have any qualifications?'

'None. I left school when I was thirteen, got a job mucking out racing stables near Randwick Racecourse. I hated school.'

'I suppose that's where you learnt your love of horses?'

Jum nodded. He was normally close-lipped where his own life was concerned, but now he felt the urge to talk.

'After that, I was a builder's labourer. My father was always away on construction jobs and, as the eldest, I suppose I just did what I wanted to. In 1906, there wasn't much on offer for a fourteen-year-old without any education. My father didn't know I'd left school, and Mum had her hands full with the other kids. I did a little boxing, but realised pretty quick that the good blokes hit a lot harder than me. I'd rather be a labourer than get my head busted every Friday night.'

'What made you join up?'

Jum thought about this. 'I suppose the excitement, travel across the world, firing guns. I had nothing to keep me in Sydney, no girlfriend, no job future as I saw it. And a few blokes from the Cordeaux Dam had decided to go – Harold, and Jim Gillies. When I decided to enlist, Bob wanted to come too. His mother went through the roof. Blamed me for it, at first. She made me promise to look after him.' Jum smiled grimly. 'I'm flat out looking after myself.'

'But you agreed to that promise?'

'I never had to worry about anybody but myself before,' said Jum. 'Being the eldest, I was always off and away. But Bob is very close to me, and the promise I made I intend to keep.'

'And if you say you'll do something, you will?'

'Even if it kills me.'

The padre chuckled. 'Let's hope that won't be necessary.'
Jum smiled.

Then Padre Jenkins asked, 'Jum, do you think about God at all?'

'No,' was the quick reply. 'I feel the same way that Jim did after Sausage Gully. I know you and Jim have sorted that out between you, but Padre, with respect, I can't think that way.' He paused. 'Padre, you know I have the deepest respect for you. Can I speak openly?'

'Of course, Jum. I wouldn't want you to speak any other way.'

'Padre, you're a little bloke, and a minister of the church, but you're one of the gutsiest buggers I've ever known. You have a great effect on the boys. But Padre, your God – that's a different matter. If He has control over the lives of men, He doesn't show much compassion as to the way they suffer and die.'

The padre leant forward earnestly. 'As I said to Jim once, God can't control our lives – we do that. We are in control of our own destiny. We can be guided by God's teachings and he can show us the way, but we must decide which way we'll travel. Jum, you must have faith.'

'Padre,' said Jum. 'I have faith in you as a person, but I have no faith in your God.'

'I understand, Jum,' the padre smiled, 'but I won't stop trying to convert you to my faith. Dear me,' he added, giving up for the moment and changing the subject, 'I'm so hungry.'

Jum bent down and lifted his small haversack. 'I got to know a corporal cook at the base hospital, name of Gibb. He heard what happened, and told me he got to my gear before the MPs. Wonder what he's left us.'

He unstrapped the pack and extracted a large wrapped parcel. The package contained thick slabs of cold corned beef and some boiled potatoes. Jum took out his clasp knife. The two set to and devoured the meal.

Late that afternoon, the train shuffled slowly into Amiens station.

***19.7.18 Arrived Amiens. Left Amiens joined
DAC in action at Villers Bretonneux.***

The ferocity of the German bombardment had eased. Taking advantage of the lull, 2nd Division Headquarters had decided that the 5th Artillery Brigade was to be floated over the River Ancre. This would allow capture of the vital high ground necessary for a continued advance against the enemy.

Conrick pored over the map with Smith-Stevens. 'There, right there, Terry,' said the colonel, pointing.

'Morlancourt? Right, sir. When can we expect orders?'

'Soon. We're waiting on a runner now. By the way, how are the men who were gassed ten days ago?'

'Bevan and Gillies are back, not too bad. The other eight in Boulogne Hospital look like staying there for some time. The other forty are on half-duty. I expect them to be right in a few days.'

A pony slid to a halt outside Headquarters, and the runner slipped out of the saddle and into the tent.

Smith-Stevens opened the folder. He read quickly and said to the runner, 'Back to 2nd Division, runner. My reply is that your orders will be implemented immediately.' He hastily scrawled his answer and the runner departed in a cloud of dust.

Smith-Stevens turned to Conrick.

'The Boche are dug in on the Western side of Morlancourt,' he said, 'and our 4th Division infantry is preparing for an all-out hit on them there. We'll be required to soften them up with pre-attack barrages by all batteries, so the sooner we float the brigade across the river, the better.' He paused. 'I hardly dare say it, but I wonder if this is the turning point.'

'I hope to God it is!' said Conrick.

The brigade batteries moved one per day without mishap to a position between Albert and Buire on the east bank of the Ancre River. Following a successful crossing, the 5th Field Artillery Brigade established its position on slightly higher ground, east of the Ancre River.

Lieutenant Colonel Smith-Stevens wrote his despatch.

To: CO 2nd Division HQ 25th July 1918
1. Our positions are subject to intense enemy fire.
2. Batteries have maintained positions.
3. Usual bombardment fire carried out by 13th, 14th and 15th Batteries, prior to Infantry raid on enemy trenches as per group order 00 No. 2.
4. Right group successfully carried out shelling and enabled Infantry to advance and secure the identification as desired.

Lieutenant Colonel Smith-Stevens
CO 5th Field Artillery Brigade

Smith-Stevens reread the despatch. 'Runner!' he called. Jum stepped into the tent. Smith-Stevens sealed the despatch and looked up. 'Driver Bevan! How are you feeling? I thought you were still convalescing.'

'Thank you, sir, I'm doing fine. Just need a couple more days.'

'HQ 2nd Division. Don't bust yourself. Just make sure it gets there.'

Jum saluted, then mounted and cantered towards 2nd Division, situated 2 miles south of Albert. A sentry stood at the entrance to Headquarters.

'What's your business, mate?' he asked.

'Despatch for HQ,' answered Jum. He eased past and stood in the dim interior.

The figure standing at the table turned. 'Despatch, runner? Where from?'

'HQ 5th Brigade, sir.'

Brigadier Robbie Tideswell moved forward. 'Is that you, Jum? Jum Bevan?'

'Yes, sir. Can't see too well in this dark.'

'Come into my office, runner.'

Once Jum was inside, Tideswell exclaimed, 'Jesus, Jum! You don't look well.' He pushed a chair forward. 'Sit down, sit down. Why are you still a runner? I thought you'd be at least a sergeant by now.'

'No time for promotion, sir. Too much work to do.'

'Have you been injured?'

Jum smiled. 'More times than I care to remember, sir. Gassed pretty bad three weeks ago with Jim Gillies and about fifty others in the brigade. I see you've made brigadier, sir.'

Tideswell waved his arm in a deprecating gesture.

'Means nothing,' he said. 'Just got to finish this bloody war and get home.'

Jum rose. 'I best be going, sir. I may be needed back at brigade.'

'Bugger the brigade, sit and relax!' Tideswell stood and moved to a small cabinet. He lifted out two tumblers and a full bottle of whisky, placing them on his desk. Pouring two large measures, he handed one to Jum.

'You need this, put some colour back in your cheeks.' Robbie Tideswell was quietly alarmed. The man before him was a mere shadow of the gunner he'd had under his command in the 5th Field Artillery Brigade.

Jum drained the whisky, the fiery liquid slamming into his empty stomach. Tideswell immediately refilled his glass.

'You hungry, Jum? When you finish that, go to the mess tent and have a big feed. And that's an order!'

Jum enjoyed the return ride to the 5th Field Artillery Brigade. The combination of food, drink and cool wind had indeed brought a healthy colour back to his cheeks.

He checked into Headquarters and spoke to Major Conrick. 'Sir, I'm buggered. Do you mind if I go and lie down?'

Conrick, like Tideswell, was alarmed. In the two and half years he had known Jum, this was the first time Bevan had shown any sign of weakness. With his endless enthusiasm and drive, he had always been the strong motivator of the 14th Battery. If Jum was tired, Conrick had fears for the remainder of the brigade.

'Of course not, Jum. Go and relax, get some sleep. You've had a hard time. I'll make sure you're awake for food.'

Jum left the Headquarters tent and walked slowly to his billet.

The draught horses, required in teams of ten to transport the 60-pound English gun, were large, healthy Clydesdales. This heavy gun, a highly efficient and effective 6-inch weapon, was the largest gun in the British artillery, and it was proving to be a dominant factor in the war against the German forces. The Brigade of Heavy Guns comprised three batteries of four guns each of the Royal Horse Artillery Brigade, and it was travelling from Amiens towards Albert, north of the Somme River.

As midday approached, the brigade paused at the 5th Field Artillery Brigade Headquarters. Lieutenant Colonel Smith-Stevens rose as the British officer entered.

'Good morning, Colonel,' Smith-Stevens said to the hard-eyed young soldier before him. 'How can we help?'

'My men are tired and very hungry. We're trying to get to Albert today. We're waiting on motorised tractors for our big guns, but they haven't arrived as yet.'

'No trouble, we only have two detachments in the mess tent. Send in your men. They can eat immediately.'

The British lieutenant colonel nodded a polite thanks.

'One thing, Colonel,' added Smith-Stevens, 'the officers eat at one end of the mess. No room for separate messes.'

The lieutenant colonel smiled. 'No problem with us at all.'

The British detachments transporting the heavy guns were finishing their meal as their officers sat down at the far end of the mess tent.

Padre Jenkins was in deep conversation with Jim Gillies as he entered the mess. The Wagga brothers, with Jum and Bob, were the last to arrive at their favourite table. Smith-Stevens and Conrick had joined the British group of officers about to begin their meal.

Lieutenant Colonel Bertrand Charles Chesterton dropped his knife in surprise. 'What unit are you, Colonel?' he asked Smith-Stevens.

'5th Brigade Artillery,' Smith-Stevens replied.

With a smile creasing his face, Bertie Chesterton asked, 'Is that Jum Bevan sitting at the far table?'

Surprised, Smith-Stevens looked across the mess. 'Sure is, Colonel. Why do you ask?'

Chesterton rose and hurried towards the group of the 14th Battery. Jenkins looked up, then said quietly, 'Don't look now, but the British brass are about to join us.'

The mess quietened as Colonel Chesterton arrived at the table.

'Are you Captain Claude Jenkins?' asked Chesterton.

Jenkins rose hastily. 'Yes, Colonel. What can I do for you?'

'I advise you to keep out of this company. They will only get you into very big trouble.'

Recognition dawned on Jum's face. He leapt up, exclaiming, 'Jesus, it's bloody Bertie!'

The table rose as one, with Jum and the boys pumping Chesterton's hand, back-slapping, yelling, smiling and laughing. 'I can't believe it, Bertie, you're a full bloody colonel!'

McErbain entered the mess and Lieutenant Colonel Smith-Stevens walked over to him. 'What's going on here, Harold?'

'Let's find out, sir. Tenshun!' he called. All stood to attention and turned towards him. At the same time, McErbain recognised Chesterton. 'Well, I'll be buggered – it's Bertie!' He strode over, grabbed Bertie's hand and shook it enthusiastically. Remembering his CO, he turned. 'My apologies, Colonel. I don't suppose you've met Colonel Chesterton?'

Smith-Stevens smiled. 'Well, I certainly have now!'

Bertie turned to Claude Jenkins, who said, 'The last time I saw you, Colonel Chesterton, you were a subaltern.'

'Yes, Captain Jenkins, and I thought you were a private. I was most embarrassed about that.'

'No apology required, Colonel. I was riding in the rear of a truck with no rank insignia. I must congratulate you on your advancement in rank.'

'Colonel Chesterton was our range operator when we won gunnery honours at Larkhill, sir,' said McErbain to Smith-Stevens. He detailed the circumstances that had led to this boisterous welcome. 'I recognised that he had potential, but – Colonel! He's only twenty-two.' He continued to Smith-Stevens, 'Jum taught him the basics – discovered he was a natural artilleryman because of his university background in mathematics. And the rest is history.'

'I reckon so,' said Smith-Stevens. 'He's CO of the Brigade of Heavy Guns parked across the way.'

The men of the 5th Field Artillery Brigade provided the drinks, and the revelry continued until late that evening. Chesterton had managed to slip away, and joined the No. 1 detachment of the 14th Battery. The story of the night at the Ram's Head in Tidworth was rehashed and grew in proportion to the alcohol intake as the night went on. At one stage, Bob swore it had been a four to one lopsided brawl.

It wasn't until mid-morning the next day that the Royal Horse Artillery Brigade set off for Albert. A group of gunners waved until Lieutenant Colonel Bertie Chesterton disappeared from sight.

The last-ditch German offensive on Amiens resumed, with extensive railway repair work being carried out by a number of German contractors. Rail transport allowed massive amounts of artillery and ammunition to be brought forward in preparation for the German thrust south-west to Amiens. If they were successful in breaking the Allied line, their next objective was Paris.

The German 207th RIR, the 14th Bavarian RIR, the 3rd Bavarian Ersatz IR and the 11th Bavarian RIR attacked with great ferocity on the east side of Villers-Bretonneux. Breaks appeared in the British line, with German Command taking the advantage and capturing most of the ground they had lost the summer before. Fierce battles were also raging at Morlancourt on the Ancre River.

Smith-Stevens, Conrick and Major Freddie Dawson met in the Headquarters tent. Smith-Stevens addressed his officers. 'We are desperately short of gas shell; we need to conserve our stocks.'

'I have an idea, sir,' said Dawson.

'Go on.'

'I propose we use harassing fire all night, then prior to dawn, change to smoke and gas shell for half an hour in concentration on the enemy front line. After three days, we use smoke only. We know that the main effect of gas is to have the Boche running for their gas masks. So, every time they see smoke, they'll think there's gas. It will give these Boche bastards something to think about, and disrupt their movements.'

'Very good idea, Dawson. What do you think, Terry?' asked Smith-Stevens.

'Yes, I'll go along with that,' agreed Conrick. 'It will conserve our gas supplies. But we'll still need more gas shell eventually.'

The plan worked well. Pre-dawn barrages with the smoke and gas shell had the German front-line troops running in all directions. When the smoke-only barrages occurred on the third day, artillery observers laughed as the German troops still ran like disturbed ants from an anthill.

To the south of Bois l'Abbé, the 4th Australian Division was successfully attacking the German lines. Hundreds of the enemy had been killed.

Smith-Stevens once again addressed his officers. 'There's a feeling at HQ – and amongst you officers, I hear – that we do not press forward enough when we have the upper hand. We now control the three German systems – front defence, counterattack and artillery. Brigade are considering strong frontal moves to coincide with our bombardment.'

'Well, sir,' said Dawson, 'the creeping barrage has been really successful. Are we to continue this pattern?'

'Yes, I expect this to be the direction. Also, we now have the power of the British Heavy Guns, 60-pounders set back at 8,000 yards, to blast the crap out of the German lines.'

Gas barrages by the Australian artillery brigades now occurred almost daily as motorised supply lines had been swiftly extended to keep up much needed ammunition supplies.

German heavy artillery had been increased to offset the advantage the Allies were now securing.

BRIGADE DIARY

25.8.18 Enemy movement reported in Starry Wood. 13th and 14th Batteries dug in west of the Somme area.

27.8.18 Our Batys to place protective barrage on enemy frontline to support and cover operations by British Inf. (1st Dorsets).

Owing to intense, hostile enemy fire, enemy completely disorganised our attack.

The morning of 25 August 1918 brought clear skies and the slightest breeze from the east. The pristine blue of the sky was in stark contrast to the ruined landscape, where Allied and German troops still fought doggedly.

The intense push by the enemy had caused protracted, close fighting, with front lines only hundreds of yards apart. Much more sophisticated heavy artillery was now being used by both the Allies and the enemy.

Ron Roberts looked across to the No. 1 Gun position about 100 yards to his right. He could see his brother Wagga laughing and talking with the rest of their detachment. After more than two years in the field, Ron's dark, curly hair was sprinkled with grey.

It was quiet. They had not yet fired a round this morning. Some 30 miles away to the south-west lay the city of Amiens where, only seven weeks earlier, the 5th Field Artillery Brigade had finished a five-day furlough.

Ron Roberts cast his mind back. In Amiens, the cobbled streets had not been entirely destroyed. The weather had been like today, warm and sunny.

The brigade had scheduled a swimming carnival. The pool at Rivery, near Amiens, was surrounded by roofed timber decking and looked out on a heavy forest of trees untouched by German shelling. The pool sides and seats were jammed to capacity. Even the slightly sloping roof was covered with keen spectators. The change rooms were at the south end of the pool. A few hundred men in shorts, their white bodies testament to a long winter, moved around excitedly, waiting for the carnival to commence. A group from the 14th Battery had gathered at the other end of the pool.

'Hey, Wagga!' called Bob. 'You and Ron getting changed?'

'Looks too cold for me,' said Wagga.

'Come on, mate. It'll be fun,' said Jim Gillies.

Wagga shook his head nervously. 'Give me a crazy horse or a bull, or drop 4.5 Howies on my head – all right. But don't put me in the bloody water. I can't swim.'

'What's with Wagga, Jim?' asked Bob.

'Somebody has to watch the clothes, mate,' Gillies replied, ending the conversation.

The races started. Good, bad and indifferent swimmers did their best, each urged loudly on by his detachment and battery.

Jim Gillies swam strongly to narrowly win the 50-metre dash, whilst Jum Bevan – though claiming to be rusty – easily won the 2-metre springboard event with a deft one-and-a-half somersault with pike. It was his favourite dive, and it had been his final dive when he won the State Championships at the Balmain Swimming Baths in 1911.

Eventually, the men began to leave the pool and return to their billets. Three gunners of 15th Battery were considering throwing Wagga into the pool for fun. A smiling Ron Roberts confronted them and offered sound advice. 'If you like living, I advise you not to take on young Wagga. He doesn't like water.' Fortunately, good sense prevailed.

Ron Roberts entered the *estaminet*, which they had drunk dry of beer the previous night. He cast his eyes over the sparse crowd. The men of the 14th Battery had moved on to another *estaminet* two streets away, close by Amiens Railway Station.

He spied the young waitress, Michelle, serving drinks to a small table. The previous night, whilst the boys had whooped it up, he had spent a long time talking to her. Her dark eyes and dark hair had made his pulse race. She had spent most of the evening making sure that every drink she served took her past Ron's table.

'Are you come here tomorrow?' she had asked.

He laughed and answered, 'Sure thing.'

'You mean, yes?' Ron nodded and sipped his beer. She gave him a radiant smile to take home to bed.

Now she moved quickly to him and asked, 'A drink, *Monsieur*?' Then she took off her apron and sat down next to him. 'The barman,' she pointed, 'he leave me to talk to you.'

Ron glanced over. The old barman smiled and waved.

They sat near the open fire in a quiet corner. With Michelle's basic English and Ron's smattering of French phrases, they understood each other well enough. Ron learnt that she had an elder brother and father active in the front line, near Ypres. Time flew by. They were holding hands as the clock slid to 10.30 pm. 'I'll walk you home?' Ron suggested. Michelle smiled and nodded.

They left the bar and once again the barman waved. Two streets along, Michelle stopped, took out her key and opened the door to a two-storey terrace. Followed by a nervous Ron, she entered, then turned, smiling, and said, '*Ma mère* has gone to Paris.' She held up two fingers. 'Two days more.'

Ron relaxed as he moved to the open fire, now only embers. They sat on the lounge. Michelle slowly encircled Ron with her arms and kissed him gently.

At the billet holding the 14th Battery, the gunners were waking up. 'The bloody stopout has just arrived home,' announced Bob.

Ron had attempted to enter quietly and make his way to his room without anyone noticing. Jum was the first to put two and two together. 'You sneaky bastard, Ron. The dark-haired waitress from the other night?'

Ron blushed. 'It's not what you blokes think. She's a lovely girl.'

'Don't give a bugger about lovely – what's she like in the cot?' came from a corner of the room. Followed by catcalls and irreverent banter, Ron eventually reached the room he shared with Wagga and Bob.

Wagga grinned. 'Come on, mate. Tell your little brother.'

Ron sat on his unused bed and felt in his pocket. With some pride, he passed the photo to Wagga. 'Jesus, she's a good sort, you lucky bugger. You seeing her again?'

'Yeah, tonight,' Ron replied.

'We're back in action tomorrow, I think, at Villers-Bretonneux,' said Wagga. 'Make the most of it, mate.'

Ron took his brother's advice. The next morning, he and Michelle had a tearful, poignant farewell.

The 14th Battery had dug in deeper than usual to protect themselves against the German offensive. Sam O'Brien, the twenty-two-year-old Queensland drover, had taken his shirt off to catch the warm morning sun.

'Don't get sunburnt, Sam,' joked Ron as the detachment lay about relaxing and smoking.

A thousand yards to the east, a German mortar group was preparing to launch their missile. A detachment of fourteen men was required to operate the massive mortar. This fearsome weapon was so large that it was set on a rail-track and required motorised tractors to move and position it. Fat and squat, the German 320-millimetre Minenwerfer resembled a massive toad with its mouth agape. It coughed loudly, spitting forth a frighteningly large projectile weighing about 850 pounds. The blast of the weapon was contained in the deep position housing the monster as it squatted on its rail line.

The German layer, carefully watching the parabolic arc of the huge missile, smiled as he exclaimed, '*Schön – schön!*' The 800-yard path of the bomb's traverse was seen clearly against the backdrop of blue sky west of Bois l'Abbé.

The shell detonated 5 feet above the ground, against the steel-plate shield of the 18-pounder in No. 2 Gun position. The effect was devastating. The eight gunners were instantly blasted to shreds by the enormous explosion.

Wagga, in No. 1 Gun position, started running the moment he picked himself up after the concussion of the blast. Dazed, he clambered into the enormous, still-smoking crater left by the huge shell and was confronted with strewn pieces of the eight men's dismembered bodies.

His face contorted in horror, Wagga dropped to his knees beside the remains of his brother.

Both Ron's legs were missing from the knees down. His left arm was severed at the shoulder. His face was strangely untouched, and small trickles of blood crept down from his curly mop of hair.

Wagga scooped up the corpse in his arms, the blood still flowing from the gruesome remains of the trunk. He staggered from the gun position. With his horrific burden, he slowly walked towards the outpost of the 14th Battery.

Sprinting to the crater, McErbain stopped in mid-stride. The sight stunned him into immobility. Jum caught up to Wagga, ran around and faced him. His senses reeled as he saw Ron's lifeless eyes peering at him from the crook of Wagga's elbow.

Wagga, his eyes wide and glazed, spoke in a monotone. 'I'm just taking Ron to see Mum, she's waiting for him,' he said, as he stepped past Jum and McErbain on the path towards the CCS.

Jum ran after Wagga, and again wheeled around to face him. 'Wagga, stop! Stop here, put Ron down!'

'I told you, I'm taking Ron to see Mum. Don't get in my way,' he said. His flat tone was now menacing.

McErbain motioned to Jum and pointed to the CCS. Jum started running.

Padre Jenkins, standing at the entrance to the casualty tent, observed the hatless figure sprinting towards him. Shading his eyes, he recognised Jum. At first the padre moved forward hesitantly, but he soon broke into a run. Muffled reports of exploding shells continued in the background.

Sobbing violently, with tears streaming down his ashen face, Jum gasped, 'Wagga and Ron!' Bent double, he pointed to Wagga and his burden. McErbain followed close behind.

Jum sank to the ground, unable to move. The padre turned and stumbled towards the casualty tent. 'Doctor! Doctor!' he called urgently.

Captain Stanley Davies strode out of the tent. He was closely followed by a large medical orderly.

'Something's not good, doctor,' stammered the padre, looking towards the approaching figures.

Wagga moved to the group waiting near the casualty tent, with McErbain by his side. 'I'm taking Ron to see Mum,' he said again. 'She's waiting.'

The orderly quietly pushed past the doctor and the white-faced padre. He spoke softly to Wagga. 'Yes, mate, your mum's out the back. Why don't you let me take Ron to see her.' He stepped forward with outstretched arms.

As Wagga carefully passed the body to the orderly, the doctor moved to his side, took his arm and said quietly, 'Come with me and we'll wait inside, out of the hot sun.'

Wagga nodded and sat in a chair near the tent's entrance. The captain hastily went to his medicine tray, selected a syringe and drew in a quantity of fluid. Swabbing Wagga's arm, he quickly sank the needle in and depressed the plunger. Another orderly applied some gauze and tape over the vein. Within minutes, Wagga was laid out on a stretcher, unconscious.

The group stood outside under the tent flap as the doctor emerged. Jum, McErbain and Jenkins waited with shocked, strained faces, as the doctor said, 'I've given him a big dose. He won't wake for some hours. I know his face, Padre, but I can't remember his name.'

'One of the boys from Wagga,' said the padre. 'James Roberts. He was carrying his brother, Ron.'

Jum had a tight grip on the tent pole.

'Fuck this war!' he said. 'Two years we've been together through thick and thin, and now this. He was twenty-three years old! And Wagga's only twenty. He turns twenty-one next week.'

The doctor, noticing Jum's shaking hands, said, 'Come inside for a moment.' Jum mutely followed the doctor into the tent and sat down. By now the orderly had disposed of the gown soaked in Ron's blood and was dressed in a clean one.

The doctor poured a strong draught and passed it to the orderly, who handed the glass to Jum. 'Here, mate,' he said, 'drink this. It'll make you feel much better.'

Jum drained the contents and twisted the glass in his fingers. 'Where did you put Ron?'

'He's out the back with two other boys from 13th Battery who were also unlucky this morning,' replied the orderly.

Jum moved his chair beside Wagga's inert figure on the stretcher and looked down at his sleeping mate. 'Don't wake up, Wagga,' he thought. 'Keep right out of this.'

The mess tent was quiet. Twelve men of the brigade had lost their lives that day. Close and binding friendships had been torn asunder. There was no joviality, no laughter. The men ate in silence.

The No. 1 Detachment of the 14th Battery, minus Wagga, sat silently smoking. McErbain, Bob, Gillies and Jum had nothing to say. Jum stood up and left. He returned a few minutes later with two bottles of whisky shoved deep in his pockets.

'Here's to Ron Roberts,' he declared solemnly as he thrust the bottle to his lips. He gulped, and a third of the bottle disappeared.

The bottle, passed around, emptied very quickly. It was smartly followed by the second.

Gillies rose and left, returning with two more bottles. 'Here's to his brother, Wagga!' he exclaimed, as he opened the first bottle. Half an hour passed. A cupful of whisky remained in the fourth bottle. The men were only now feeling the soothing effects of the alcohol.

Bob lay on his bunk, hands behind his head. They had all retired to Bob and Jum's tent. Jum sat on the edge of his cot, the half-empty bottle of jimjam juice in his hand. 'Wan' some?' he slurred. Bob nodded as he took the bottle and drained the contents.

'I thought we were safe, we couldn't be touched!' The tears started slowly. 'He was so strong, Jum. So quiet, so strong. Remember at Larkhill? He could've beaten those three Tommy bastards on his own. And now he's gone.'

There was silence for a few moments until Bob spoke again. 'I wonder where the padre is.'

'He's been sitting with Wagga all day. I'd say he's still there,' said Gillies. 'Is Wagga awake yet?'

'I don't know. I hope not,' said Bob grimly.

Captain Stanley Davies was worried. It was now three days since the death of Ron Roberts. His brother had not spoken since awakening from the sedative-induced sleep. He ate and slept, but had to be helped with simple toilet needs. He gazed at the hills, the shredded trees and his mates of the 14th Battery, but made no sound.

The divisional medical officer, a major, was more interested in what was on the menu for the evening meal than the condition of the men under his care. 'Put a rifle in his hand or toss him back in the gun position,' he said brusquely.

'Sir, with respect, I feel that to put him back where this happened, in the gun position, would damage him deeply and permanently,' said Captain Davies.

'We don't want cowards or shirkers being given a free ride at the expense of the others,' was the response.

Captain Davies knew it was useless to argue. He eyed the major with disgust. He was fed up. 'I'd like to see you in the front line, in the mud, under enemy fire for half an hour, you gross, fat toad!' he shouted. In fury he turned on his heel without saluting and made his way back to the brigade CCS.

'Shell shock', the term being used to describe Wagga's condition, covered all the mental disorders the troops had suffered for the previous three years. Captain Davies had seen plenty of men in a much more advanced stage than Wagga. There was no accepted treatment of such cases. His dilemma was that in order to get a man suffering shell shock out of the line, he had to list him as suffering 'mental disorder'. He knew what that meant – incarceration in a mental asylum.

He was convinced Wagga had suffered a mental breakdown and that he would be useless for further active front-line service.

'One thing's sure,' he thought, 'there's no damned way you're going back into the line.' He wrote the required analysis in Wagga's Casualty and Service Record Book, stating strongly that he should be repatriated as unfit for further active duty. With sadness, he closed the file.

That evening, he discussed the situation with Jenkins. 'Padre, you've spent days with Wagga. What do you think?'

'Well, he hasn't uttered one word since the day Ron was killed. He just sits and stares into space. It's as if he's in another world.'

'Exactly, Padre – the boy's been so damaged mentally by the experience of his brother's death that he's lost the ability to act in a normal way. The army has no labels for what's happened. The DMO – whom I consider to have no medical integrity at all – refuses to address the case. He says we should send the soldier back into the line, or in this case, back into the gun position. If you put your hand on a hot stove and burnt it badly, would a doctor say, "The best way to fix that is to put your hand on the stove again"? I've never heard anything so stupid.'

Padre Jenkins sadly shook his head and answered, 'Wagga can't go back into the line. He'd be useless in his present condition, and a burden to the rest of the detachment.'

'Exactly. I've recommended him as medically unfit for further duty.' Captain Davies paused. 'I worry about men like Roberts. I've seen many less affected, but still very disturbed, unable to maintain their basic abilities to think and act.'

The two men spoke for some time regarding various other men of the brigade who were suffering similar disturbances.

'Well, Stan, do you have a cure?' asked the padre finally.

'No, but I believe that rest, good food, a return to a normal civilised life and some caring attention will help at least some of these poor fellows return to normality. As for the rest, they'll go back to find that their problems aren't recognised by the Australian government. They'll be left on their own, a burden on their families forever, or until they recover from their mental conditions,' he finished flatly.

In late August, the enemy shelling was particularly aggressive, concentrating on the front line of Allied positions around Villers-Bretonneux. Orders arrived at Headquarters: the 5th Field Artillery Brigade was to be relieved by the 10th. There was no great joy amongst the men, only pure relief that for a short time they would be away from the nightmare of the Somme. They lost no time in making ready for the handover.

Arriving at the relief camp, a mile north of Amiens, the brigade settled quickly, and most of the men fell instantly asleep. But relief from the front line was brief. After four days' rest, the 5th Field Artillery Brigade was ordered back into action at the Warfusee–Aban Court Valley. From there, orders were received to advance – not just infantry, but also artillery, including the British Heavy Gun Brigades.

The brigade rumbled to a stop on the congested road to Saint-Quentin. The rain began, then increased in volume, soon turning all access roads to a quagmire. The brigade stubbornly fought the mud, and eventually made some ground during the night.

Morning brought clear weather. The impending Allied attack was only hours away. The preparations were complete, with Allied expectations running high.

Jum sat in the driver's seat of the towing rig for the 18-pounder as Gillies swung around and surveyed the scene behind.

'It looks like the whole Allied army is behind us!'

'This looks like the big advance we've been waiting for. We'll keep these Boche bastards on the run now,' Jum replied.

The determination of the Australian infantry was at its highest since the start of the war. Wave after wave of men swept eastwards, overcoming all opposition and capturing all objectives before them, some of them hours earlier than anticipated. The English brigades north of 5th Field Artillery Brigade endured some very heavy fighting and severe casualties.

Lieutenant Colonel Smith-Stevens was seething. His brigade was now to the rear, out of position, due to what he considered the lack of initiative of the English officers.

Brigade Diary

8.8.18 The English Officers do not seem to have the grim desire to overcome unexpected difficulties which every yard confront advancing infantry, which calls for immediate, individual action.

It is feared the average English soldier is not so bold and grim as he is hesitating, and dependent on higher authority, both very weak and undesirable characteristics in an attacking force. It is some proof of this, that when the 3rd Corps took over from the 5th Australian Division, the Germans attacked near Morlancourt, capturing over 200 prisoners, probably getting priceless information about the impending operations. However, it is recognised that such criticisms are in a way bad for the morale of an Army, but the Australians at least see that it will be a good thing for the solidarity of the Empire when the English soldiers really do something to redeem their ancient heritage gained in many battles, and illustrated in many a heart thrilling story of fights to a finish and handed down through the centuries, such awe-inspiring names as the Black Prince, Moore and Wellington.

The next few days were quiet. The 4th and 5th Field Artillery brigades made Headquarters at Bargonvillers. The 2nd Division Ammunition Column had maintained a steady flow of ammunition to the brigades throughout the action.

In keeping with the new trend of relief, days out of the line were more frequent. The 4th and 5th Field Artillery brigades were relieved and moved back behind the wagon lines as Corps Reserve. After four days of inactivity, 5th Field Artillery Brigade was moved back again into the line to relieve the current brigade in action.

The villages of Framerville and Vauvillers suffered extremely heavy German artillery bombardment. Many civilians were killed, and many more severely distressed by constant German gas shelling. 'Yellow Cross' gas had been developed in 1916 and its effects on the nose, mouth, eyes and lungs were devastating. But the Allies were prevailing. Over 400 German prisoners were marched past the brigade, adding to the growing list of captured German troops.

The German prisoners passing by evoked intense interest as the Allied troops eagerly scanned their enemies' faces, nervously expecting to see superhuman monsters. Instead, they gazed with surprise at an enemy similar to themselves in age and physique, with young, scared faces. The trickle of prisoners had increased to a constant stream of grey-clad soldiers, whose air of dejection was mixed with relief. Food and safety, away from the ferocity of the front line, were certainly appealing to the young prisoners. Under interrogation, one young German officer had admitted that his men had refused to face the Australians due to their fierce and unorthodox methods of infantry warfare. Wave after wave of screaming, yelling Australians with gleaming bayonets fixed was enough to drain the resolve of even the bravest of the German defenders.

Lieutenant Colonel Smith-Stevens felt a growing confidence amongst the men, from officers right down through the ranks. Though quietly excited, he hardly dared to acknowledge that the balance of power had shifted slightly in favour of the Allied forces.

The brigade had encamped on the bank of the River Somme, a mile from the small village of Frise near the Canal du Nord. Smith-Stevens glanced 100 yards down to the water's edge. Fifty or so naked men were cavorting and splashing in the river, despite the water's icy cold. Yelling, diving, wrestling, the men were exhibiting healthy signs of release from the gut-wrenching ordeals they had suffered under constant bombardment.

Smith-Stevens smiled. 'Just a bunch of excited young boys having fun.'

An hour previously, a naked young gunner had fled from the water, shivering not only from the cold, but also from fright.

'What is it, Andy?' asked Jum.

'There's a fucking great snake over there under that tree in the water,' pointed the boy. Jum and a couple of the men inspected the muddy pond the boy had indicated.

'You silly bugger – it's a freshwater eel!' Jum turned to Gillies, who was already dressed. 'Quick, Gill, get 2 yards of strong wire and some raw meat from the kitchen.' Gillies ran towards the mess area, returning quickly with the wire and scraps of meat.

Jum carefully lowered the baited wire into the pond. The eel slowly edged its head out from the reeds while a dozen pairs of eyes watched from the bank. The eel slowly took the bait. Jum let out the wire carefully.

'Go, Jum, you've got him!' hissed one of the men.

'No, no,' whispered Jum, 'he has to get it right down into his belly.' After what seemed an agonisingly long time, Jum suddenly snapped the wire that he had carefully wound around his wrist. The wire tightened and three of the men dragged with all their strength. The surface of the water broke as the eel came hurtling out of the river. The men jumped and yelled, pointing and gesticulating.

'Watch he doesn't bite!' called one. Another, braver than the rest, attempted to grab the 6-foot, writhing, squirming mass, which slipped through his hands.

'Hit him on the head!' yelled Jum, as he fought to stop the eel heading for the water. A heavy branch appeared, swung high and descended sharply on the eel's head. The eel lay still, and the men gasped and panted. Jum removed his beloved pocket knife and cut the bait free.

'There'll be more. Get the bait back in the water,' he said. Half an hour later, the men marched triumphantly back to the tent lines with seven large eels strung on a stout branch.

The cook was excited – anything to break the monotony of tinned beef, biscuits and strong horsemeat.

'What do you think, cookie?' asked Bob.

'Mate, tonight you blokes'll have the best soup you've ever tasted.'

Enticing aromas wafted from the large cauldron that the kitchen staff proudly placed on the serving table, eagerly watched by a horde of hungry men.

Lieutenant Colonel Smith-Stevens called for order and the din quietened.

'We have a special treat tonight, courtesy of No. 1 Gun Detachment – fresh River Somme Eel Soup.' Cheers rang out. Smith-Stevens continued, 'Drivers Bevan and Buchannen, please come forward.' Amid yells and laughter, the two moved to the serving table.

'Well, men,' said Smith-Stevens, 'you caught it, you taste it.'

Jum took a cupful of the steaming brown soup, sipped slowly and grimaced. 'It's bloody terrible, but I'll have some more.' The table was rushed by the hungry men, while the cooks and kitchen staff smiled.

The head cook turned to his staff. 'We should've put more water in. These hungry bastards have nearly finished the lot.'

Corporal O'Brien, the large cook, snarled to no one in particular, 'Should've put some arsenic in to fix up those bastards, Bevan and Buchannen.'

BRIGADE DIARY

29.8.18 Infantry in the line still advancing with few casualties and no resistance.
Reserve not required.

30.8.18 *Infantry unable to cross the marshy portion of the Somme, south-east of Clery. Our Batteries ordered into the line immediately and forthwith into action. For two hours, all Batteries shelled the rise ahead held by the Germans, which overlook all our forward areas. Our Infantry are slowly gaining ground, but with heavy losses. Péronne is close!*

1.9.18 Our Batteries instructed to fire at 'intense rates' on Mont St Quentin and Anvil Wood until 1500 hrs. Our Infantry rushed the town of Péronne and met with very heavy German Machine Gun fire. Casualties heavy. Enemy balloons are a headache. They have uninterrupted sight of our infantry and gun emplacements. Ammunition supply is unable to be carried out. Our wagons cannot approach the Battery positions when balloons are up. Requests for the RAF to destroy were of no avail. Much enemy movement reported along the road leading to Cardinal Wood.

About 50 Germans have just passed our Brigade HQ. They were captured in Péronne by the 5th Division. Notwithstanding this, the objective has not been secured. The 2nd DAHQ has instructed us to move our Batteries immediately across the Somme River in order to support an operation tomorrow morning.

During the night the Boche shelled the 14th and 15th Batteries with HE and gas, no casualties resulted.

We are expending, daily, an average 6,000 rounds of 18-pounder and 1,200 rounds of 4.5 Howitzer shells. The workload is so enormous that, unless we can get a spell very soon, a large number of the men will become useless in a little time.

2nd DAHQ instructed Brigade to move all Batteries and wagon lines forward to the Cappy area immediately. Enemy artillery exceptionally quiet. Weather fine, cool.

4.9.18 The CO of 298th Brigade, Royal Field Artillery, visited our Brigade to discuss relief by their Brigade. At 1400 hrs all Batteries relieved by the 298th Brigade, Royal Field Artillery. 5th Brigade moved to an area on the River Somme between Bray and Cappy. Brigade Headquarters located east of Bray at the 'Mill'. Horses let out to graze and recover after six weeks of intense work.

The men of the brigade relished their break. In groups of 150 men at a time, they were transported to Bray and given hot baths and clean clothing. During this time, the mules that had endured the worst of the conditions were replaced with fresh horses. The troops were unhappy with this arrangement, as the mules withstood harsh work better than horses and rarely seemed to suffer illness or injury.

September to October 1918

Rain, sleet and snow greeted them at Albert station. They reported to Headquarters and were loaded onto a motorised truck, which set out for the Doingt area between Cambrai and Bapaume.

The 5th Field Artillery Brigade, encamped in a large, muddy field, had suffered four days of unrelenting rain and sleet that heralded the onset of a vicious winter.

The sullen, set faces of the men of the 14th Battery spoke volumes about the previous weeks' activity.

'We've been ordered into the line,' said Gillies, as the men sipped their tea. Jum felt disheartened by the numbing cold and the dreaded news.

McErbain entered the tent. 'We move in three hours into the line. Best get packed and ready.'

The men rose wearily. In twos and threes, they slowly left the mess tent. With horse teams hitched, the batteries moved eastwards to their new camp. Heavy mud, up to the wagon axles, made forward movement slow and laborious.

The 18-pounders and detachments were the first to arrive. Icy cold rain, blown by the north-west wind, drenched the open field. McErbain squatted, hunched down, on the lee side of a wagonload of stores. 'Doesn't get much worse than this!'

Jum nodded, too cold to speak.

Bob turned his head. 'Jum, I saw a couple of bombed farm houses about half a mile back. What say we go and scavenge some sheet iron for shelter?'

Jum turned to McErbain. 'What do you think, Harold?'

'Good idea. Take a wagon and get whatever you can.'

Three hours later, the bedraggled figures of Jum and Bob, sitting atop a massive load of corrugated iron, appeared through the dusk. The rain had eased, but the wind was still blowing in violent gusts. The men, aching with cold, fell to the task of unloading and preparing a shelter in the muddy field.

They dug shallow trenches for the iron sheeting walls; other sheets were tied down as roofs. Mud and hessian were then packed into any cracks or holes.

These rough huts were a massive improvement on sleeping under wagons in the savage weather. The men, four to a hut, slowly began to warm up. The wind eased. But they slept restlessly, as the enemy bombardment had begun, searching and sweeping the area.

The sporadic shelling, fired by very long-range guns, had no set pattern of concentrated fire. 'These bastards are a long way off, Jum,' said Bob.

'Yes, mate. I'd reckon this stuff is from the Boche "Big Boys" 12 miles away behind the Hindenburg Line.'

Rain fell steadily over the next few days. The Allied advance met no resistance as it moved rapidly eastwards towards Cambrai. War-weary German prisoners revealed that they had been ordered to put up a fighting defence, but it had withered in the face of the fierce Allied infantry attack.

2.10.18 Back to old job, mounted runner from Gunpits to HQ and wagon lines. Everything going OK at present.

The German retreat had become a rout. Along the Hindenburg Line, from Belgium to Vailly, east of Paris, the enemy was in full flight.

The Allies captured batteries of guns intact and took hundreds of the enemy prisoner; they offered no resistance. The feeling of excitement, and even euphoria, in the Allied ranks escalated as they recorded success after success.

The Allied divisional artillery, not accustomed to rapid advance by the Allied infantry, struggled to keep up. The advance was halted. It had become increasingly harder for stores, ammunition and covering artillery to maintain the hectic pace. Commanders prudently regrouped and reassembled a cohesive fighting force. After three days of regrouping and replenishment, the Allied advance recommenced in rain and sleet. The nightmarish mud was up to 3 feet deep in places.

The brigade was separated whilst performing a creeping barrage to support infantry capturing the small village of Louvencourt. Brigade signals could not locate the 14th and 15th batteries, and search groups were unable to pinpoint the missing 18-pounders. Heavy German retaliation made movement difficult, with men now pinned in their forward trenches and the artillery, further back, suffering heavy casualties.

The following day, two runners on exhausted horses finally found the 14th and 15th batteries some 1,200 yards forward of the area they should have been occuping. They had run out of ammunition and were dug in, waiting for the fierce German bombardment to end.

McErbain, deep in conversation with Conrick, was fuming. 'If it hadn't been for the bloody Yanks, the whole brigade could have been 10 miles further east, virtually to the Hindenburg Line. They reach their objective, then sit on their arses; no get up and go at all! They're bloody good infantrymen, but their officers have no initiative. Anyway, their sheer numbers counted for a lot.'

Conrick nodded in agreement. 'We were wondering where the hell you blokes were. A day and a half missing twelve 18-pounders is no laughing matter!'

'Well, Terry, we were out of ammo and the Boche had us pinned down. They must have regrouped. We knew they were running, but they must have stopped well short of Hindenburg.'

'We haven't seen the last of the Boche, Harold. They're not going to give up easily.'

Smith-Stevens joined the two officers. 'Our failure to get the batteries over the Canal du Nord has caused a big setback. We must try again tomorrow morning, early. The 1st and 2nd divisions are being joined by the 30th American Division for a big push right up to Hindenburg.

'We're to be supplemented by the 7th and 8th Australian Field Artillery brigades at Joncourt. The three brigades of artillery are to lay on a forty-eight-hour continuous barrage.'

He paused before adding, 'We have a minor operation tomorrow for the 14th Battery, to support infantry in straightening their advancing line between Mont Corchan and Ponchaux. Unfortunately, we're expecting heavy rain at about the same time.'

Conrick smiled grimly. 'So what's new? I don't know how long our men can last, though, without a break. They're on the go for thirty-five hours at a time. I'm concerned for their health, mental and physical.'

'We're all buggered, Terry,' replied Smith-Stevens, 'men, officers and horses alike. Let's hope this big push is the beginning of the end.'

The Allied attack, all along the line, was very successful. The German retreat was so rapid that the Allied forces found it hard to keep in contact with the enemy.

The Allied infantry, with full artillery support, had moved forward as far as the River Selle between Saint-Benin and Saint-Souplet, where they encountered very strong German opposition. Here, German Minnenwerfer bombardment was successfully repelled, allowing the Selle to be held by Allied forces. The villages of Saint-Benin, Saint-Souplet and Molain were overrun and secured by the Allies.

The excitement of these successes was tempered by a desperate German onslaught. The German infantry penetrated the Allied line near the village of Hail Mennereuse, dangerously close to the 5th Field Artillery Brigade.

8.10.18 Big stunt postponed this morning till tomorrow morning. Yanks hopping over.

10.10.18 Another stunt today, successful. Civilians delighted.

Lieutenant Colonel Smith-Stevens addressed his officers. 'The 15th Battery lost about twenty horses in last night's action. These bloody Germans are shelling unprotected French villages with gas. Of course, the French civilians have no gas masks and are suffering severe casualties. Six men of the 105th were also gassed and have been evacuated. Luckily, the 14th, 15th and 105th have now moved forward and are in position on the front line. And the 30th American Division has now been formed up, ready for a final push to the high ground east of the River Selle.

'Tonight, we see the big push postponed for a few hours, to allow us to regroup – but this may be it; this may be the end of this abysmal, stinking war. Let's do the best we can to bring it to an end!'

The officers rose and applauded their commanding officer.

'Well, Harold, let's hope he's right,' Conrick said to McErbain as they left the Headquarters tent.

11.10.18 I fired fifty rounds of Fritz's 5.9 ammunition back at him.

In the continued Allied advance, the 5th Field Artillery Brigade captured a German gun emplacement east of the River Selle. Jum, Bob and Gillies, with three new recruits to the battery, were examining the German 5.9 gun.

'Handy little bastard, Gill!' said Jum.

Bob had moved to the left of the trench. 'Look, they've left ammo here too.'

'How much Bob?' asked Jum.

'About fifty rounds.'

'You thinking what I'm thinking, Gill?'

Grinning in reply, Gillies nodded.

'Let's get it round then!' said Jum.

The six men rapidly turned the weapon around, facing east towards the retreating enemy. They quickly loaded the weapon. 'Give us plenty of range, Bob,' called Jum. 'Don't want to drop short on the Yanks.'

In an almost frivolous manner, the detachment started firing the German shells at the retreating troops. But towards 2300 hours that evening, the men of No. 1 Gun, relaxing and smoking in the captured German pit, were hit by a barrage of enemy shells.

Jum jumped up. 'These bastards aren't finished yet! These are the heavies from behind Hindenburg, I'll bet.'

The bombardment grew heavier. 'We better scatter and find some decent cover!' Gillies shouted as another salvo of shells exploded nearby. The men ran from the position in various directions, seeking the safety of a deep shell hole or trench.

Jum and Bob ran about 400 yards to the left, finally jumping into a deep trench. Light from the bursting shells split the dark. The two huddled together, flinching each time a close explosion occurred. The bombardment brought with it icy rain, and the cold intensified. Ear-splitting explosions, interspersed with thunderous mortar shelling, continued unabated. Jum and Bob were accustomed to the horrific nightmare of heavy artillery, but this attack was as bad as any they had experienced.

When it arrived, the explosion was enormous. A shell landed on the western edge of the trench, illuminating their horror-stricken faces with stark brilliance. Shell fragments flew in all directions.

The two men lay still.

Fifteen minutes before dawn, the roar of exploding shells subsided. One of the most horrific and relentless barrages of Jum's war had finally ceased. Now, with the first streaks of a grey dawn, came the stillness. The rain had stopped. Jum had regained consciousness; he had kept his eyes firmly closed for the duration of the shelling.

'I think it's over, Bob,' said Jum, squinting in the soft early light. His heavy woollen tunic was soaked and icy cold. Both men were motionless, locked in an embrace for mutual protection. Jum eased his cramped back away from the earth bank. 'I'll have a quick look around. You stay here,' said Jum. Then, 'Shake a leg, Bob – can you hear me?'

Bob could not hear, or see, or feel, and would never answer another question. Most of the left side of his head was missing, the left eye hanging from the mangled remains of its socket. Jum moved back and Bob's head lolled to his right shoulder.

Jum looked at Bob's face. It seemed to grin at him. He rose to his knees, his own face twisted in disbelief. Jum cried out. With three years of horror behind it, his cry rose to a shriek. Sobbing, he fell forward, his trembling hands covering the mangled head of his mate.

Two hours later, a small group approached the trench. 'Two more here, sir,' said the corporal, over his shoulder. The lieutenant nodded and answered, 'Very well, get their tags and papers and bring the bodies out.'

As a hand touched his neck, Jum recoiled, grabbing the corporal's throat in a fierce grip. The sight of this blood-soaked demon screaming incoherently made the men panic. Two soldiers quickly grabbed Jum from behind as the lieutenant jumped into the trench, jamming his revolver into Jum's face. 'Pull the trigger, you bastard! Pull the fucking trigger!' Jum shouted, loosing the corporal and sliding to the duckboard floor of the trench.

'I promised his mother! I promised his mother!'

The lieutenant holstered his revolver. 'Get him back to the CCS. He needs help. Leave that other bloke for the moment.'

He and the corporal moved to the waiting dray, while the two soldiers lifted Jum, now limp and unresisting, from the trench.

As they staggered towards the dray with Jum between them, a voice exclaimed, 'Jesus! It's Jum!' Harold McErbain, on his way to rejoin the 5th Brigade, had recognised the slumped and bloody figure. He joined the group, and went with them to the CCS.

The CCS was overflowing with bleeding and broken bodies. As Jum had suffered no obvious physical injury, he was seated on an empty ammunition box, a blanket over his shoulders. The grey sky cast a deathly pallor over his drained face. An over-worked doctor administered an intravenous sedative that dulled his responses.

'I see you're artillery,' said the interrogating captain. 'What unit are you from?'

Jum cast vacant eyes on the captain, answering in a flat monotone. '14th Battery, 5th Brigade.'

'Do you know where your unit is?'

'No.'

'How did you happen to be in the trench, separated from your unit?' Jum was silent and the captain asked the question again.

'Our battery had been under constant bombardment since 2300 hours last night. We were out of ammunition, and under heavy attack. The German artillery must have had forward spotters – they had our position to within a few yards. We were ordered to act alone and seek cover, so we ran out of the position, across the knoll, where we found some infantry trenches. We dived in just in time – they were sending in their 230 mortars. A couple of wild ones came astray, and one landed 30 yards down the trench.'

'Who was in the trench with you?'

'Bob Buchannen, my mate.'

'You realise, Private Bevan, that Private Buchannen was killed?'

'Hard to stay alive with half your fucking head missing!' Jum's stomach started heaving; the bile rose in his throat. He began to sob and retch. His retching turned dry, but continued until blood started to flow from his ruptured throat. Streams of bright blood gushed from his open mouth.

'Orderly, Orderly!' yelled the captain. 'Hurry, for Christ's sake, he's about to choke!'

The orderly quickly administered an injection to control the bleeding and retching. When it at last subsided, Jum was carried to an empty stretcher. The injection had done its job. He lapsed into a deep sleep for hours.

McErbain stood at the end of Jum's stretcher, quietly talking to a white-coated orderly. 'They were in this stunt together from the beginning,' said McErbain. 'Bob was like a younger brother to Jum. He looked out for him for three years. God knows what Bob's death will do to him.'

284

NOVEMBER 1918

Jum stepped down unsteadily into the gun position. He held onto the steel-plate shield of the 18-pounder for support. Only two other gunners were in the pit; one was asleep, the other smoking.

The heavy, dark cloud from the north west indicated rain or possible early winter flurries of snow.

Jum had shared breakfast with a few of the boys, then immediately returned to his tent. Bob's kit was still on his bed. Each time Jum looked at his dead mate's pile of gear, his stomach churned and a bitter taste filled his mouth. With shaking hands, he found the bottle of whisky hidden under his pack. He tipped the bottle and gulped the contents, then wiped his mouth on the sleeve of his jacket.

Technically, he was on active duty, although the fighting had eased considerably. The last thing on his mind was sitting in a gun position, waiting for a highly unlikely order to commence a highly unlikely barrage. He stood up and tucked the bottle out of sight in his tunic.

He made his way through the mud towards the gun positions, answering greetings from various men with a casual wave. The whisky was only now beginning to take effect. Fifty yards from the gun positions, Jum emptied the bottle.

In a sudden rage, he hurled the bottle at a lump of twisted metal. The crash, with its flying pieces of sharp, glistening glass, intruded on the early morning quiet.

He sank to his knees, breathing heavily. 'Why? Why?' he muttered over and over. Then slowly he rose and stumbled towards the position.

Jim Gillies had asked a number of people if they had seen Jum. All had shaken their heads. Finally, a corporal from the stores depot said, 'Yeah, I saw him headed for the gun positions about twenty minutes ago. He seemed a bit unsteady on his feet.'

On his way, Gillies was passed by Captain Henry Chilcott, riding in a horse-drawn dray. He made no acknowledgment and did not offer a lift. Gillies watched the disappearing back of Chilcott and thought, 'Typical, you bastard!' Now that the fighting had been curtailed, Captain Chilcott had become even more pompous and officious than he had been before the easing of hostilities.

Jim sensed trouble as he approached the artillery position. The driver of Chilcott's dray was attempting to drag Jum from the No. 2 position. Voices were raised in argument. He hurried to the scene.

Chilcott called loudly to Gillies, 'I want this man arrested, Corporal.' He pointed to Jum, standing beside the 18-pounder.

'What's happened, sir?'

'This man is drunk on active duty. It's the second time this has happened, and I won't stand for it.'

Gillies jumped into the position. Jum was ready for anything, preferably a brawl. Gillies could smell the alcohol.

'Come on, mate,' he said. 'We'll go back to the wagon lines and sort this out later.'

As he recognised Gillies, Jum's aggressive attitude dissolved. He said brokenly, 'He was my mate, Gill. I can't stop thinking about him. I can't get it out of my mind.' Jum's hands were shaking.

Gillies helped Jum to the wagon. Chilcott climbed aboard, the driver took the reins and they headed towards the HQ area.

Lieutenant Colonel Smith-Stevens read the charge sheet and turned to Harold McErbain. 'What do we do with Bevan, Harold?'

'I don't know, sir, but I do know that that bastard Chilcott is a pain in the arse! The fighting's nearly over, we're only a token presence here now. And Bevan's suffering badly. His mates say they hear him at night, calling and yelling in his sleep. The padre and I are quite concerned about him.'

Smith-Stevens rubbed his forehead pensively. 'You know, Harold, Bevan could have risen in rank dramatically these last three years, but his AWLs and drinking have held him back.'

'Yes, sir. I think he feels responsible for too many people, takes it all on board, and when something like Buchannen's death happens, he can't handle it. A drink is his way out of the stress he puts himself under. But he's one of the toughest and bravest men I know.'

Harold glanced through the window. He saw men relaxing everywhere, laughing and at ease. 'The padre and other men owe their lives to him,' he said.

'Confidentially, Harold, Chilcott wants Bevan court-martialled.'

'What?' McErbain turned in surprise. 'That bloody Chilcott never put his head near the front line. He's hung out in HQ ever since he bloody well joined the unit! And now he wants to ruin one of our best men.'

'Don't worry, Harold, it won't happen.'

The following morning, Jum, suffering a severe hangover, made his way to the CO's tent. He knew he would face charges. 'But then,' he thought, 'what can they do to me now?'

Sergeant Charlie Hill read the charge. 'Drunkenness whilst on active duty.'

Smith-Stevens looked at Jum. 'What do you have to say for yourself, Driver Bevan?'

Jum looked at his CO with slightly bloodshot eyes. 'Sir, I thought the fighting was over,' he stammered. 'I ... I haven't been handling things too well lately, sir.'

'Driver Bevan, we have all been under enormous strain these past three years; and I mean everybody. If we allow ourselves to let go now, we will not have completed the job we set out to do.

'I cannot allow this matter of "drunk on duty" not to be dealt with. I sympathise with you; I realise you have been under severe duress. Given all the circumstances, I award you five days' forfeiture of pay, No. 2.'

Jum stood to attention.

'Sergeant, march Driver Bevan out.'

Charlie Hill spoke gently. 'About turn, quick march!'

Outside, Charlie Hill walked with Jum. 'Mate, I'll see you tonight. Just a couple of drinks for Bob, OK?'

Jum smiled sadly. 'Thanks, Charlie.'

Brigade Diary

11.11.18 The trek was continued in fine weather at 0900. En route, in Péronne, news of the signing of the Armistice reached the column. After these many hard months and years, the news was hard to understand and take in. The silence of the men demonstrated the strong heartfelt thankfulness of the men.

11.11.18 Up the line again, passed through Péronne the day Armistice was signed.

The fighting was over. The Great War, the 'war to end all wars', had finally run its course.

The 5th Field Artillery Brigade, now out of the line and any further action, had been transported to Allonville for rest and recuperation.

For Jum, the days blended into one another, but the memory of that horrifying night was etched on his mind forever.

Padre Jenkins was troubled. 'I don't know what to do, Jim,' he said to Gillies. 'He just stares into space the way Wagga did when Ron was killed. But at least he talks.'

Gillies nodded. 'How are we going to handle Jeanne, what with her being seven months pregnant and all?'

'Jum will have to travel to Zillebeke to break the news. I think I should go with him,' said Jenkins resignedly.

'What about Bob's body?' asked Gillies. Bob's body had not yet been buried. The cold winter of the Western Front meant that temporary interment, prior to final burial, was not required.

'Usually it would be interred in a designated war cemetery, but under these circumstances, I don't quite know what will happen.'

A week passed. Jum was passed as fit for active duty.

'It's a tricky case, Padre,' said Lieutenant Colonel Smith-Stevens. 'The Australian Army does have rules and regulations for the burial of their men killed in action. But you really think Driver Buchannen's wife will want to take care of his burial?'

'Knowing the young lady in question, I feel sure she will insist,' replied Jenkins.

'Very well, Padre, I will recommend to Divisional Artillery HQ that Buchannen's body be released to his wife. You and Driver Bevan may have compassionate leave to attend the burial. Major Conrick will organise passes for you both.'

Thanking his commanding officer, the Padre left Headquarters and sought out Jum.

'I've received leave for us to go to Zillebeke,' he said. 'We can leave whenever it's convenient.'

'I don't want to go, but I suppose I have to,' said Jum listlessly.

'Yes, Jum. It's going to be bad, but we can help each other,' said Jenkins.

The train carrying Jum and Padre Jenkins ground to a panting halt in the town of Ypres. Their orders secured transport and the two were quickly on their way to the village of Zillebeke. At the village, they drove down rue de Dorp and past the church, now a pile of rubble.

In the motor omnibus, Jum turned to Padre Jenkins. 'Look outside the post office, Padre. That's Jeanne's horse and dray.'

The driver halted the vehicle, and Jum and Jenkins climbed down. A light dusting of snow had covered the street. Dull grey skies promised heavier snowfalls.

Anna Meaux emerged from the post office as Jum called, 'Anna, Anna!'

She ran excitedly to the two men. Three paces from Jum, she saw the looks on their faces and stopped. Her small bag of mail dropped to the ground. Jum moved forward and embraced her. Her body was rigid.

'It's Bob, isn't it?' she said.

Jum nodded dumbly.

Padre Jenkins moved forward. 'Where is Jeanne, Anna?' he asked.

'Back at the farm. It is too cold for her to come out.'

The padre steered the couple to the warmth of the nearby *estaminet*. They removed their coats.

'What happened, my Jum?' she asked.

'About a week ago,' he said, 'we were near the River Selle. We thought the war was almost over. We'd been ordered to stay behind. The infantry had overrun the German line and we weren't required for any further action. So we were resting, awaiting orders. The Boche started one of the heaviest bombardments I've ever been in. It was awful. Anyway, a large mortar shell landed in our trench. Bob suffered a critical head wound. The doctor said death was instantaneous, if that helps at all.'

Jum paused while Anna took in the news. 'Is the baby all right, Anna?'

'So far, yes, but now ...'

'Well, we'd best be getting this over,' said the padre.

The horse and dray stopped outside the farmhouse. As the three stepped down, the door opened. Jeanne appeared in the doorway.

As she saw the three approach, the welcoming smile faded from her face. She held her hands up as if to ward something off as she stumbled backwards into the room. 'No, no!' she cried. 'Not Robert!'

Jum closed the door gently behind them. Jeanne had fallen to her knees. Nothing was said as Anna dropped to Jeanne's side. The two men remained standing.

Jeanne raised her face to Jum. 'Tell me it's not true. Tell me he's not dead.'

Jum's grief overpowered speech. He moved stiffly to a chair and sat down, without speaking.

'I knew it would happen!' she cried. 'It was too good to last. He was a beautiful man, so full of love and compassion. He really loved me, you know? And he loved this child of ours so much.'

'He not only loved you, Jeanne – he adored you,' Jum said through unashamed tears. 'He couldn't stop talking about you. You were in his thoughts constantly.'

Jeanne stood up and moved over to Jum. She embraced him, holding his head against her swollen abdomen.

'Feel his heart beating in my body. He will always be with me, Jum. Feel his heart and remember – feel his heart!' Jum sobbed uncontrollably, sick with grief.

Later that night, as Anna lay trying to sleep, she heard Jeanne crying softly. A wave of deep compassion overwhelmed her. She slid from her bed and went into Jeanne's room. She slipped into Jeanne's bed and embraced her tenderly, murmuring consoling words.

'Oh, Anna, what am I to do?' Jeanne cried.

'We'll face this together, Jeanne,' said Anna. 'I'll be here for you.'

A horse and dray, bearing a coffin covered simply with a black sheet, slowly made its way up the slight rise to Jeanne's farm. Bob's slouch hat sat atop the coffin, a reminder of the sacrifice this young Australian had made on the Western Front.

For some time, light snow had been falling. Jeanne stared at the covered coffin; its thickening mantle of snow suggested to her the cleansing of the soul, an absolution.

Jeanne watched as the coffin was lowered into the grave. She supported her stomach with entwined fingers, hugging her unborn child.

She bent and cast one handful of soil onto the coffin. '*Adieu*, my love,' she said softly, then turned and walked with great dignity towards the house.

The grave was gently but quickly filled. Not one of the mourners moved until the burial was complete. Finally, the stream of quiet, local people headed back to Zillebeke. Jeanne stood at the gate of the farmhouse, thanking each person as they passed.

Sergeant Alan Casey turned to Jim Gillies. His mouth was set in a grim line. 'What a bastard waste of young life!'

Jum settled into a routine. With the fighting over, the men had plenty of spare time to relax, play football, or simply sleep and write excited letters home. The brigade, now billeted at Cartignier, was lavished with care by the delighted civilian population. They provided the men with free billets and food, and refused to accept payment from the weary soldiers. The days became weeks, and the weeks extended into a couple of months. Jum left Thuin, in Belgium, for Le Havre, en route to Blighty for his final furlough.

Jum considered visiting Jeanne and Anna before his departure for England. But in his current mental state, a further emotional encounter was beyond him. He did not contact either girl before he left Thuin.

APRIL 1919

24.4.19 *Left Liverpool on TC* Runic *for home.*

The troop carrier HMAT *Runic* eased its way south through the calm waters of the Indian Ocean.

'Forget him, Jum, he's only a loud-mouthed bully,' said Jim Gillies, leaning on the rail.

'Any more of his crap and he'll get more than he bargained for!'

Earlier, after finishing their meal, Jim Gillies and Jum had poured tea into their pannikins. The obnoxious cook O'Brien was standing behind the serving table with a sneer on his face. 'The war's over, Bevan. You can forget about being tough now. Your pansy mate Buchannen isn't here to back you up anymore.'

Jum halted in mid-stride, then turned and flicked the pannikin of hot tea at the cook's large belly. O'Brien screamed as the steaming liquid soaked through his singlet.

He charged at Jum. Shouting obscenities, the cook was held by two men in front of Jum. 'I'll get you, you fucking smart arse!' he yelled.

Jum moved forward. 'Let him go,' he said, seething with anger. But the cook was hustled away into the kitchen area.

Padre Jenkins cast a glance at Jum. 'What was that about?'

'He thinks he's so tough, that bloody O'Brien. Four or five times now I've had to give him a reminder that he's not as tough as he thinks he is.'

The morning sun shone in a brilliant, clear sky; there was not a cloud in sight. The *Runic* sliced neatly through the calm water, her cargo of war-weary men rejuvenated by the fresh salt air. The padre stood by Jum on the foredeck, watching sea birds wheeling across and under the bow of the ship. 'Did you see Jeanne and Anna before you left France?' he asked Jum.

Jum stared at the bow wave splashing white against the deep blue of the Indian Ocean. 'No, Padre, it was too hard. I thought, why open old wounds? Just let them get on with their lives.' He paused. 'I have three letters from Anna. They finally got to me after three months. I haven't opened them.'

Jenkins glanced at Jum, then returned his gaze to the wheeling birds. 'I thought something might have come of your relationship with Anna.'

Jum wearily pressed his hand to his forehead. 'I've thought long and hard about Anna, Padre, but my mind's too jumbled to come to any smart decisions. When Ron was killed, I somehow felt responsible, don't ask me why. Now Wagga's in a nut farm somewhere and Bob's gone.'

Jum drew a deep breath. 'When Bob died, a chunk of me died with him. I feel like there's a hole in me; a part stayed in his grave in Zillebeke. To have seen Anna again — I don't know, I don't think I could have handled it.'

This time the padre's glance was full of sadness. 'I wonder how Jeanne and her child are,' he mused, after a moment.

Jum answered a little too quickly, 'I don't even know if she had a boy or girl, or how they are.'

The padre rose, and put his hand on Jum's shoulder. 'If you open Anna's letters, you may find out.' He smiled and gave Jum's shoulder an affectionate squeeze before moving away.

Sailing on the *Runic* were men who were still lightly disabled by battle as well as others who were physically untouched. Two weeks of inactivity had them champing at the bit for action, anything to relieve the boredom.

Gillies led Jum to the notice on the 'tween deck. 'Look, Jum, boxing today. You having a go?'

Jum shook his head. 'Not interested, Gill.' They looked at the 'Boxing Tournament' notice, which listed the various boxing weights and named Corporal Harrison as referee.

The main deck was crowded to capacity. Half a dozen bouts had been completed. Enthusiasm was triumphing over serious technique, with the boxers receiving standing ovations for their gladiatorial efforts. The announcer, an infantry lieutenant, called for quiet after the last bout.

'Well, men, that's about it. We do have one more contestant, but no opponent for him.' Paddy O'Brien, seated near the temporary ring, stood and waved to the crowd. He beckoned the lieutenant over and muttered in his ear. Once again, the lieutenant raised his hands for silence.

'Paddy O'Brien, a cook from 5th Brigade Artillery, is disappointed not to have had a bout, so he's offered to spar in an exhibition with any one of you blokes who wants to get square after two years of his food in France.'

Roars of laughter greeted this announcement. The lieutenant looked around.

'No one? No takers?'

Jum Bevan stood up. 'I'll take him on,' he said quietly.

A murmur went through the crowd. Many knew of the bad feelings between the two.

'Right, then, we have an exhibition,' called the lieutenant. 'Five minutes to get changed.' He detailed the statistics of the two boxers for the crowd.

Harold McErbain, Padre Jenkins and Jim Gillies sat four rows from ringside. The padre was uneasy.

'Don't worry, Padre,' said McErbain. 'Jum can look after himself.'

'It's not Jum I'm worried about,' the padre replied, 'it's the other boy.'

The two boxers were called to centre ring.

'Nothing low, break clean and come out boxing,' intoned Corporal Harrison.

Although out of condition, and overweight from indulging in too much of his own cooking, O'Brien knew the rudiments of boxing. 'No Buchannen to help you today, Bevan,' he taunted. The bell rang.

Moving to centre ring, O'Brien did not touch gloves. Instead, he stepped forward, unleashing a wild right that had Jum backfooting rather quickly.

'So much for the boxing exhibition,' muttered the padre.

Jum – ducking, weaving, swaying – did not throw one punch for the first minute of the round. Content to let O'Brien chase him from corner to corner, Jum began to feel good as his body warmed to the exercise.

'Stand still, you bastard!' panted O'Brien.

Jum smiled in reply.

The round ended with Jum not breathing any harder than when they'd begun, while O'Brien, chest heaving with the exertion of carrying an extra 2 stone of body fat, fought to regain his breath.

The bell rang again. Jum moved in, stepping outside a vicious left hook and countering with a short left. O'Brien's head snapped back and a welt immediately appeared under his left eye.

Jum danced. A flurry of body blows into O'Brien's bulging midriff had him on his heels. Jum moved in, his face set and eyes baleful as he snapped a quick left, right, left combination to the head.

Jum sensed O'Brien's guard had dropped, and slammed home a series of telling body blows. He did not want to hear O'Brien speak Bob's name again. Jum landed a vicious left hook, followed by a savage right.

O'Brien's eyes glazed over and he stumbled back into a corner, his arms hanging over the ropes, an easy mark. Jum followed and landed a torrent of violent blows. The referee stepped in, only to be pushed over by the frenzied Jum.

Left, left, right to the head, to the body. The blows continued to rain down on the now semiconscious O'Brien.

Jim Gillies leapt for the ring at the same time as O'Brien's two corner men reached Jum and tried to restrain him. One went down after a snapped left jab; the other grabbed Jum's waist. Now back on his feet, the referee also attempted to hold Jum. Gillies jumped between them and held Jum's arms.

O'Brien's face was a pulped mess. His broken nose, squashed between his now closing eyes, dripped blood onto his chest. Jum's face glared at him over Gillies's shoulder. 'You ever mention his name again,' Jum yelled, 'I'll fucking kill you!'

Jum was escorted out of the ring, and taken to the showers by Gillies.

The crowd was quiet. What had promised to be an exhibition had turned into a vicious beating.

'You knew this was going to happen, Padre?' asked McErbain.

'Not this badly, Harold, but O'Brien's been overheard slinging off at Bob Buchannen, and I know how Jum feels about Bob. My advice to O'Brien would be – don't badmouth Bob Buchannen in front of Jum Bevan.'

JUNE 1919

The *Runic* passed the entrance to Botany Bay, south of Sydney Harbour. The men lining the ship's rail were talking and yelling excitedly as the troop carrier ploughed her way past the heads. A large crowd had gathered at Circular Quay to await the ship's arrival after the long voyage from Liverpool in England.

Jum stood at the stern of the ship. Now that the time had arrived, he had no stomach for returning to his earlier life. He winced at the thought of meeting Maude Buchannen. How in hell could he explain Bob's death, his responsibility, his complicity? His promise to Maude some three-and-a-half years earlier had not been kept. Her son was dead. Wasted in France. 'If only I had been closest to the trench entrance that night,' he thought. One moment he sought to shoulder the blame, and then, just as quickly, he sought to extinguish his failure.

It was in this state of mental confusion that he walked down the gangplank at Circular Quay. There were tears of joy as long-lost fathers, brothers, uncles and sons were reunited with families and loved ones on the dock.

Jum, his head bowed, made his way from the dock. He had deliberately not informed his family of his arrival. It was a bleak and lonely homecoming. He arrived as an alien in a land of hope, heroes and gallant victors.

Jum stood nervously in front of the door. He knocked loudly, feeling out of place in his khaki uniform, with his kitbag by his feet. The door opened. Millie, Jum's younger sister, looked at him curiously then, as recognition dawned, she turned to scream down the hall, 'It's Jum! He's home!' She jumped, wrapping her limbs around him. In an instant there were people everywhere, hugging, crying and laughing. They made their way excitedly to the rear of the house.

Jum sat at the table with his sister and brothers as they all fired questions at him. Amelia, Jum's mother, anxiously searched her son's face. What she saw unsettled her – a deep weariness; eyes that had witnessed too much; the hair thin and greying, accentuating her son's pale complexion. 'What you need is a good feed, Jum,' she said.

'What I need is a good drink, Mum,' he said with a wan smile.

The tram ride from Randwick seemed to take an eternity. Jum alighted at Taylor Square and walked east along Oxford Street towards the Victoria Barracks.

It was eleven days short of four years since he had enlisted in 1915. So much had happened. So much life had been wasted. The nightmare spectre of the Western Front had returned with him, and haunting memories resurfaced.

As he approached the stone walls of the barracks, he felt nervous and unsure. His life of the past four years was about to change irrevocably. He walked through the imposing wrought iron gates of Victoria Barracks into a large, grassy parade ground. It was ringed by three-storey Victorian sandstone buildings that housed the administrative offices of the 2nd Military District of the Australian Imperial Force.

A short time later, Jum felt both relief and trepidation as he moved towards the exit gates. His discharge from the AIF had been brief and to the point. 'Thanks for your service and goodbye.'

He walked past the sentry and into Oxford Street, Paddington. He felt depressed. Four years out of his life, and his army family had bade him this curt farewell, barely acknowledging his service.

The civilian clothes hung slackly on his gaunt frame, though his step was strong as he made his way to Taylor Square. Aboard the Randwick tram, he was deep in thought as the tram passed the showground. He was now on his own – no mates, no guns, no wild drunkenness and no insubordination. He had spent years in hell, living on adrenaline, under constant threat of a horrific death. Now he contemplated a return to humdrum civilian life.

On the return voyage aboard the *Runic*, he had resolved to leave the nightmare behind him. It was 12 August 1919, two days before Jum Bevan's twenty-seventh birthday. The battle of the Western Front was over. Little did he realise the battle for the rest of his life was about to begin.

Aftermath

...

2002

Upon reaching the last entry and closing my father's diary, I experienced a strange feeling of sadness mixed with relief – sadness for my father's war story ending and a strange relief that my father had survived the terrible events he had recorded with such matter-of-factness and brevity.

A week or so later, I spoke with my younger sister, Patricia.

'Well, I've finished the diary.'

'What did you think of it?'

'I had no concept of what the men went through – the extent of their suffering or their appalling experiences.'

She thought for a few minutes before answering. 'I remember Mum telling me about our father's awful nightmares, when he sweated all night and couldn't stop shaking. Mum put up with it all their married life.

'You know, George, it broke Mum up badly to leave him. But she'd had enough. She couldn't continue like that, and we were all too young to do anything about it.' She paused. 'Do you realise that Mum told me everything – everything that happened?'

I answered carefully, 'I know that you and Mum were very close.'

'We were closer than sisters, soul mates, for many, many years. There's so much more to the story than just Jum and the war – the bit you know about; there's the Jum and Alma story– which I know about. You can't just give half the story.'

She looked at me seriously. 'Mum was only fourteen and a half when she first met Jum. He was thirty-two.'

I waited for her to go on, unsure of what I was about to hear.

SEPTEMBER 1919

Jum moved to the ticket window in the Central Station concourse. There were few travellers about.

'When's the next to Douglas Park?' he inquired.

The seller looked at his departure schedule. 'Two hours, mate,' he replied, as Jum fumbled for coins in his pocket. He started trembling as he attempted to get his change out.

'You going to be long, mate?' came a testy voice from behind. Jum turned to see four or five people waiting in line behind him. He moved away and eased onto a nearby seat. He felt the sweat coursing down his back, though the early September weather was cool. He sat back, his heart thudding in his chest.

'How the hell can I front Maude?' he thought. He wiped his brow, trembling.

This was the third occasion on which Jum had stood in Central Station, ready to purchase a ticket to Douglas Park. Twice before, his nerve had failed him. On this, the third attempt, he was eventually successful.

As the train approached Douglas Park, he looked nervously at the passing countryside. 'Nothing like France,' he thought.

The train slowed as it puffed its way into the station. There had been no contact between Jum and Maude Buchannen since he'd left the farm in late 1915.

Jum alighted from the train and walked slowly to the end of the station. He'd decided to speak to Tom Grady, the store owner who had given him and Bob the clasp knives, before he attempted to find Maude.

He slowly entered Grady Providores. There was only one customer, who was casually examining bolts of cloth. Jum approached the counter and stood waiting.

Tom Grady looked at Jum. His mouth opened but no sound came out. He turned to the small office and called, 'Maude! Maude! It's Jum!'

Jum turned to the office. Maude Buchannen was framed in the doorway. Her once fair hair was streaked prematurely with grey. Her lips trembled as she ran towards Jum and clasped him to her. As they moved apart, she dabbed at her eyes with a corner of her apron.

The lone customer had gone. Tom Grady locked the door and put up the 'Closed' sign. They walked quietly to the lounge area of the residence behind the store, where they sat in silence. Maude moved her chair next to Jum's, and held his hands in hers.

'I'm sorry, Maude,' he whispered.

Jum broke down at last. His shoulders rose and fell, and tears streamed down his distraught face. Maude laid her head on his shoulder. After some minutes, Jum's tears subsided. He wiped his eyes carefully.

'I'll get tea going,' said Maude, as she hurried to the kitchen.

'It must have been tough,' said Tom quietly.

'I can't begin to describe what it was like.' Jum paused. 'So much suffering, so much death.'

Maude arrived with a tray of cups and a pot of tea.

'We heard from the War Office when Bob was killed,' she said, 'and from the padre, Captain Jenkins. He said you'd tell me about your time with Bob when you got back home. He said there was too much to tell in a letter.'

Jum nodded. 'Yes, the padre said he would write for me. I was in no condition to do anything much.' Jum looked at Maude earnestly. 'I want you to know, Maude, that I really tried my hardest to ...' He trailed off as Maude held up her hand in a silencing gesture.

'Jum, I know you would have done anything you could to protect Bob. We blame no one for Bob's death, except the Germans.'

'Twice he saved my life, but in the end I couldn't save his,' Jum said brokenly.

Again Maude took Jum's hands in hers. 'Thank God you're safe, Jum.'

Jum searched her face in a plea for understanding.

Tom's arm was around Maude's shoulders. 'About a year after Hector died,' Maude said, 'Tom asked me to marry him. We're so happy. The future is now up to us.'

'After Bob ...' Jum bit his lip and paused. 'After Bob died, I had no stomach to face up to anything. Bob and I had both got involved with Belgian girls, two wonderful people, Anna Meaux and Jeanne Ricaud. Bob's girl, Jeanne, had been married to a young Frenchman who was killed at Verdun in late 1915. My girl, Anna, had lost her fiancé six months before we met. We just seemed to hit it off. We saw them as often as we could get leave.

'Jeanne fell pregnant, and Bob and Jeanne were married in 1918.'

Maude's hand went to her mouth, and tears started in her eyes.

'The fighting was so intense,' Jum continued, 'he never had a chance to let you know. He was going to stay in France, and planned to bring you over to meet his wife and their child,' Jum smiled, 'your grandson. They all wanted me to stay too. I was close to agreeing. But after Bob died, I couldn't face it. I couldn't even bring myself to see Anna and Jeanne before I left for home.'

'My grandson,' Maude said wonderingly. Then, 'Have you contacted Anna since you left France?'

Jum shook his head. 'I've thought of her, and I've had letters from her, but there's no way I could stay there without Bob. I'll give you Jeanne's address,' he added, 'so you can contact her.'

'You won't go back to France again?' asked Maude.

Jum shook his head emphatically. 'No, Maude. The war is over and everything that happened can stay there.'

The following morning, the train moved slowly out of Douglas Park station. Tom and Maude waved, as they had waved four years earlier to two excited young men about to embark on the adventure of a lifetime. Jum waved slowly in return. He was worn out, aged before his time.

'Well, what trade qualifications do you have?' asked the bald, bespectacled manager.

'I'm pretty bloody quick with an 18-pounder or a 4.5 mortar – they're my fucking qualifications!' Jum rose and stamped out of the office.

'Who was that bloke?' asked the clerk of the manager.

'Another returned army type. We get so many looking for work. Some are good and some are bad. Some have a bad attitude problem, like that one. Aggressive, short-fused. So they won the bloody war, so what! It wasn't our war, we weren't invaded. I'm only glad conscription got defeated twice, otherwise I might have been dragged over there. The other problem,' he continued, 'is that they're usually young, and a lot are pisspots. They drink so much, they'll maybe miss a day or two a week. Can't have that in a business.'

It had been the same for weeks: no work for anyone not qualified. Jum saw the same faces at every job position that was advertised. The slowing economy was flooded with returned soldiers who had little or no training, and unemployment soared.

Finally, Jum's persistence was rewarded. Labouring did not pay well, but it required heavy physical exertion. His complexion gained some colour and his thin frame acquired a little muscle. His drinking, on the other hand, did not decrease.

The years in France, where staying alive sometimes depended upon the support of close friends, had created an unbreakable bond amongst the front-line soldiers. This mateship nurtured a need for close male company. And so it became typical for large groups of the same army unit to congregate in pubs and clubs where they could drink freely.

DECEMBER 1919

The sun splashed off Fiona Roberts's brilliant red hair as she sat on the wide verandah of the Wagga Wagga farmhouse. For some time she had been chewing the end of her pen as she tried to capture her thoughts in a letter to Reverend Claude Jenkins.

> *So, Reverend, I'm aware that you knew my brothers well during the years of their service. I haven't been able to get any useful information from the army or the Department of Rehabilitation as to how my brother Ron died, or what happened to James to cause his current condition.* ·

She looked up at Wagga. He sat quietly, staring out over the green hills. Then the stench hit her. She sighed. 'Damn! I wish you'd let me know.'

She went to prepare a bath, then helped Wagga to his feet and walked him to the bathroom. She slipped off his soiled trousers and undergarments and helped him to get in.

'Here you are. Here's some soap, wash yourself. I'll be back in a minute with clean clothes.'

Fiona went to his room and collected fresh clothing. Wagga liked the warmth of the bath and would happily sit in it for hours.

After drying off, he stood patiently waiting for Fiona to help him dress.

Back on the verandah she finished her letter.

> *Would there be any way you could help me find out what happened to Ron, and to James? I'd be most grateful if there was. If not, do you have any suggestions about where else I could enquire?*

As Fiona signed the letter, her father walked onto the verandah. Unsmiling, he greeted Fiona with, 'He looks clean!'

'Yes, Dad, he's just had a bath.'

'A bath, at 11 o'clock? Shat himself again, eh?'

'Dad, he's ill. At times, he doesn't seem able to control himself.'

'If he's sick, he should be in hospital.'

'Don't start that again!' she said. 'I thought we had this out a month ago. I'll look after him until he gets better.'

'Who helps me around the farm, then? He does nothing!' He stamped into the house.

Fiona knew that Ron had been their father's favourite, and that his son's death had nearly sent him over the edge. To have the younger brother at home in a vegetative state, unable to do even the simplest chores, had turned her father from a cheerful, hardworking man into a bitter cynic.

Reverend Claude Jenkins read and reread the letter. His sister Adele had also read the correspondence. 'I feel you must go to the farm at Wagga, if only to talk to her. It must be awful for her to try and handle this horrible situation,' said Adele.

'I believe you're right, Adele. You know, I could maybe get Jum Bevan and Harold McErbain to come along, and I'm sure Jim Gillies would come too.'

It was swiftly arranged. Jum, AJ Casey, Jim Gillies, Harold McErbain and Reverend Claude Jenkins travelled together to the Roberts's farm to spend the evening with the family.

Fiona arranged camp stretchers in the shearers' quarters and eagerly prepared the house for visitors. She cleaned the silver, polished the furniture and tidied the grounds surrounding the house.

An overcast sky, hinting at rain, greeted the *Southern Flyer* as it rolled into Wagga Wagga Station.

Fiona, nervously awaiting the train's arrival, paced up and down outside the stationmaster's office. She stood silently as the train puffed to a halt.

The carriage door opened, and the five men alighted. She quickly surveyed the group, then smiled and said, 'You're the Reverend, and you're Jim Gillies, and you must be Harold, the slightly serious one is Jum Bevan, and you are?' she asked, her heart skipping a beat.

'I'm Alan Casey. You're the image of Ron,' Casey added, only to see the smile fade from her face.

'It's only twenty minutes to the farm,' she said.

Alan Casey had expected to see a thin, bespectacled middle-aged spinster. But this stunning, red-haired beauty in her mid-twenties – a commanding, assured and confident young woman – stopped him in his tracks.

'If you like, I'd be happy to drive,' he offered.

Fiona looked at him and grinned. 'Why? You think you blokes are the only ones who can drive? Climb in and hang on!' With everyone seated, she slipped the Essex 'Super Six' into gear, dropped the clutch and roared out of the railway yard.

The men hung on grimly as Fiona punched the car along the gravel track to the farmhouse, where they clambered out, happy to be in one piece.

Sitting on the verandah, 20 yards away, was Wagga. He looked ahead, completely still. They stood in front of him but he showed no sign of recognising them.

Jum stepped onto the verandah. 'Hi, Wagga,' he said, gently, putting his hand on Wagga's shoulder.

'He won't recognise you, or speak to you,' said Fiona, as she kissed Wagga on the head.

Jim Gillies turned. 'He looks good, Fiona. Lost a little weight, though.'

To Jum, Wagga looked like death warmed up.

They moved into the large lounge room that opened onto the verandah. Fiona introduced the men to her parents before seating everyone comfortably.

There was an awkward silence, then Fiona said, 'We received many letters from Ron before he was killed. I feel I know all of you; especially you, Reverend, though Ron always referred to you as "the padre". I thank you for your letter after Ron died.' The reverend nodded, and Fiona continued, 'We know nothing about how Ron died, except that he was killed in action. As far as my younger brother is concerned, there was a mention of shell shock.'

Jum rose suddenly. 'Can I use your lavatory?'

'Yes – out the door, towards the harness shed,' said Fiona, surprised by his abrupt behaviour.

Jum grabbed his Gladstone bag from the verandah and headed for the outside lavatory. He sat on the closed lid, opened the bag with shaking hands and extracted a bottle of whisky. He quickly drained a third of it and replaced the bottle. He returned to the lounge where Fiona was still speaking.

'Yes, that's it – knowing what happened to Ron and how James got the way he is will help us get on with our lives.'

'James?' said Jum.

'Wagga,' said Mrs Roberts. 'He was christened James Watson Roberts, but he was Wagga from the time he was very small.'

Claude Jenkins spoke quietly. 'I don't think you would benefit by knowing what happened to Ron. Wagga is different.'

'You can't explain one without the other,' said Jum resignedly.

'I can handle it. Tell us,' said Fiona. Her parents waited quietly.

Jum stood. The whisky had calmed his shaking hands and eased his feelings of foreboding. 'Ron was operating in No. 2 Gun position, about 50 yards from us in No.1. Wagga and myself were knocked over by the explosion in Ron's position. Wagga was the first one to reach what remained of No. 2 Gun.' Jum paused and took a deep breath.

'Everyone, all eight men, died instantly in the blast. Wagga jumped into the position and picked up Ron's body. He carried him to the casualty clearing station with Harold and myself trying to stop him. Then the padre came running out with a doctor.'

Fiona's hand had gone to her mouth. 'Was Ron already dead, then?'

'I'm afraid so, he had shocking injuries. Wagga said to the doctor, "I'm taking Ron to see Mum, she's waiting out the back."' A gasp came from Mrs Roberts, who then slumped down in her chair. Her husband sat transfixed. Alan Casey quickly picked up Mrs Roberts and carried her to the bedroom.

Reverend Jenkins moved to Fiona's side. 'The shock of Ron's death was too much for Wagga. He didn't speak again. The brigade doctor had no option but to classify him as unfit for active duty.'

Trying to control his sobs, Mr Roberts left the room to join his wife in the bedroom.

Fiona, ashen-faced, looked at Wagga. He stared blankly.

The reverend asked, 'Do you think he knows we're here?'

'I don't know, Reverend,' Fiona replied.

Jenkins stood up and turned to Jum. 'Over here, Jum. Play something we all know, and loudly,' he said, opening the upright piano in the corner. Jum slid onto the seat and began thumping out the chords of 'Mademoiselle from Armentières'. Gillies, McErbain and Casey jumped to the piano and started singing along with Jum at the top of their voices.

She pulled its tail instead of its tit
And all she got was a bucket of shit,
Inky pinky, parlez-vous.

Jum shouted, 'Second verse!'

Their voices became louder as Jum thumped the piano. He shouted, 'Third verse!' Fiona stood in amazement as the roaring voices filled the house. Then Wagga stood and moved to the piano. He screamed out, 'Fourth verse!'

The four men turned to him, amazement etched on their faces. Jum continued to play. The five men built to a raucous shout and finished the song.

Wagga sat down. Fiona moved slowly towards him. He stood up again as she reached him. The men watched nervously. 'Ron's not coming home, Fiona,' said Wagga slowly. 'He's staying in France.' The blank look was gone. He put his arms around his sister.

Later, Alan Casey sat on the verandah with Fiona. The drizzling rain had eased, and occasionally a watery moon peeped out from behind the clouds.

Casey was a powerful man, in mind and body. The war in France had only hardened him. He had come to accept the killing, and he had been determined to complete the job as quickly as possible. Back in Sydney, he had managed to put the war behind him as he turned his considerable energies to building up his engineering business. He had little time for pursuing women. But now he was completely captivated by Fiona.

'Aboard!' the guard yelled. Four of the men were seated in the carriage, but Casey was still talking to Fiona on the platform.

'If you need anything, Fiona, just call me,' he said.

The engine jerked forward and the carriages banged together. AJ Casey stepped aboard, waving. The four men grinned. Alan Casey blushed a deeper red than Fiona's hair.

'We all thought you were staying, AJ,' said Jum.

Jim Gillies smiled. 'She's sure got AJ interested.'

January 1920

A month later, Wagga shot himself with a Steyr revolver – the same gun Jum had taken from Captain Junge and given to Wagga as a souvenir. After several days, the coroner released his body with a verdict of 'Accidental death by firearm'.

Claude Jenkins, Harold McErbain, Jim Gillies and Jum Bevan sat silently in the softly rocking train. Each man was deep in thought, contemplating the shattering news of Wagga's death. They knew that it had not been accidental. They had heard the truth from AJ Casey, who was still at Fiona's side.

Wagga was to be buried in a small section of the local cemetery that had been dedicated to soldiers who had died since returning to Australia. A granite monument bore the names of locals who had not returned to Australia. For such a small town, the monument was inscribed with a tragically long list of names.

The Reverend Claude Jenkins had finished his brief but solemn service. A brisk wind whipped leaves over the fresh mound of earth above Wagga Roberts, who was now at peace.

The men were standing in the lounge of the farmhouse. Fiona had been busy making scones and sandwiches for Wagga's wake. She rushed to and fro, offering food and a warm smile.

Noticing Jum's relaxed face, McErbain moved beside him. 'Funny-coloured tea, Jum. Got any more?'

Jum grinned sadly. 'Always for you, Captain.'

McErbain gently emptied his tea into a pot plant. Jum tilted the bottle of whisky, still in its brown paper bag, into the cup. McErbain gulped quickly, shivering as the raw spirit bit, and smiled. 'That one was for Wagga. What about a double for me?'

'Sure, mate.'

Gillies arrived. 'What are you two buggers up to?'

'Just giving Wagga a send off,' said Jum.

Gillies snatched up a teacup, which Jum quickly filled. The three clinked their cups, drained them, then relaxed as the whisky took effect.

Casey moved across the room. 'I've been watching you cheeky bastards. What's going on?'

'Well, AJ,' said Jum, 'we're just toasting Wagga.'

Casey thrust his cup forward. 'Not without me, you aren't.'

Jum sloshed a double whisky into Casey's glass. 'Wagga!' he said solemnly.

'Wagga!' the others responded.

Later, Gillies, Jum, Casey, McErbain and Reverend Jenkins sat quietly as dusk slowly settled over the yard. Fiona had finished cleaning up the lounge and wondered where the men had gone. At that moment, Jum's voice softly began the soulful pleading song of the trenches.

> *Take me over the sea,*
> *Where the 'Alleyman' can't get at me!*

The others joined him. At first their voices were soft, in respect for dead and lost mates.

> *I don't wanna live in the trenches no more*
> *Where whiz-bangs and shrapnel do rattle and roar.*

Their voices rose, the men seeking release from the continuing nightmare of the Western Front.

> *Take me over the sea*
> *Where the 'Alleyman' can't get at me.*
> *Oh, my! I'm too young to die, I wanna go home!*

The last few words roared across the yard, and were followed by silence. Fiona stepped onto the verandah. Her voice broke. 'Wagga would have loved that song. Thank you all so much for coming.' Her manner changed. 'Anyway, enough of that. I thought you blokes might have had enough tea and scones.' She went back into the kitchen and reappeared with a number of glasses and two bottles of whisky. 'Just to remember Wagga,' she said.

'Just what we need, Fiona,' said Jum, a gleam in his eye.

They toasted Wagga again.

Claude Jenkins carefully observed the men. 'No amount of alcohol,' he thought, 'will ever take that look off their faces.' Pain, relief, guilt and fatigue were all etched into the sometimes forced smiles. He looked at Jum, leaning against the sideboard, his eyes bleary and unfocused. He saw a man in conflict – outwardly strong and composed, but racked by inner turmoil.

'Why can't he understand he's not guilty of Bob's death, or Ron's, or Wagga's?' Jenkins was angry – angry at the war, at the people who had caused the decimation of a generation of young men, at the perpetrators of this foul blot on the history of humanity. 'This is what we have now,' he thought. 'Men whose minds are so badly damaged that alcohol is the only way to ease their nightmare.'

Jum stared at the open door leading to the rear yard. Wagga's death had brought long-suppressed memories to the surface. His memory dragged him back to scenes that he had desperately tried to erase since the end of the nightmare in France. He felt his hands shaking and looked at them in disbelief. He thought, 'Will this ever end?'

He surreptitiously picked up the whisky bottle, three-quarters full, and walked onto the rear porch. He looked at the sky. The faraway stars appeared to blink at him from the blackness beyond. 'I wonder if Bob and Ron and Wagga are up there somewhere.' He swallowed some whisky and held the rail for support. The old guilts returned. Tears filled his eyes as he looked at the stars again.

'They're gone and I'm here alone.' In his jacket pocket he felt the smooth hardness of the Steyr revolver, which Fiona had returned to him. His mind raced. He removed the Steyr from his pocket and stared at the weapon's evil shape. Then he slowly replaced it.

Claude Jenkins, standing unseen in the shadows, breathed a sigh of relief. He moved to Jum's side. 'I know what you might be thinking, Jum, but this isn't the way. It's not the way of strong men such as yourself, and – you may disagree – it's not the way of

God.' He placed his hand on Jum's shoulder. 'As a man of God, it is my duty to protect you, whether it be from other people or yourself. Understand that I will do whatever I can to help you. We'll work this out together.'

Now he took Jum gently by the arms. 'So many died that others might live. We must be grateful to our fallen comrades. We have all lost friends. Do you think that I don't agonise at the losses? But we must get on with our lives, we must return to normality, for that is the way of God. It is the only way.'

There was a brief silence, then Jenkins said, 'Let's go inside, Jum, and join the others.'

They walked back into the house as groups of mourners started to leave.

By 8 pm, the only sounds on the farm were heavy whisky-induced snores drifting from the shearers' quarters. The following morning, the four men left Wagga Wagga for Sydney on the *Southern Flyer.*

At Randwick, Jum proceeded to the nearest hotel and drank several large beers to ease his recurring jimjams. Wagga's burial had depressed him greatly. Once again, he felt savaged by guilt.

The deaths of his three friends were now peeling away layers of self-control. He would always see the remains of Bob's head. His body jumped as the images flashed into his mind.

He drained a large beer and purchased a bottle of sherry. Beer would not succeed in erasing his thoughts, and whisky was too expensive. He walked to his mother's house in Waverley, draining the last few drops from the sherry bottle as he fumbled with his key at the front door.

He found his mother, Amelia, in her kitchen. She looked disapprovingly at her son as he held onto the table for support. 'You're drinking far too much, Jum. You come home like this most nights now, ever since you came back from the war.' He had changed dramatically from the young man who left Sydney in 1915; he had been so lighthearted, so full of life.

Jum shook his head, and said slowly, 'We buried Wagga yesterday. He was twenty-one years old. He suicided with a gun I gave him in France.'

Jum sat at the table and ate the meal his mother served. He thanked her and walked unsteadily to his room.

During the night, Amelia Bevan woke to a sudden thud. She heard a raised voice, then another thud.

Alarmed, she wrapped a knitted shawl about her shoulders and hurried along the hall. Flicking the light switch on in Jum's room, she gasped in fright as Jum screamed, 'Star shell, star shell! Down! Down!'

Amelia ran to Jum. He screamed again. 'Douse the light, douse the fucking light! We'll get the .77s! Get down, get down!'

Jum was scrabbling on the floor, wearing only a singlet. His eyes, wide with fear, showed no recognition; his body was bathed in sweat.

Amelia tried to lift him. He dragged her to the floor, covering her head with his arms.

'Mortars! 230's! They're coming! Stay down, stay down!' he screamed.

Amelia grabbed Jum's head. 'Jum, Jum! Wake up! It's me, your mum! Wake up!'

Jum's eyes slowly focused on Amelia; his fierce grip on her nightdress eased. He allowed himself to be dragged up on his knees as she sat on his bed.

Amelia hugged her son to her bosom and gently kissed the top of his head as he shook uncontrollably. His body relaxed now, and he laid his head in her lap. With an aching heart, she cried gently and smoothed his hair. 'What have they done to you, my boy? What have they done?' she sobbed.

She gently rocked, and eventually helped the half-asleep Jum back into bed. Softly, she turned the light off and eased the door shut. Then she sat at the kitchen table, her head on her folded arms as she sobbed uncontrollably for her son and his tortured soul.

In a simple but moving ceremony, Fiona Roberts and AJ Casey were married at St Mary's Anglican Church at the top of Birrell

Street, South Bondi, overlooking the blue Pacific Ocean. Among the invited guests, Beatrice Wenban sat enjoying the celebrations. She had met Jum before, with two of her brothers who had served on the Western Front.

She and Jum enjoyed a whirlwind affair, announcing their engagement within weeks.

But the marriage was a dismal failure. They were mismatched, and Jum, still drinking heavily, was in no fit state to tackle a full-on relationship.

One night, Beatrice slid carefully into the bed, ensuring she did not wake her snoring husband. She turned her back, falling asleep instantly. In his drunken half-sleep, Jum's hands found her. He whispered, 'Anna! Anna! Come to me.'

Beatrice sat up hurriedly, pushing Jum's arms away. 'Leave me alone! Go and find your Anna.'

She moved out the following day. Three months of enduring Jum's drunkenness, with the accompanying smashing of doors and furniture, left her with no choice. She left, never to return.

Alan Casey spoke into the receiver. 'Where do you think I'll find him, Mrs Bevan?'

'I don't know, Alan. He didn't come home last night, he seemed pretty upset. Maybe at the Doncaster Hotel in Kensington or the Coach and Horses in Randwick.'

Casey knew Jum's marriage was shaky, but he did not realise it was over. He had telephoned Jim Gillies and the pair had arranged to meet and try to find him.

Casey pulled on the car's handbrake outside the Doncaster Hotel. They made their way into the public bar. Smoke and noise filled the central bar area. Jum was not in sight. Casey, followed by Gillies, edged his way to the end of the bar.

At the far end, Jum Bevan sat on a low, built-in seat, his head back and his mouth slightly open. He was unconscious, wedged against the timber panelling. Three laughing young men were tossing peanuts at him, the target his open mouth. The nuts bounced off his forehead, his chin and his ears. Jum did not move.

Casey reached the loudest of the three laughing men. He grabbed his shirt with his large left hand and dragged the man from his stool. The bar fell silent.

'What the – !' exclaimed the man in surprise.

Casey bunched his fist, lifting the man on to his toes. 'What the fuck do you think you're doing?' he demanded, glaring into the young man's eyes.

'We're just tossing peanuts at that old drunk,' the man replied.

Casey slammed the man against the bar, and tightened his grip. 'That old drunk you see has just spent years in hell, fighting German bastards so the likes of you can sit in this pub and enjoy yourselves. I've seen him take on three Germans barehanded. He's got more courage in his fucking toenail than you three together, and you throw fucking peanuts at him!'

Casey dragged the young man over to Jum. 'Look at him!' Casey thrust the hapless man's face at Jum. 'Take a good fucking look. How old are you?'

'Twenty-nine,' the man said quietly.

'How old do you think he is?'

'I dunno, maybe forty, maybe older, I can't tell.'

'Well, I'll tell you what, you slimy piece of pig shit, that man is twenty-seven, two years younger than you, with a life that's been destroyed. I see you treat him with anything less than the respect he deserves, I'll tear your fucking head off.' Casey's voice was tense with anger. 'Understand?'

The man nodded dumbly. Effortlessly, Casey carried Jum past the now subdued trio. He deposited Jum in the rear seat of his car and, with Gillies, drove the short distance to Amelia Bevan's home.

Meanwhile, the bar had returned to its usual noise level.

'I could have whacked him one,' said the man with the crumpled shirt.

A bystander turned and said, above the noise, 'Bloody lucky you didn't, mate. Do you know who that was?'

Crumpled Shirt shook his head.

'Well, that was Alan Casey, a sergeant in the 3rd Pioneers. He saw three years in France. I've heard he killed twenty Germans, some barehanded. That bloke you were throwing the nuts at is Jum Bevan, and they're good mates. I wouldn't advise you doing that again in a hurry.'

Beatrice Bevan filed for divorce, citing violence, drunkenness and fear for her life as substantive evidence in support of her case. The court agreed. In late 1920, the marriage of Jum and Beatrice Bevan was dissolved.

RANDWICK 1922

Jim Gillies sat with his shoulders slumped and his elbows on the bar. He surveyed his few fellow drinkers. He felt lonely and empty, devoid of emotion.

His position at the bank, although secure, paid only a moderate wage. The work was predictable and boring, and gave him very little satisfaction. He felt in limbo, in a state of stalemate.

His nightmares were now less frequent, although Wagga's suicide had affected him more than he could admit.

The Australian government was not about to acknowledge the kind of trauma Gillies was suffering, and there were no criteria for gauging degrees of mental damage. The extent of the trauma was never fully examined or documented, though it was severe and widespread. The affected men were left to fend for themselves.

Jim Gillies was neither an alcoholic nor a heavy drinker. It was true that during the course of the horror of the Western Front he had indulged in heavy drinking, along with a large percentage of other Allied soldiers. It was a peer-group response, an attempt to hold on to sanity in the face of the unbelievable mental stresses placed on men constantly living and working in battle conditions.

Jim Gillies drained his glass. He went up to the room he rented at the hotel and removed his coat, tie and shoes, then lay on his bed, hands clasped behind his head, staring at the ceiling.

The images flashed by – Wagga carrying his brother Ron's mutilated body; the long string of covered corpses outside the CCS; the flickering candle held by Padre Jenkins as he moved slowly amongst the crosses at Pozières, praying for the dead; and his own humiliating outburst at the padre on the Sunday morning after Sausage Gully.

Sleep came slowly to Gillies. The light was still blazing. Suddenly he woke with a start and sat up abruptly, breathing heavily. He wiped his brow, which was drenched in sweat.

Gillies undressed quickly, climbed into the bed and fell into a disturbed sleep.

It was mid-morning, and the bank was quiet. Gillies reached for the telephone on his desk. 'Operator, could you connect me to the Wenden Village Presbyterian Church, west of Berowra Waters?'

'Yes, sir, calling that number for you now,' the voice replied.

Gillies waited as a female voice came on the line.

'Wenden Village Church, who's speaking please?'

'Could I speak to Padre Jenkins, please?'

'Yes, of course. Whom may I say is calling?'

'Jim Gillies from Sydney.'

'Oh, hello, Jim! One moment.' The voice called, 'Telephone, Claude! Jim Gillies!' Then, 'He's coming now.'

'Good morning, Jim. How are you?'

'Very well, Padre. Just thought I'd call and say hello.'

Claude Jenkins had a feeling this was no casual call.

'Padre,' Gillies went on, 'I was wondering – could I call and see you sometime, just to have a chat?'

'Just name the time, Jim.'

'Maybe this Saturday, Padre?' asked Jim.

'I look forward to seeing you, Jim. You'll stay for lunch with Adele and me?'

'Thanks, Padre, I'd love to.' A relieved Jim hung up the telephone. A burden seemed to slide from his shoulders.

The train thumped its way north out of Hornsby station. Walking down the western side of the station, Gillies was surprised to see Padre Jenkins standing beside a neat little Austin 7 two-seat tourer. 'Wow, Padre, mobile faith! How long have you had the motor car?'

The padre, his face smiling in welcome, clasped Gillies's outstretched hand. 'It's so good to see you!'

The conversation continued uninterrupted on the 15-mile trip. Jenkins slid the car to a gentle stop outside the beautiful, century-old church. Lichen and green moss covered the southern wall, and an atmosphere of quiet stability surrounded the building. The gravel paths were raked and immaculate.

Adele Jenkins stood at the entrance, awaiting their arrival. Gillies shook her hand. They had met once before, several years previously. Adele, a plainish woman who was slightly older than Claude, exuded warmth and comfort. She was devoted to both the church and her brother. She left the men comfortably seated in the rectory while she made tea.

'Well, Jim,' smiled Jenkins, 'you look fit and healthy.'

Gillies forced a smile. 'Not too bad I suppose, Padre.'

'Well, what brings you to our far-flung outpost?'

Gillies lowered his eyes, not quite sure where to start. 'I'm having trouble sleeping, Padre. A lot of the stuff we went through in France keeps coming back to me. Wagga's suicide, Sausage Gully, what I said to you that Sunday morning ...'

Jenkins interrupted. 'We sorted that out, Jim, remember?'

Gillies nodded. 'Padre, I feel empty and ill at ease. I woke the other night and I couldn't ...' He paused and bit his lip. 'I couldn't stop crying. My life feels flat. I know a lot of the boys drink to wipe out the memories. I've tried it, but it doesn't work for me. Talking about it helps, but you're the only one who understands. You were there, you know what I'm talking about.'

As the padre listened, Gillies's hesitant confession became a torrent of despair, an outpouring of the repressed horror of the war. Death, destruction and the years of hell had left their indelible mark.

Jenkins realised that Gillies was a man of great emotional sensitivity. It was a testament to his fierce strength of character that he had withstood the onslaught and resisted the trauma for so long. But finally the dam had burst.

Adele appeared behind Gillies in the doorway. Jenkins shook his head slightly. She moved back into the kitchen, closing the door behind her.

Gillies talked of blown-apart bodies, the stinking mud and the decomposed, bloated corpses bursting with gas; the frost, the endless, bone-shattering cold, with men frozen to death at their posts. He began to sob uncontrollably.

Jenkins stood up and put his arm around Jim. 'Come, my boy, it's over, it's all over,' he said.

As his sobs subsided, Gillies dried his eyes. He looked at the padre, who returned his gaze with compassion. The fear and the horror began to fade.

'You, Jim, are a fortunate person, for you have a remarkable sensitivity. You have tenderness, but you also have strength. Your inner strength comes from your unrealised belief in a Greater Being.' He paused. 'We can't explain these senseless atrocities, and we were powerless to stop the madness. Why God allowed it to happen, I don't know. Why God allowed it to continue, I'm at a loss to understand. Possibly, He wanted man to really understand the vile futility of such death in a lesson so dreadful it would be learnt for all eternity, for all peoples in the future.

'What we have witnessed, you and I, we will take to our graves, with never a day passing that we don't ask ourselves why? And if by the suffering we have witnessed and endured we can make this a better place – if we can offer comfort and the love of God to people in need – then we are lucky.

'I believe, Jim, that you are a chosen person; that you possess the qualities required to be a servant of the Greater Being.'

Gillies lifted his head. 'What do you mean, Claude?'

'I'm asking you to join our church. You have all the attributes of a man of God. Don't waste your life any further. Come and join us.'

Gillies was astonished. Jenkins smiled at him as he laid a hand on his shoulder. 'Think about it, Jim. Peace of mind doesn't come easily.'

Adele arrived with tea and scones. 'Enough talking, you two. After tea, why don't we walk to the river? It's so beautiful at this time of year.'

The sun poured through the rectory window as they helped themselves to scones. Gillies felt a dawning sense of liberation.

In due course, Jim Gillies took his vows and entered the church. He became a tireless worker for the poor, the needy and the lost. Through the torment and horror, he found peace within himself.

RANDWICK 1924

At fourteen-and-a-half years of age, Alma Marion Johnson, born on 27 June 1910, was a confident, strong-willed young woman. She was quite tall and boasted a superb figure, which she was more than happy to show to advantage in daring neck-to-knee costumes that featured revealing shoulder straps instead of sleeves.

At the rear of her family home, six stables housed a number of first-class racehorses. Alma often rode these horses to track work at Randwick Racecourse. She was a more than competent horsewoman. She also excelled at swimming, and spent much of her time at Coogee Beach, enjoying the surf and sand.

The Sunday nor'easterly breeze had picked up, whipping up the sand and making it difficult to enjoy the sun. Alma stood up and said to her sister Eda and two friends, 'Come on, let's get out of this wind and over to the pool.'

The tram terminus at the northern end of Coogee was adjacent to Hobson's Baths, a tiled 50-yard pool that was a favourite meeting spot for younger people. The girls paid the 1-penny entrance fee and climbed to the top deck.

Alma, sitting with her arms folded over the safety rail, idly watched as a lean, muscular man walked to the 10-foot springboard. He climbed the ladder and casually dropped his towel over the rail. He moved to the end of the board, tested with one bump and returned.

He paused a moment before taking three graceful steps. Alma watched with interest as the diver came off the end of the board, performed a layout one-and-a-half somersault and entered the water with scarcely a ripple.

'Bloody hell, Eda, did you see that?' asked Alma. 'That bloke that just dived – he was great!'

Jum slipped easily from the pool and climbed the ladder again. Alma called to the girls. 'Watch him, he's going again!' Jum took a slightly longer run this time, then leapt off the end and completed a masterful two-and-a-half somersault, again entering the water cleanly.

For about the next half hour, Jum Bevan entertained the crowd with a series of complicated dives, all executed with style and precision, ending with a high, graceful swan dive.

'I can do that!' Alma exclaimed.

Climbing to the 10-foot board, she tried to imitate Jum's action, mistimed the leap, was slow in the turn, and landed ignominiously on her backside in the water. Red with embarrassment, she climbed the ladder again. This time the result was not quite as bad as the first. Her head held high, she stamped up the stairs to the top deck and rejoined her friends.

'Are you all right, Al?' said Eda. 'You hit pretty hard.'

With her towel around her shoulders, Alma nodded. 'I'm fine.' The only thing hurt was her pride. She sat shivering gently as the sun slowly warmed her skin.

'That was a pretty good try you had back there,' said a voice beside her. The diver sat down beside her. Unable to speak, she just nodded dumbly. 'You weren't that far from a good dive, really,' he said.

Alma looked at the man. He had auburn hair tinged with grey, clear blue-grey eyes and a mouth that quirked up at the corners.

'But you were attempting one hell of an advanced dive, that one-and-a-half forward. Maybe you should try a straightforward somersault first, feet into the water.' Alma listened while Jum explained how the step-off was an important part of gaining the required height.

Half an hour later, she was at the board again. With few people left in the pool, she was able to concentrate.

'All right, do as I told you. Get height, and don't rush the action,' called Jum. Nervously, she stepped along the board. She timed her leap to perfection, rose, turned lazily and entered the water feet-first with very little splash. She surfaced, grinning, to see Jum clapping his hands and smiling.

'How'd I do?

'You were great. Now do a few more.'

In the following weeks, Alma spent all her spare time at Hobson's Baths. Under Jum's tutelage, she quickly became an accomplished diver. Jum Bevan had purchased a Rudge Four motorcycle and after a diving session, Alma would often enjoy a lift home.

The motorcycle changed down to second gear and slowed to a stop outside her home. Alma stepped off the back and waved to Jum as she moved across the wide, grassed pavement. She was surprised to see her father collecting mail from the letterbox at the gate.

Henry George Johnson was 6 feet 4 and wore small, round glasses. He was nearly bald, with just a ring of white hair above the ears.

'You're home early, Dad,' said Alma as they entered the house.

'Early enough to catch you, young lady.'

Alma recognised the tone. She was about to receive a dressing down.

'Dad, Jum's been teaching me diving for two months. He's an expert – ask Eda,' pleaded Alma. Eda, sitting stiffly on a sofa opposite them, nodded. Five years older than Alma, she was as plain as Alma was attractive.

'Yes, Dad,' she said, 'he sure can dive, and he's taught Al a lot.'

'That's just what I'm afraid of,' said Henry.

Born in Hobart, Tasmania, in 1862, Henry Johnson was the eldest son of a strict, close-knit family of six. He had grown up in a tightly controlled home where neatness, cleanliness and punctuality were the order of the day. He, in turn, was obsessive and punctual, with an extremely sharp business mind. When he gave an order, others did not think about it – they obeyed.

He had arrived in Sydney from Tasmania as a hard-working businessman in 1899. He employed eight joiners in his workshop, and was very successful. With a shrewd eye to the future, he had started acquiring properties in the early 1900s. He now owned properties at Central Railway, St Peters, Randwick, Woy Woy on the Central Coast and Leura in the Blue Mountains.

'You are not to ride on that motorcycle again, and that is an order. Understand?' he said.

Alma looked him directly in the eye. She was her father's daughter. 'Do you understand?' he repeated.

'Yes,' she replied, glaring.

'Gee, Al, you get Dad so annoyed,' said Eda later.

'Bugger it, Ede, he gets *me* so annoyed!' replied Alma.

One Friday evening three months later, Alma failed to arrive home. Henry Johnson knew where Jum lived and police were called in the following morning. A dejected Alma returned home, but no charges were laid against Jum.

'I warned you, Alma, but you took no notice. I will not be disobeyed,' said Henry Johnson. 'I'm committing you to the Parramatta Home for Girls, as of Monday. You will stay there until you turn eighteen. Maybe that will teach you to do as you're told.'

He left the room. Eda moved over and put her arms around Alma. 'There's nothing I can do, Al. You know what he's like,' she whispered.

Alma held her head high. 'He can go to blazes. He won't tell me what to do!' she vowed.

For a little over three years, Alma lived at the Parramatta Girls Home. It was her good fortune that the director of the home was a quiet, understanding family man, happily married with three daughters near Alma's age. She was quickly recruited into the family as a maid, ate with the family and, when not employed, spent many hours with the three daughters in a strict learning regimen. She enjoyed being part of a loving, caring family and receiving expert schooling for those three years, which she later recalled as some of the most enjoyable of her life.

The decision of what to do after she left the home had been discussed by her surrogate family for months.

'I suppose it looks like nursing at Broughton Hall,' Alma said eventually. There was general agreement.

Broughton Hall, a reception centre for people suffering mental problems, was a halfway house for Callan Park, a home for the insane, the criminally insane and any others deemed too dangerous to themselves or the public to be free in society. A fourth-grade nurse at Broughton Hall earned 4 shillings a week plus full board, and uniforms were supplied. Alma Johnson began her career as a psychiatric nurse grade I.

'I'm eighteen, Jum, he can't stop me seeing you,' said Alma. It was a superb sunny day, and the two sat under some shady trees in the Sydney Domain.

Jum turned to face her. 'I'll bet your diving has suffered.'

She smiled. From then on, on her days off, Alma would go riding with Jum on his faithful Rudge Four motorcycle. They explored areas they would never have found by public transport.

Alma's profession gave her insight into the mental damage Jum had suffered. As a nurse, she had handled and cared for many patients much worse than Jum, and she was confident of her ability to cope with what she considered Jum's depression.

Alma knocked nervously on the door of her father's home. Her sister, Eda, opened the door and gave Alma a spontaneous hug.

'Come in, come in!' she cried. Alma nervously walked down the hall to the large lounge room and paused.

Henry Johnson sat at the large dining table, with business papers neatly laid out in front of him. He looked up. 'Well, Al, seems we did the right thing. You look well and healthy. What are you doing now?'

'I'm nursing at Broughton Hall, near Rozelle,' she replied stiffly.

'I've heard it's a very rewarding profession.' Her father waited for Alma to speak.

Finally, she quickly said, 'I want to marry Jum Bevan.' Her sister gasped softly.

Henry Johnson's gaze was rivetted on his daughter. 'I thought that was all behind us, Alma.'

She slowly shook her head. 'No, I love him and I want to marry him.'

Henry Johnson laid down his pen and folded his hands on the table. 'I forbid you to marry this man,' he said. 'He's twice your age and I think such a marriage could only end in disaster. You realise that you can't do anything until you turn twenty-one?'

Alma was as defiant as her father.

'The day I turn twenty-one,' she said, 'I'll marry Jum Bevan.'

Henry Johnson glared. 'That's up to you to decide. But remember this,' he stood slowly to his full height, 'if you marry this man, you no longer belong to this family, you will not be asked into this house in the future, and I shall never speak to you again.'

Alma felt as if she had been punched in the stomach. 'If that's how you want it, that's how it'll be.'

Her sister saw her to the door. 'I'll keep in touch,' she whispered.

Henry Johnson surveyed the view through the large leadlight windows his firm had constructed. The sweep of grassy slope and bush reflected the setting sun. He removed his glasses carefully and began to polish one lens with his handkerchief. He was not about to capitulate to his wild young daughter. But he felt unaccustomed tears well in his eyes.

He loved Alma for all the things in her that rankled him – her strength and determination, her refusal to bow to anyone, her daring and love of life. She was his pet, his favourite, and now she was gone.

1928

Alma Johnson enjoyed her work at Broughton Hall. A deeply caring person, she showed understanding and compassion towards the inmates.

During one morning break, a nursing colleague, Celia, said, 'Don't waste too much time with the likes of Benson, he's as cunning as a shithouse rat. He'll get your confidence, then one day when your back is turned, he'll try to rip all your hair out.' She grinned. 'I know, so keep your hair short.'

The matron approached them. A large, pleasant woman, she carried her substantial figure lightly. Her darting eyes took in everything around her.

'Good morning, girls. After your break, will you clean up Matthew and his room, please?'

'Yes, Matron,' answered Celia in a resigned voice. 'Jesus, not again,' she muttered.

'Who's Matthew?' asked Alma, as the matron continued on her rounds.

'You'll see, he's a special,' said Celia glumly.

Celia glanced through the glass peephole into the room. The patient sat quietly on the floor, dressed only in pyjama trousers. Celia turned to Alma. 'He seems quiet, but be ready,' she hissed. She carefully inserted the master key on her chain into the door. The two nurses slipped in, locking the door behind them.

Celia said quietly to the figure sitting in the corner, 'Will you come and have your shower now, Matthew?'

The figure sitting in the corner raised his head from where it rested on his folded arms, which were propped on his knees. His dark eyes glared at the girls.

Celia said, 'Come on, Matthew, don't make it hard for us.'

Still glaring, the patient slowly shook his head from side to side.

Celia moved forward slowly and Alma followed. The smell of human excrement assailed Alma's nostrils.

The patient stood up, trembling. 'Don't touch me, don't touch me!' He bent down and scooped up a handful of his own faeces, then smeared it over his face and upper body.

'Now you won't touch me!' he announced with a harsh, triumphant cry.

'Let's go, Al,' called Celia, as she grabbed the patient firmly by an arm.

Together, the girls had no trouble marching the patient from his room, along the corridor to the shower block. A small man of slight build, he did not put up much resistance.

'Here we go, Matthew,' said Celia, as she turned the cold water on full. The two nurses and their patient, all fully dressed, struggled under the shower. Then, with the water off, Celia started stripping the cold and wet patient.

'He's all right once he has his shower,' she said, towelling down the now naked Matthew. She cast a dry robe over his frame and the three of them returned to his room. Alma set to and cleaned up.

Later, after lunch, Celia and Alma were enjoying a cigarette. 'It's very sad, Al,' said Celia. 'Matthew was only about eighteen when he was on the Western Front and he suffered very badly. I don't know the details.'

Later, Alma stood respectfully in front of the matron in her office.

'Of course, Nurse Johnson, this file is confidential. You may not take it past the outer office.'

'Yes, Ma'am,' responded Alma quickly.

Alma read the report. Attached to it was an extract from a 1924 Australian medical journal. The case study of Private Matthew Reynolds, an infantryman of the 3rd Division, had caused disquiet in government medical circles. The report had been compiled from numerous interviews with the patient over a period of years. It described in detail the circumstances surrounding Matthew Reynolds's ordeal in the front-line trenches during the Third Battle of Ypres in 1917.

Report on Neuroses: Hysterical Type Reactions

MR was a twenty-year-old infantryman from New South Wales at the time of his ordeal. Prior to his enlistment, there was no evidence of any psychiatric problems. The patient, MR, had been involved in constant fighting in the front line at Passchendaele in Belgium in 1917 for three weeks.

The main trench, where MR was in action, was over knee-deep in mud and slush, with temperatures around 36°F, MR having been on 'stand to' for twenty-four hours.

During the night, a number of attacks by German infantry had been repulsed, although the Allied Line had suffered heavy casualties.

MR was a Lewis gun operator. After one gruelling attack, MR could see only one other infantryman on his left. The heavy rain made for poor vision as MR concentrated on any activity in 'no man's land'.

MR remembers a shell exploding on the front of his trench, a few feet from his position. A shard of steel, three feet in length, had been blasted with great force by the explosion, spear-like into MR's shoulder, hurling him backwards and impaling him by the shoulder upon the rear trench wall. On his knees, unable to stand, MR had to endure the trench water level rising as the deluge of rain continued.

By dawn, the water had risen to his chin. MR, by this time, would have been suffering extreme shock from loss of blood and the mental stress of the possibility of a slow death by drowning.

MR has recurring nightmares of the next phase of his ordeal. Large, voracious rats inhabited the trenches and the vermin were attempting to attack the impaled MR. From this point, he remembers no more.

The report by the Brigade Medical Officer states that when rescued by the stretcher-bearing party, MR was screaming incoherently and attempting to ward off five or six rats with his broken right arm, to no avail.

He had suffered a number of bites from the vermin to both ears and his neck.

He was repatriated to England for treatment for his physical injuries and classed as unfit for further active service. MR was repatriated to Australia in 1918. He has been in psychiatric care since arriving in Australia. Long-term prognosis has determined that MR will be unable to return to normal societal activity in the foreseeable future.

Dr John Ainstey

Alma slowly closed the file.

Alma and Jum sat in the grounds of Broughton Hall, enjoying the hazy, blue view to the south-west. Alma had told Jum about Matthew Reynolds's experience. Jum lowered his head, his half-eaten sandwich still in his hand. His face clouded.

'Passchendaele was worse than the Somme, if that's possible. The 1st, 2nd, 3rd and 5th divisions were all there. The rain didn't stop for weeks. The mud was up to our waists, and sometimes deeper. Many of our blokes, mainly Poms, drowned in the mud.'

Alma squeezed his arm as he continued to eat his sandwich. 'No wonder the poor bastard hates water,' Jum said softly.

With zeal and application, Alma progressed in her profession. After two years, she was awarded a grade II advancement. Now living together, Alma and Jum were enjoying life. He had reasonable labouring work, and Alma's steady income provided a much needed boost.

But the Great Depression of 1929 was approaching.

1929

A cool, clear Sunday provided welcome relief from the heatwave of the preceding week. Alma had finished her night shift at Broughton Hall, and she sat waiting for Jum at the main tram stop on Balmain Road.

He brought the motorcycle to a halt. 'Jump on, Al, we're having a special day!' he called. With the wind in her face, her fatigue eased and her spirits rose. Jum was an expert rider and handled the bike with skill.

'Where are we going?' she yelled in his ear.

'You'll see, just be patient.'

He rode through the city down to Circular Quay, where the Manly ferry banners proclaimed 'Seven miles from Sydney, a thousand miles from care'. Locking the bike under a tree in Macquarie Street, Jum took the haversack off the rear of the bike.

'Where are we going, Jum?'

He grinned as they set off for the ferry terminal. They ran, and got aboard just before the gangplank was swung away. As the large ferry set course for the main harbour, Jum and Alma stood on the western side admiring the two spans of the Sydney Harbour Bridge that were gradually coming together. It was a massive construction that many said would fall into the harbour, taking half of Sydney with it.

The ferry picked up speed as it moved rapidly into the main channel. Alma and Jum stood on the foredeck, enjoying the morning sun on their faces. The light breeze was refreshingly cool.

Thrust into reverse, the ferry glided into the wharf at Manly. Scores of sightseers thronged the pier and walkway that formed part of the shark-free swimming enclosure to the west of the wharf.

'I've brought your togs and a towel, Al. Change in the ladies'.'

The pair walked along the deck. Jum pointed. 'That's what we're here for.' Alma looked up. The diving tower loomed in the blue sky.

Amidst great excitement, scores of young men were leaping off the first diving platform, 10 feet from the low water mark. The second platform, at 30 feet, sported only a few damp patches, a testament to the frolickers' lack of interest.

Jum and Alma performed a few warm-up dives from the first level, then moved to the second highest tower. A small crowd gathered and the group of swimmers under the tower dispersed.

Jum turned to Alma. 'You haven't dived from this height before. You don't have to, Al,' he said.

She looked down, her stomach tightening. 'I'm OK, Jum. I don't want to wait too long, though.'

Jum nodded. 'Just follow me, a simple, straight dive.'

He launched off the platform, completing a well-executed swan dive. Alma stepped forward. She leapt out, arched her back and executed a stylish, flowing dive. Upon breaking the surface, she received a smattering of applause. Jum grinned broadly. 'That was good. Up to the top now!'

She began to climb the ladder to the 60-foot platform. She felt as if she were climbing a skyscraper. Jum was hard behind, and his firm shoulders bumped reassuringly against her trembling thighs.

Standing on the 60-foot platform, Alma could not believe the height they had reached. The open-mouthed spectators below, craning their necks to see the action, seemed as small as ants. The wind whistled and the tower trembled.

Jum stepped forward, turned and said, 'Just remember – big leg push and dive for the horizon.' He reached back, gave her arm a squeeze, turned and launched himself into a sensational one-and-a-half layout dive. He hit the bright, shimmering water with an easy entry that brought excited applause from the crowd. Grinning, Jum trod water and called up to Alma, 'Let's go!'

Alma could not remember ever having been so scared. The water glistened like wet concrete. The wind whistled across her back. With a dry mouth and a pounding heart, she plunged forward.

Jum knew immediately that Alma was in trouble. She valiantly spread her arms in a swan dive. Her heels came forward, her head ducked, and with a body-slapping smash, Alma hit the unyielding surface of the pool. Pain flooded her body. She had completed a classic 'belly buster' from 60 feet.

Jum sprinted to her entry point and dived into the water. At 8 feet under, he grabbed her waist and kicked for the surface. She burst from the water, gasping for breath. Jum supported her as her breath returned.

'Oh, Jesus, Jum, I'm going to die!' she gasped.

'No, you're not – you're going up again,' he said.

With her face twisted in pain, Alma shook her head. 'No, no more, not today,' she pleaded.

'Bullshit, you're going up even if I have to carry you!'

There was no applause this time, only murmurs of concern from the onlooking crowd.

The pair climbed to the walkway. Alma, her arms and thighs bright red, clung to the ladder for support. Jum, his voice soft but insistent, said in Alma's ear, 'If you don't do it now, you never will again.'

Reluctantly, she began the torturous climb to the 60-foot platform. They stood, Jum with his back to the water, enticing Alma forward. 'Look, Al, it's easy. Jump for the horizon, as far as you can, stretch out!'

So saying, Jum slapped her thigh, moved to the edge of the platform, turned his back to the water, grinned and launched himself lazily into a stylish reverse one and-a-half. With his arms together, he broke the water perfectly, attracting excited applause from the crowd of onlookers.

He waved to Alma as she stood on the edge of the tower. Her determination dismissed any residual doubt. She bent and leapt out, concentrating on the horizon over the Norfolk pine trees. She floated gracefully, head back, arms wide, in a classic, controlled swan dive. There was scarcely a ripple as she broke the water cleanly. She surfaced with a smile.

'You bloody beauty!' yelled Jum. 'I knew you could do it!' The crowd clapped enthusiastically as the pair climbed the ladder to the walkway.

A number of people patted Alma on the back. 'Good girl!' they said, and 'Gutsy effort!'

Jum and Alma then entertained the crowd for an hour with their expert diving. Afterwards, they walked along the Corso to Manly surf beach, where they lay in the sun. Returning to the wharf later in the day, they hungrily devoured a Devonshire tea before catching the return ferry to Circular Quay. Jum's arm wrapped reassuringly around Alma's shoulders as they sat in the stern. Alma turned her face to him. The firm lines of his face were highlighted by the bright, setting sun.

'I'm glad you made me repeat that dive,' she said.

He smiled. 'I didn't know whether you would or not. It's the only way to beat the bogey, though.' Alma didn't answer. She snuggled contentedly into Jum's warm coat. Her love for this man knew no bounds.

1931

'Pregnant?' asked Jum. 'Are you sure?'

''Fraid so,' replied Alma.

He hugged her gently, his arms soft against her firm young body.

On 27 June 1931 – the day Alma turned twenty-one – she and Jum Bevan were married at St Jude's Church in Avoca Street, Randwick. Her sister, Eda, was bridesmaid. It was a simple ceremony, which her father did not attend.

Early one morning, shortly before their wedding, Alma had opened the door to an unexpected visitor. Jum had left for work an hour before. A well-dressed woman, twenty years older than Alma, stood before her.

'Yes?' asked Alma. 'Can I help you?'

'May I come in?'

Bemused, Alma showed the woman into her modest home. The woman sat down at the kitchen table and removed her gloves. In a strained voice she said, 'I believe you are going to marry William Bevan.'

'Jum? Yes, in a couple of weeks,' replied Alma.

'I suggest you think seriously about whether you want to do this,' said the woman. 'I believe if you marry this man, you'll be making a grave mistake.'

'What gives you the right to come into my house and question anything I intend to do?' Alma bristled with anger.

'My name is Beatrice Wenban. I was married to Jum years before you came on the scene. And I can tell you he is nothing but a violent drunk and a layabout. You won't be happy.'

Alma considered the woman before her. 'Miss Wenban, I thank you for your concern. Good day.'

A stony silence followed. Beatrice Wenban stood up.

'Don't ever say you weren't warned,' she said.

As the woman shut the gate, Alma called out, 'Did my father send you?' Beatrice Wenban looked back at Alma then, without answering, turned and walked across the street.

'Your first wife came by today,' said Alma as she served Jum his dinner that evening.

Jum laid down his knife and fork. 'And what little gems of information did Beatrice pass on?'

'She warned me against you,' said Alma.

Jum sat back. 'It was a bad time in my life. My friend AJ Casey had just married, a couple of my army mates had died, and I was lonely. We married, and it was a mistake – we had nothing in common. She divorced me as soon as she could.'

1932

For most people, the Great Depression meant a lack of work, and low wages. Jum and Alma did not escape the privations caused by this worldwide economic collapse.

Alma, nursing her first child Reg in her arms, said softly, 'We have to move, Jum. The landlord wants to increase our rent.'

'How much?'

'Three shillings a week, from 8 shillings to 11 shillings.'

Jum dropped his chin onto his hands and said forlornly, 'We can't afford that!'

Alma smiled. 'We can – I've saved a few pounds this last year – but we should look around.'

The Waverley stock and station agent was barely polite. 'Not much for rent around here,' he said as he turned to his key board. 'Go and look at this one in Hooper Street.'

Jum reached across the counter for the key. The agent withdrew his hand.

'I need a deposit.'

Alma opened her purse and passed over 1 shilling.

They walked to Hooper Street, pushing their baby boy in his pram. 'Hooper Street isn't far from Mum's place in Albion Street,' said Jum.

Hooper Street, Randwick, was neat and tree-lined, between Randwick and Waverley. As they walked, searching for numbers, Jum said, 'It's a nice street.'

'Here it is,' said Alma tentatively.

A narrow, single-storey Federation cottage sat on the southern side of the street. Alma took in the peeling paint, overgrown grass and general shabbiness of the property.

'Needs new gutters and downpipes,' grunted Jum.

Jum opened the door and walked in. Alma followed with the baby in her arms. The air was foul and musty.

'Turn the light on, Jum.' He flicked the switch. Nothing happened. Their eyes, becoming accustomed to the gloom, took in the piles of newspaper and garbage spread across the floor.

Alma turned suddenly, startled by a rustling noise. 'What was that?'

Jum felt the hair rise on his neck as Alma moved to the door. He saw a pair of eyes, then another, then more. Rats, twenty or more of them. Jum watched transfixed as they darted about the room.

Not since Sausage Gully on the Somme had he seen so many vermin. Those rats had been fat, black monsters, as big as small cats. They had moved from corpse to corpse, from dead horse to dead horse, gorging themselves on stomach, intestine, liver and kidney. These rats were smaller, brownish grey and hungry.

Jum grabbed a broom leaning against the wall and slashed it at the rats. One of them ran squeaking up Jum's trouser leg. Alma fled the house as Jum dropped the broom and ran for the door, slamming it after him.

Alma ran to the gate, holding her baby tightly. 'What is it, what is it?'

Jum, ashen-faced, yelled, 'The bastard's in my trousers!' He grabbed the squirming shape and squeezed his hands together with a strength bred of fear. The raucous squeaking in his trousers subsided. He kicked the offending brute out of his trouser leg. The rat began to move slowly. Jum, with a rage that Alma had not seen before, snatched up a brick from the edge of the path and smashed the rodent to a pulp.

He turned to Alma, the blood-covered brick still in his hands. There were blood spots on his face, shirt and arms. 'Rats!' he said. 'These bastards were everywhere on the Somme – in the trenches, in our beds, everywhere.' He dropped the brick, turned to the garden tap and washed off the blood as best he could.

He marched back to the stock and station agent, with Alma finding it difficult to keep up. The agent was casual. 'Back so soon? Was it to your taste?'

Jum furiously smashed the remains of the rat, wrapped in dirty newspaper, on the counter.

'To our taste, you bastard?' he growled. Startled, the agent took a pace backwards.

'That damn place is alive with rats!' said Alma.

The agent turned to his key board, his white face full of concern. 'I gave you the wrong key – that place is down for fumigation.'

Armed with the new key and a different address, they reluctantly went back to Hooper Street. This time they were pleasantly surprised by a small cottage that was full of light, airy and comfortable. They immediately signed up with the agent, who atoned for his initial mistake by offering them two weeks' free rent.

Jum had been sitting in the kitchen for two hours. The left side of his jaw was swollen and red. Alma came in from the outside laundry. 'Has that tooth flared up again?'

Jum, obviously in severe pain, nodded slightly. 'It's driving me through the roof!'

'You'll have to go to the dentist.'

Jum gave a hollow laugh. 'And pay with what?'

Later that day, Jum made his decision. Alma was surprised to see him down three or four double-overproof rums, for she knew he was not a rum drinker. He went out to the rear shed. Alma looked up from the stove as he walked back into the kitchen.

'Get a towel, Al, a bowl and a glass of warm water.'

'What are you doing?' she asked.

'I'm getting rid of this blasted tooth.'

He did not realise that his tooth was badly abscessed and in need of urgent dental and medical care. Jum withdrew a pair of metal pliers from his pocket. He had just spent five minutes cleaning them with solvent.

He clamped the pliers onto the offending tooth, working it with a sideways motion. Very quickly the tooth became loose and, after a few moments of determined tugging, slid easily from its abscessed cavity. Jum found that the rum did little to alleviate the pain.

Discoloured blood welled for a few seconds after Jum's amateur dental procedure.

Jum rinsed his mouth and grinned at Alma. 'That's better. Maybe I'll sleep tonight.'

As Alma emptied the bowl of bloodied water, she watched Jum put the rum bottle to his lips and take a large, well-earned swig. She gently wiped his face with the towel. His face relaxed at her soft touch.

Two years passed. Jum had found intermittent work, but jobs were few and far between. In 1933, Alma was pregnant again.

'When the baby arrives, we'll need another bedroom,' she said. Jum nodded in agreement. As Alma handled the finances, Jum was well aware she knew about their financial predicament.

Later that year, before the arrival of their second child, they found a large house in Caerleon Crescent, Randwick, for a rent slightly less than they had been paying. Greatly relieved, they moved their belongings.

1935

Alma hummed quietly as she cradled her five-day-old son, George, in her left arm. She was happy and content. The dreadful depression was over. Jum had a secure job as a builder's labourer in the southern suburbs of Sydney.

Her toddler pulled at her leg. Alma smiled as she looked down at her daughter, Valerie. Both Jum and Alma were besotted with this delightful, angelic child with her blonde, curly hair. At twelve months old, she had become the centre of the family.

'What more could I want?' thought Alma. 'A sturdy three-year-old boy, Valerie, and my second son.' She glanced at the newborn resting peacefully in her arms.

Valerie's birth had had a huge impact on Jum. He drank only on Friday and Saturday nights, and even that had eased, except occasionally, when he and his war mates got together. At the age of twenty-five, Alma knew that Jum, now forty-three, was getting on. He spent hours playing with his 'Little Blossom', as he had named her.

Alma placed the tall mug of boiling water on the edge of the bench top, and reached for the egg she was about to coddle for Valerie.

A piercing shriek ruptured the air. Valerie lay spreadeagled on the floor, screaming shrilly, the empty mug beside her.

Alma lay her son on the floor and scooped up the tiny girl. Her screams intensified.

Frantically, Alma ran from the house. Her neighbour's car came slowly to a stop 20 feet from her. Crying hysterically, she ran to the driver. 'Please, please, get me to a hospital!' Then she remembered her other children. 'My little boy and my baby are still inside. What'll I do?'

The neighbour responded quickly. He ran to his house and knocked furiously. His wife appeared, and in a short, sharp sentence he explained.

'Go! Go!' his wife cried. She ran to help Alma into the car. 'I'll watch your kids until you come back. Go quickly!'

The child's screams were split by choking sobs. The neighbour jumped behind the wheel. 'I'll get you to Prince of Wales Hospital. What happened?'

Through her sobs, Alma answered, 'She grabbed the mug of boiling water. It's all over her head and chest!'

The driver made no attempt to obey speed or traffic rules and finally screeched to a halt at the hospital. Valerie was rushed into emergency with a flurry of doctors and nurses in attendance. A nurse attempted to console Alma, and put her arm around her shoulder.

On the verge of collapse, Alma clutched at the nurse. 'My baby boy – he's only five days old. He's at home with my neighbour.'

'What's the address?' asked the nurse.

'Caerleon Crescent, number 15,' sobbed Alma. 'Could you telephone my sister? She lives close by.' She gave the nurse the number.

When the nurse returned, she said, 'Your sister's on her way. Your father is driving her to your house.'

An hour passed. A doctor came into the waiting room. 'Mrs Bevan?' he enquired.

Alma trembled. 'How is my little girl?'

'She's been seriously burned. We've sedated her and applied dressings to her burns. She has third-degree burns to her head, chest and back.'

'Will she be all right, doctor?' asked Alma, her apprehension growing.

'We hope so; we are doing our utmost. But I would have to say her condition is critical.'

Alma slumped. The doctor helped her to a seat.

Eda Johnson opened the door. The light was on and the baby boy was sound asleep in the neighbour's arms. The offending mug still lay on the floor.

'Reg is having a nap,' the neighbour said. She carefully gave the sleeping newborn to Eda and left.

Later, Jum Bevan quietly inserted the key into the front door lock. He always enjoyed the moment when his tiny 'Blossom' toddled through the house to greet him. But this time there were no pattering feet to greet him. He walked down the hallway to the lounge room.

Eda, pacing quietly, heard Jum enter. 'Is that you, Jum?'

'What's going on, Eda?'

'I don't know the details, but there's been a terrible accident. Al and Valerie are at Prince of Wales. Valerie's been scalded.'

'Fucking hell!' Jum dropped his coat and ran, leaving the door to slam against the wall. He sprinted down to Alison Road, up to Avoca Street and along to the hospital. Fifteen minutes later he arrived at casualty. Sweating and panting with exertion, he saw Alma sitting hunched in the waiting room. He grabbed her by the arms and jerked her to her feet.

'What's happened?' he shouted, shaking Alma forcefully.

'Valerie pulled a mug of boiling water over herself. She's badly burned,' sobbed Alma.

Jum rushed towards the front desk. 'Where's my baby? Where's my little girl?'

The large, elderly matron gave Jum a stern look.

'Sit down, young man. The doctor will be out soon.'

'What?' shouted Jum. 'Don't stuff me around! My daughter's badly injured. Don't tell me to sit down!'

The matron hurriedly retreated to the operating theatre, then re-emerged with the young doctor who had spoken earlier to Alma. Jum's hands were shaking. The visions of burns the men had suffered in Western France were only too clear.

'How bad is she, doctor?' he asked.

'Look, I must be honest with you, Mr Bevan – your daughter has suffered severe burns to her head, chest and back. We're doing all we can. She is alive, and at the moment she's asleep. She's being monitored carefully. There's someone constantly by her side.'

The large matron sat next to Alma in the waiting room.

'You should go home to your baby. He'll need feeding,' she suggested softly.

'I'm going nowhere!' retorted Jum.

Alma stood up. The matron said, 'I have my car outside. I'm off-duty now, so I can drive you home. I know your street.'

Alma nodded, and whispered, 'Thank you.'

She moved to Jum. He had a dreadful look on his face, the one she feared. His eyes were blank and hard, his mouth set in a harsh, straight line, exuding cold fury and hatred.

Alma put her hand to her mouth, turned and walked out to the car with the matron.

In Caerleon Crescent, Eda was waiting on the porch. Alma walked unsteadily to the gate. The two sisters entered the house together. An hour passed. They had gone over and over the accident suffered by the little girl.

'You couldn't be expected to realise how much more active she'd become in the week you were in hospital,' Eda said.

Alma was inconsolable. 'I'm staying here until Val comes home,' said Eda.

Alma rose at 6.30 the following morning. She fed the baby and prepared food for Reg, then hurried to the hospital, leaving Eda at the house.

'Yes, your little girl has been taken to dedicated care, second floor, up those stairs,' the desk secretary informed her.

A nurse beckoned. 'Are you Mrs Bevan?' Alma nodded. 'Please follow me.'

They entered the room. Jum sat by the bed. Tiny Valerie, swathed in dressings, was quietly asleep. Alma was shocked by Jum's appearance – white, drawn face, sunken black eyes, body hunched over. He stared intently at his little girl, as if the fierceness of his look could give her strength.

Alma looked at the nurse, the unspoken question obvious on her face.

'There's no change. Your little Valerie is fighting like blazes. All we can do is hope and pray.'

At the word 'pray', Jum looked up. Alma had never before seen the cynical sneer that contorted his face.

'Pray?' he said. 'You've got to be joking!'

At last, after four days' constant vigil at Valerie's bedside, the baby opened her eyes.

Jum took her small hand in his large grasp. The tiny pink fingers gripped his thumb. But Valerie suddenly coughed – a gurgling, racking cough.

The doctor hurriedly appeared. 'Outside, everyone, quickly!'

In the hallway Jum and Alma waited. Jum paced up and down the corridor.

At 11 o'clock, the door to the ward opened. The doctor and two nurses stepped into the corridor. The younger nurse was crying softly.

The doctor stood before Jum and Alma. In a low voice he said, 'That brave little girl fought her hardest. Unfortunately, she lost the battle, and she has passed on. She caught pneumonia, and was too frail to withstand the harshness of her injuries. I'm sorry.'

Alma slid to the floor unconscious. Jum knelt and supported her. Two orderlies carried Alma to an open ward as Jum slowly followed, despair etched in every line of his face.

A clear, bright day, with brilliant sun filtering through the trees, greeted the mourners at Rookwood Cemetery. Alma, her face covered with a veil, stood by Jum as they faced the grave.

Rector Claude Jenkins waited, Bible in hand. Behind him stood Reverend Jim Gillies. AJ Casey, with his wife, Fiona, waited nearby. Harold McErbain, after greeting a few of the mourners, stood silently with his wife, Lucy. They had all lost close friends in France, but for Jum it seemed that terrible grief and loss were to continue in his civilian life.

The small white coffin lay beside the open grave. Claude Jenkins surveyed the group of people gathered at the graveside. He said strongly but gently, 'A death amongst friends or family is the one situation we never wish to encounter. The death of a loved one is especially cruel when the departed has not had time to experience the wonders and joys of life. It is hard to find solace in this situation.

'For the bright twelve months of Valerie's life, we thank the Lord. Her departure so early from this life we can only mourn, and ask Him to help us make sense of the loss.

'William and Alma have lost a child. They have two sons. They are a strong family and I firmly believe their strength will overcome this sadness that has befallen them. May God rest her tiny soul.'

The coffin was lowered into the grave. Alma leant forward. Jum gently placed his arm around her waist and drew her back. She sobbed quietly, fighting for control. Eda moved in and led Alma away.

Claude Jenkins and Jim Gillies approached Jum. He was staring vacantly at the grave as two attendants filled it with soil. Reverend Jenkins said, 'Jum, I'd like to talk to you and Alma together.'

Jum turned towards Jenkins, glowering. 'What about, Padre? The good Lord Jesus, and some bullshit about how lucky I am?'

Jim Gillies stepped forward. 'Jum, please.'

Jum, his whole body shaking, held up his hands in silent protest. 'No, Gill. No more, not now,' he pleaded. Alma joined Jum and tightly clutched his arm, holding him steady.

Claude Jenkins's voice caught in his throat. 'Jum,' he said brokenly, tears slowly forming in his grey eyes, 'we've been to hell and back, you and I and countless others. Some are here, and some are not. We've suffered, and witnessed events that no one would want to be part of. But of all the nightmares you've suffered, all the horrors you've been part of, I believe nothing will ever cause you as much pain and grief as your and Alma's loss today.'

'How many times, Claude, am I going to be given a love and a life, only to have it ripped away again? And every time a part of me is torn out. I'm being dragged apart, piece by piece.' Jum stepped forward and grasped Jenkins by the arms. His voice broke. 'How many more times, Claude?'

'I don't know, Jum. I honestly don't know.'

'Well, Claude, here's what I think,' said Jum. He dried his tears and a hard, uncompromising look appeared on his face. 'There is no God. No God could take a young life so cruelly, without cause, without reason. There – is – no – God!' Jum accented each word with a gentle tap on the padre's chest. He turned on his heel, holding Alma by the arm as he moved to the funeral car waiting nearby.

As they drove away, Jenkins and Gillies stood silently together. 'If only Jum could understand what Claude Jenkins has shown me over the years,' Gillies thought.

Jenkins prayed, 'God, please forgive this man, your servant. He is suffering more than many others because of the burden of guilt he carries. He feels he is being singled out by you for punishment.'

Later that afternoon, Jum and Alma travelled by tram to Randwick. Jum stepped off the tram a stop early and said in a hollow voice, 'I'll be home sometime.' Alma stared straight ahead and did not answer.

She lay awake for hours, waiting for his return. At the sound of the front door opening, she tiptoed quietly along the hall.

Jum stood over the baby's cot. He held the cot sides with both hands as he glared at the sleeping infant. 'You bastard!' he spat. 'This is your fault!' Leaning lower, he mumbled hoarsely, 'You'll pay, you'll pay for this.'

Alma forced her way between Jum and the cot. 'You leave my son alone!' she hissed. 'He had nothing to do with this. You touch my boy and I'll do for you!'

'Now you're on his side, are you?' he yelled deliriously. 'On the side of the bastard God, who took our little girl!'

Jum began weeping uncontrollably. Alma wept too, for her baby and for the desolation of the man before her – lost, grief-stricken, destroying himself.

COOGEE,
APRIL 1935

The loss of his baby daughter affected Jum dreadfully and added to the intense emotional damage he had suffered on the Western Front.

His was a complex character: he was both a risk-taker and a staunch and abiding friend, fiercely protective, but also violent. These opposing traits drew him into seemingly endless conflict.

Jum found that exposing himself to extreme risk helped to exorcise – at least temporarily – the demons that plagued him constantly. He rode his motorcycle dangerously, at breakneck speed. He was constantly involved in vicious hotel brawls. Though this risk-taking behaviour provided some relief, it was not sufficient to release the pent-up anger that had grown in proportion to the misfortunes in his life.

Little did Jum realise that through this behaviour he was about to become embroiled, unwittingly, in one of Sydney's most notorious murder mysteries.

James Smith, a forty-year-old billiard marker and SP bookmaker, lived at Bateman's Road, Gladesville. He was about to become famous – or infamous, depending which side of the law you were on.

As an SP bookie, he inhabited smoky dens, mixing with a large cross-section of the demi-monde of post-depression society.

Obviously, some persuasive characters would have been his frequent companions.

Jack Hobson, a professional fisherman, operated his 16-foot clinker-built boat from the northern end of Coogee Beach. Ten or so boats of similar design and construction, usually covered by strapped-down tarpaulins, were permanent fixtures on the beach. Their owners took advantage of the relatively calm water at the northern end of Coogee to safely launch their craft and putt-putt their way to their favourite fishing grounds.

Jack and his brother, Charlie, held the lease of the Coogee Aquarium Swimming Baths at the Coogee tram terminus.

Murray Stewart, known to his friends as 'Muzza', was eleven years old at the time. He and his close friend, Kevin McCormack, also eleven, spent all their free time fishing, surfing and hanging about the fishing boats and their owners, hoping to be asked to join the next fishing expedition.

Jack Hobson stood watching Muzza Stewart neatly and expertly tie hooks onto his fishing traces. Jack's companion turned and said, 'That bloody kid's good, Jack!'

Jack smiled. 'I reckon! He's only eleven, and he's one of the best fishermen on this beach. We can be out about a mile, fishing 60 feet deep, and if he gets a bite, he'll name the fish – snapper, traglin, bream, tailor, flathead or whatever – before he gets it to the boat. He knows this whole area like the back of his hand.' Jack waved his arm, indicating the large sweep of water to the east.

'When are you going out again, Mr Hobson?' asked Muzza.

'Friday night, Murray,' said Jack, turning to Muzza and Kevin. 'You know that reef where we get good snapper and bream?'

Murray nodded. 'You mean your mark about 600 yards north-east of the island?'

'That's it. A bloody rogue shark is hanging round. We hooked a good fish, and were just about to get him into the boat and bang! This big bastard flashes up and takes it. So we're going out Friday night to set-line a big bait and see if we can catch the bugger.'

On Saturday, 19 April 1935, Murray and Kevin stood watching the small fishing boat labour its way slowly towards Coogee Beach from Wedding Cake Island.

'He's going slow ... He's towing something!' yelled an excited Murray. The two boys sprinted from the clifftop to the beach.

The tide was low at 11 am, as Jack Hobson neatly steered his craft through the small break. Half a dozen excited onlookers rushed to help drag the boat through the shallows. Jack Hobson stood up and waved his arms.

'Keep back, keep back!' he yelled. 'This bastard's mad and mean!'

A 14-foot tiger shark, with a large hook still embedded in its jaw, was held captive by a rope tied to the stern of the boat. The monster stared malevolently at the knot of gathering onlookers.

Jack Hobson called, 'Hey Muzza! You and Kevin grab that plank from the boatshed. Quick!' The boys ran off and returned with a timber plank, which they dropped into the water. 'Be careful you blokes. This bastard's still alive. He'll take an arm off if you're not careful,' he warned.

The first hand that touched the monster sent it into a paroxysm of thrashing and jaw-snapping. When the frenzy had subsided, half a dozen lines were cast around the huge shark, and willing hands eventually lifted the wildly twisting brute onto the plank.

The shark was quickly transported to the aquarium and rolled into the pool, which had been filled with fresh saltwater. With a gentle splash, the shark sank into the pool. One propelling kick of its tail sent it circling its new confines. The size and raw power of the monster shark were both thrilling and intimidating.

Charlie and Jack Hobson cleared the crowd of onlookers from the poolside. There were to be no free looks at this sensation. The front gate was locked, and the two brothers sat in conference. They agreed to charge threepence entrance. The news spread like wildfire. The Coogee trams disgorged their packed carriages at the entrance to the baths.

At the end of the next day, Charlie Hobson turned to his brother. 'We've taken more today than in the last four weeks.'

Jum Bevan waited patiently as another tram, packed to bursting point, careered past without stopping. Tired of waiting, he jogged down from Randwick to Coogee, a refreshing swim on his mind.

Over the past two years, Jum and Alma had given diving exhibitions at the aquarium. At forty-three years of age, Jum had lost none of his athleticism or diving skill. As he approached the tram terminus, he was amazed to see the pushing, shoving hordes attempting to gain entry to the pool. He forced his way to the gate, calling out to Charlie Hobson, 'What the bloody hell's going on, Charlie?'

A beaming smile lighting up his face, Hobson unlocked the gate. Jum squeezed in and they walked to the pool. The pool sides were jammed with excited people, pointing, gesticulating and shivering in imagined terror as the maneater circled the pool.

Jum watched, fascinated. The shark swam around the perimeter under the two diving boards in a continuing, lazy circular path, its lithe form brushing the pool edge.

Jum watched the shark for an hour. He went to the beach and swam in the surf but returned later to the aquarium pool. Jum, Charlie Hobson and his brother, Jack, had a serious discussion. 'No worries, Charlie,' said Jum. 'It'll be easy!'

Jum left the pool and boarded a tram to Randwick. The two brothers sat quietly talking.

'If he's mad enough to take the risk, it's fine by me,' said Charlie.

'It'd keep the crowds coming all right,' smiled his brother.

Printed placards were soon produced and placed in various areas around Maroubra, Randwick, Coogee, Bronte and Bondi. They invited onlookers to witness the greatest daredevil feat of all time. 'Man takes on shark in pool!' The entry fee jumped from threepence to sixpence.

When Jum told her about it, Alma was beside herself. 'What if you slip and knock yourself unconscious?' she asked angrily. 'What do I do – what do the children do – if you get bitten in half by a crazed maneater?'

But Jum was adamant. The 5-shilling fee he was getting for each encounter far outweighed any concern for danger. He had observed the shark carefully for two days. Its unchanging swimming pattern meant he was relatively safe. He had discussed with Jack Hobson how the stunt would be performed. The plan was that, after the shark had passed under the board, Jum would wait five seconds, launch off the springboard into a spectacular dive, quickly kick to the surface on the far side and slip out of the pool.

On the first day, the pool was packed to overflowing, as onlookers strove to get a clearer view of the action. As Jum approached the board, the crowd hushed into silence. Jum waited on the springboard as the shark gracefully passed under him. He glanced casually at the shark and then at the silent, open-mouthed audience.

Three steps, then off the end – a beautiful one-and-a-half front somersault into the water. A hard kick, then his arms pulled him to the tiled edge. One jump and he was clear of the water.

The shark, hearing the splash, had accelerated slightly and changed its path to explore the spot where Jum had entered the water. The crowd went wild, clapping, cheering and whistling, as Jum smiled and waved.

The following night, a Thursday, Jum was to perform twice. He had argued for and won a fee of 10 shillings per dive – £1 for the night! He was excited.

The first dive was as uneventful as the previous night's performance. The crowd erupted. Jum donned a robe as sandwich- and drink-sellers moved amongst the patrons.

Jum prepared for his second dive. What he hadn't counted on was that sharks, amongst the oldest living inhabitants on earth, had not survived for millions of years by being stupid. The shark had worked out that the splash at the far end of the pool signalled a potential food source, and the Hobson brothers, Jum and Alma, and the hundreds of excited fans all knew this. What they didn't realise was that the shark had also worked out that the sound of the bump from the board – which travelled very quickly underwater – meant that a potential meal was about to enter the water at the familiar splash point.

Jum watched warily as the shark passed underneath him. Then he ran, sprang off the end and floated gracefully in his layout one-and-a-half.

Halfway to the end of the pool, the shark reacted instantly to the bump on the board.

Arcing viciously, the maneater accelerated rapidly towards the splash. Jum, who'd taken two strokes under water, broke the surface smiling, only to be greeted by screaming pandemonium. The shark, no more than 15 feet away and travelling at full speed, opened its massive jaws.

Desperate hands grabbed Jum's arms and ripped him out of the water. One leg still dangled in the water. The shark's open jaws broke the surface. With one last heave, Jum was dragged out as the abrasive surface of the shark's skin flashed by and tore skin off his ankle.

Alma gasped, ashen-faced.

The crowd dispersed, babbling with excitement, witnesses to a near-disaster. The police arrived and immediately put a ban on any further such activities.

The next day – Friday, 25 April, Anzac Day – only a few people were in the Coogee Aquarium. Without Jum's diving, the shark in the pool was not so sensational.

Late in the afternoon, Murray and Kevin stood at the deep end of the aquarium pool. The shark's tail splashed the surface. A large, swarthy man dressed in a long coat pushed past Kevin, muttering, 'Out of my bloody way, kid!' He disappeared quickly through the pool exit.

A piercing scream broke the quiet. A woman, holding her hand to her mouth, was pointing at the pool. A human arm floated on the surface.

Jum and the Hobson brothers ran from the office. The Randwick police were summoned, and the arm retrieved from the pool. A short piece of rope was found knotted tightly around the wrist. The forearm featured a tattoo of two boxers in fighting pose. Jum looked on quite calmly. This was a Sunday school picnic compared to what he had witnessed on the Western Front.

Murray and Kevin stood listening to the police.

'The shark disgorged the arm?' asked the sergeant.

'I suppose so,' answered Jack Hobson.

Young Murray stepped forward. 'No way that arm came from that shark's gut. If it had been there for a week, there would've been nothing left!'

'Piss off, kid, who asked you?' snarled the police sergeant.

The boys moved back. The crowd dispersed and the police left, taking the arm with them.

The boys were in the office. Jack Hobson said, 'I agree with young Murray here. That arm would have had no flesh on it at all after a week in that shark's belly.'

The shark was netted, taken away and dissected. Two weeks after the discovery of the arm, a fishery expert, Mr D. G. Stead, stated that the strong gastric and intestinal juices of the shark would normally digest any flesh within thirty-six hours, and that there was no case on record of flesh remaining comparatively intact in a shark's alimentary canal for longer than that period.

And so James Smith, once positively identified, found his place in criminal history because of his severed arm. On Friday, 10 May 1935, at the Central Police Station, a man was formally charged with having feloniously and maliciously murdered James Smith at Cronulla during April 1935.

After hearing the news, the Hobson brothers sat with Jum in the Doncaster Hotel.

'That bloody shark was awake to you, Jum,' said Charlie, with a rueful shake of his head.

'Trust our luck,' said a peeved Jum. 'We were about to make a killing. Why couldn't the bastard have tossed the arm into the sea?'

The conversation lapsed as the three men disconsolately drank their beer.

Due to inconclusive evidence against the accused, the charges of 'murder' and 'illegal dealing with a body' were dropped by the police prosecution.

Muzza Stewart sat on the beach with Kevin McCormack.

'That arm was tossed into the pool, Kevin,' said Murray emphatically.

'I know, Muzza. And who was the big bloke that pushed me out of the way just before the arm was spotted in the pool?'

Both boys gazed at the white water crashing onto Wedding Cake Island.

'I guess we'll never know, Kev.'

SYDNEY, 2002

My sister, Patricia, sipped her hot tea. We had been talking for some time. 'Do you remember the house?' she asked.

'Yes, but very little of the big shed in the rear yard. So Mum built the house, you say?'

'She did – every stick of timber, weatherboard and even the roof. Although Colin Treweeke, a carpenter, set out and cut the roof for her. Mum fought the Repat for two years to get them a Returned Soldiers Settlement block of land at Matraville. She was dogged; drove them mad. But they agreed at last, I think more to get her off their back than anything.' Patricia smiled, 'She was damned determined, our mother.'

SYDNEY, MID-1937

Alma stood at the counter of the Repatriation Department, facing an exasperated clerk. 'Now listen carefully,' she said, 'and I'll tell you again. My husband, William Bevan, served in the AIF for three years in France and Belgium. He was gassed twice, injured by enemy machine-gun fire and served with distinction. He satisfies all the criteria required for allocation of land under the *Repatriation Act*.

'I've written numerous letters to you over the last two years, of which I have handwritten copies.' She waved a sheaf of papers. 'And all I've received are evasive replies.'

The clerk mumbled, 'Just one moment,' as he walked to a door behind the counter.

His superior was sitting at his desk. 'Who is she?' he asked, with annoyance.

'Her name's Alma Bevan, she's married to a William Bevan and they have two children.'

The manager withdrew a file from his cabinet. 'Here we are. Bevan, William. Served in the 5th Brigade Artillery for four years.' The manager read on. 'Quite a boy, our William! Pretty wild by his service record.'

He seemed momentarily lost in thought. 'I was a lieutenant in 2nd Division in 1916. We were attacking at Pozières, about five weeks after that bloody Haig had botched the Battle of the Somme raid on the 1st of July in 1916. The 4th and 5th Brigade Artillery had given us great support for over a month. They worked their backsides off to keep the Boche pinned down. Their work saved a lot of Australian lives.'

He signed the application form on the bottom of the page and smiled. 'Process this immediately.'

Alma was overjoyed. As she waited for Jum to arrive home from work, she could barely contain her excitement. Jum merely smiled quietly, although inwardly he too was excited. 'Our own land!' he thought.

The next Saturday, Jum, Alma and the two young boys travelled south on the La Perouse tram to Matraville. Alma had the subdivision map in her hand.

'Here it is!' she exclaimed. 'Lot 12.' The 50 by 150-foot block was level and bare, with an established fence and houses abutting on the eastern and southern boundaries. Alma dropped the plan into the pram where George, her two-year-old, was asleep. She turned and hugged Jum with glee.

'It was worth all the trouble!' she laughed.

'First things first, Al,' said Jum, becoming animated. 'Now, let's see – I can build a large temporary shed in the back corner that will do us for a year or so until we complete the house. I suppose they have a standard design for a house?'

'Yes, three designs. I like the two-bedroom with a front sleep-out – that's what we need.' They continued to discuss their options as they walked over the land, scratching lines in the sandy soil, working out where the various rooms would be.

Jum waited apprehensively in the outer office of the Australian Paper Manufacturers at Botany. After a brief interview he was employed as a factory hand in the boiler room, where the primary paper pulp was mixed before being formed on huge felt rollers. The paper mill was close to Jum and Alma's block of land in Matraville, and offered permanent employment.

Each afternoon, after the factory shut down, Jum would scavenge the area for any old building materials. There was an abundance of derelict sites in the Botany/Matraville area. He would often work until 8 or 9 o'clock at night, dragging and carrying disused corrugated iron, old timber or any other items that could be used in the construction of their house. It was demeaning and backbreaking work.

The proposed large shed at the back of the block took shape quickly. It was not exactly picturesque, but it was their home, their stronghold. Once it could be locked up, the family would often spend a Friday or Saturday night in the shed so they could get an early start on building the house the following day.

Jum had procured a large, unwanted roll of thick felt from the paper mill. The manager was only too happy to have a lorry drop it off at the block. With meticulous care, Jum had already wetted down the sand floor of the shed and levelled the surface. Straining and grunting, he and Alma carted the felt into the shed, where they carefully rolled it out over the sand base. They were over-joyed to have the next best thing to carpet underfoot.

As water had been connected, they were now self-sufficient, and gave notice to the agent of their rented house in Randwick. The shed was bare and primitive, with only kerosene lamps for light at night. A kerosene primus stove meant that Alma had to work culinary wonders. The toilet, a long-drop enclosed in an outhouse, sat against the rear fence.

In the course of his scavenging raids, Jum had come across a large brick warehouse that had fallen into total disrepair. The walls had collapsed and the roof structure lay in a tangled heap of bricks, timber and corrugated iron. It was a treasure trove for Jum, who used it as the family's building supplier.

One evening Jum surveyed the debris, wondering how he could transport the pile of bricks the mile and a half to his block. He remembered how in Belgium, especially in Passchendaele, they had transported the 18-pounder shells through the deep mud on 'limber packs' strapped across the donkeys' backs. He quickly made a pack that could carry five bricks on either side and hung it on his bicycle seat. When fully loaded, it meant a tough walk uphill, but downhill, it was a wild ride.

The stack of bricks grew and grew, until one day a brick fell on his finger, splitting the end.

Cyril, a fellow worker at the paper mill, could hardly believe his ears. 'You're carting bloody house bricks on your bloody pushbike?' he asked incredulously.

Jum nodded. 'I'm trying to build my house.'

'Well, we'll sort this out today. I've a mate with a horse and cart.'

At 6 pm that evening, a horse and cart, groaning with a load of 500 bricks, turned into Jum's street. The men offloaded the bricks into a large pile as Alma and the boys watched.

'OK, mate,' laughed Cyril, 'same time tomorrow. We'll get your bloody house started!'

The building plan was pegged out on the land and, as Jum had to work, Alma took over the construction of their dream home. She had a sharp mind, and no one was surprised that she could read and understand building plans, procedures and most other aspects of building. As a young girl, she had often spent Saturdays in her father's joinery shop at Railway Square in Sydney. She had spent many hours watching the joiners craft windows, doors, cupboards and a host of other items. She knew about timber: how to saw it, how to plane it square and how to handle a hammer and nails.

She set to work with gusto, working constantly on the house. To her great joy, each afternoon Jum would praise her, amazed at what she had been able to achieve that day. Alma was then only twenty-seven years of age.

One evening, the family sat around their kerosene heater in the shed. It was bitterly cold outside, and they huddled together for warmth.

With a soft laugh, Alma said, 'Well, Jum, a neighbour from down the street came up today, an old bloke. I was on the roof nailing down the last of the ceiling joists. He walked over and called out, "You're a wonderful daughter to be slaving so hard while your father's out working!" I nearly fell off the roof laughing,' she giggled.

Jum smiled. 'Either you look very young, Al, or I look very old.'

After nine months of constant work, usually seven days a week, the house was liveable. Amid much joy and celebration, the family moved into their new house. With electric light, a large Metters fuel stove and warm, comfortable bedrooms, the house seemed like heaven.

KENSINGTON, 1938

Jum suddenly stopped walking, causing the pedestrians around him to bump and jostle each other. Staring at the approaching hunched figure, Jum stood in his path and saw a flicker of recognition in his eyes.

'Ernie, is that you, you old bastard?'

A bright smile creased the drawn face.

'Jum! Long time, no see,' Ernie replied hoarsely. 'When was it? 1918, in France?'

Jum nodded slowly. 'Twenty years ago. Christ, where's it gone?' They moved to the edge of the pavement. 'Got time for a drink, Ernie?'

The pair walked up to the Doncaster Hotel. At 10.30 on a Saturday morning, the public bar was very quiet. With two icy beers in hand, Jum moved to the table where Ernie was sitting. They sipped slowly.

'How've you been, Ernie?' asked Jum.

'I've been diagnosed with TB, mate. Pretty advanced, the doctors say.'

'The bloody gas wouldn't have helped,' said Jum.

Ernie smiled, remembering. 'Saw AJ about two years ago, Anzac Day. He said a few of the boys are gone.'

Jum's face tightened. 'Bob Buchannen copped it our last night of action. We were hit by a 230 mortar. Took half his bloody head off.'

'So AJ said,' replied Ernie. 'He told me about Ron, too.'

'And poor bloody Wagga went mad because of it, and ended up blowing his brains out with a revolver.'

'Any good news?' asked Ernie, sadly.

'Well, Gill joined the church with Claude Jenkins and he's done well. It's funny to see him in his white collar,' Jum laughed.

'Doesn't fit too well with the images I have of him pissed legless.'

The two finished their beers and Ernie bought another two. 'What happened to Jeanne after Bob bought it?' asked Ernie.

'I ... we went to the funeral. Anna organised it. Bob was buried in the yard at Jeanne's farm. It stuffed me up badly,' said Jum. 'I was in pretty bad shape and got on the piss for a few years.'

'Didn't we all,' smiled Ernie. 'What happened to Anna? I thought you two were hot for each other.'

'She was some girl, Ernie. If Bob hadn't been killed, I think I would have stayed and married her. Anyway, my wife Alma is a gem. How she puts up with me, I'll never know. I think I'm a lucky bloke to have her.'

Small talk followed. Ernie's eyes lit up. He said, 'I've two lovely kids. Andrea, my eldest girl, is eight, and my boy, John, is four.'

Jum smiled. 'I have two boys, one six and one three.' His face clouded. 'We lost a little girl at twelve months. A dreadful accident.'

They continued to talk, the 'what abouts' and the 'do you remembers' coming thick and fast as the memories unfolded.

'What about the night of Bob and Jeanne's wedding? I remember Harold saying, "That bloody Ernie is putting the hard word on Madame Grigor," and, of course, you sure were. I didn't blame you though. What a beautiful woman!'

Ernie's eyes lit up. 'I was scared shitless. Here I am, a twenty-four-year-old shit-kicker private going for this French general's wife. When she asked me into her room and locked the door, I thought she was going to stab me to death for being such a smart arse. It was only after she dropped her clothes, smiled at me and put her beautiful tits in my face that I thought, "I've half a chance, here!"'

Jum laughed uproariously.

They talked about the horse race and the idiotic danger they had placed themselves in.

'Why on earth did we do that, Ernie?'

'Well, Jum, I don't want to sound like a ratbag, but I reckon we had to keep doing stupid things to keep the edge. If we'd started to look for safety, we surely would've bought it. I think the more danger we found, the less liable we were to get knocked over.' Ernie sipped his beer. 'Do you ever miss it, Jum? The excitement, I mean.'

'I know what you mean,' said Jum. 'Even though it was dangerous, I suppose there was a lot of excitement in dodging bullets and hand grenades and staying alive while we killed the Boche. And after all, Ernie, we were only twenty-four. It was sort of a game, but with high stakes.' He paused. 'There's nothing in civvy life to match it, putting your life on the line every day. I suppose that's another reason why we find it hard to adjust.' He smiled. 'Sometimes I wish the milkman would lob a hand grenade in the front yard, just to relieve the fuckin' boredom.

'So, Ernie,' he continued, 'when did you leave France? I thought your Military Medal might have got you home a little earlier.'

'No way, mate. Made it harder, if anything. I left in November 1918, straight after it finished, and got home in December.'

'First Brigade was in action at Villers-Bretonneux. You were there for a while?'

'Well, we were in Amiens, waiting to move to Villers-Bretonneux. The Boche was blasting Amiens with their long-range stuff. A large number of our blokes were killed at Amiens station, waiting to entrain. That was in April 1918.'

Jum said, 'I was a mounted runner then at Ribemont. We had the 2nd Div in front.'

'Our 1st Div had been sent up north to Hazebrouck,' said Ernie. 'The Boche bastards were attacking there too.'

'Villers-Bret was the key,' said Jum. 'The Boche knew the railhead at Villers had to be taken. If they took Villers-Bret, it was only 10 miles to Amiens. If Amiens fell, it was all over for the Allies – the Boche would hold the main rail line to Paris. They threw everything they had into Villers. We were told, no matter what, Villers-Bret had to be held.'

A few older drinkers had gathered silently as Ernie and Jum continued. One asked 'Were you both there?'

'Yeah,' said Jum. 'Ernie here was in the village, virtual hand-to-hand combat, vicious stuff. The village was bombed out, only ruins remained, but it was the high ground. About 1,000 yards north of the village was the plateau, a great place for German artillery to control everything, and all around were the trees.'

'And to the south,' joined in Ernie, 'Hangard Wood, Monument Wood and Bois l'Abbé held thousands of Boche, jammed in trenches, waiting to attack. The German bastards broke the Tommy line in late April, but our 13th and 15th Brigades made some mad, wild charges and drove them back. Those Victorian boys were the mainstay. They held Villers-Bretonneux, but at great cost. They lost over 1,000 men.'

The bystander spoke again, as the others listened intently. 'Didn't the 13th Brigade come from the Somme, north of Villers-Bretonneux?'

'They sure did,' said Jum. 'Also the 15th Brigade, more bloody Victorians! The 59th Battalion led the way and made such a bloody racket the 60th Battalion joined in too – still more Victorians!'

Ernie mused, 'Those Victorians saved Villers. The hand-to-hand fighting was insane. Boche machine guns were every 20 or 30 yards apart, right through the village, hiding in doorways, behind piles of rubble, everywhere.'

He sipped his beer. 'Those Victorian infantry blokes would stand and run, toss two grenades and go to ground. Then the next bloke would do the same. Some lived. A lot were cut to pieces by the Maxim guns.' He paused. 'But they kept coming at those bastards, not suicide stuff, but desperate individual attacks. They all knew they had to win or three years were wasted.'

Jum spoke. 'Villers-Bretonneux was devastated, hardly a house was standing, the school was flattened. Few acts of bravery will ever be greater than at Villers-Bretonneux. After three days of unbelievable shit, the town was recaptured. The Allies had every reason to be proud. The Germans' greatest all-out attack had been stopped. The turning point of the war was Villers-Bretonneux, thanks to those mad bloody Victorians.'

A slight pause, then Ernie said, 'Don't forget the British 8th Division, Jum – as tough a bunch of bastards as you'll ever see. They had lots of eighteen- and nineteen-year-olds, but their core of veteran men were the best. They were great infantrymen, hard as nails.'

Jum looked at Ernie as he finished his beer. It was 3 pm. 'We'd best be going,' he said. 'We've been here bloody hours.'

Ernie looked at his watch. 'What's the time? I'm too pissed to read my watch.'

'It's late. Come on, I'll walk you back.'

As they left, the pair waved to the crowd, who had listened attentively, and received waves in return.

The cool air was refreshing. They made their way slowly up High Street beside Randwick Racecourse. They paused. The Saturday race meeting had only two races left to run.

Ernie smiled as he remembered. 'Galloped round that bloody track a few times, mate.'

'Not as exciting as our race in No Man's Land,' laughed Jum.

'Nothing could ever beat that,' said Ernie, his face creased in delight. They moved on.

'Nearly there, mate,' gasped a wheezing Ernie. The Prince of Wales Hospital, a large, imposing sandstone building, sat on a rise in Randwick. Whenever Jum passed the hospital, he felt a sharp stab of pain as he remembered his tiny daughter, Valerie.

'I'm down the south end, in the chest clinic,' said Ernie. The two shook hands firmly and parted company.

Not long after their meeting, Ernie's TB and chest problems, exacerbated by gas inhalation on the Western Front, deteriorated badly. Ernie Fitzroy Buckleton, forty-five years of age, soldier, awarded the Military Medal for 'conspicuous gallantry, bravery and devotion to duty', horseman, bookies' clerk, lover of life and daredevil, faded. Unsung, he departed.

1939

Australia was well and truly at war – again. The German nation was fighting the world – again.

Jum turned the official-looking brown envelope over in his hands while Alma watched. 'It's from the Army,' he said. 'What the bloody hell are they writing to me about?'

He tore the envelope open. His face paled. 'I don't believe it! They want me in the bloody militia.' Jum was dumbfounded. 'I did my bit in the first bastard! I'm near fifty years old. I don't want to touch a gun again as long as I live. I'm not going!' He threw the letter on the table and stamped out.

Alma picked up the letter and read it. It said that William Bevan was to report to Malabar Rifle Range Camp for a four-week introductory course the following weekend. Full infantry kit, complete with rifle, was to be issued.

Alma talked long and hard to Jum to make him see the wisdom of obeying the letter. Reluctantly, he walked the 2 miles to the camp and presented himself.

During the course, Jum's demeanour soured. He became taciturn, sullen and moody. With the chance of overseas service remote but possible, he endured what he considered the idiotic soldier games with toy rifles at the Malabar camp.

The camp ended, but his presence was required on weekends every month. Insubordination, drunk on duty, AWL – nothing much had changed in twenty years.

Jum was demobilised out of the 7th Garrison Battalion on 30 October 1941, being considered 'unfit for the duties of his corps'. His days of fighting, firing weapons, insubordination and AWL were at an end.

1940 TO 1942

Jum carefully held the newborn baby as Alma rested in the comfortable white bed. It was quiet in the maternity section of the Royal Hospital for Women in Paddington.

'She's a beautiful, tiny girl. Another Little Blossom,' said Jum, with tears in his eyes.

Alma smiled. 'I think Patricia will be a lovely name for our daughter.'

Jum nodded as he smiled at the baby. And so Patricia Joan became the next addition to the Bevan family.

In 1942, Alma and Jum's fifth and final child, Terry, a boy, was born. Jum and Alma now had Reg, aged 10, George, 7, Patricia, 2, and baby Terry, all with healthy appetites. Money was very short.

But Alma was resourceful. The chicken coop was always full of activity and brilliant colour. Black and white Orpington hens, White Leghorns, Bantams and Rhode Island Reds threw themselves into a fierce free-for-all each day when feed and scraps were thrown into the coop.

The boy often watched the birds' antics for long periods. The large Rhode Island Red rooster was king of the coop. He would strut arrogantly amongst his hens, clucking and occasionally pecking at a hen to keep her under control. He was the boys' favourite. They had named him 'Red Man'.

Alma had nurtured a growing demand for eggs and fresh chickens. Sales of eggs were steady, at a shilling per dozen. After receiving orders, Alma would select the chickens from the coop. Jum would kill the birds, but Alma did the plucking and dressing, stuffing each fowl with tasty seasoning. She supplied an eager and reliable market and greatly boosted their family finances during the extended periods when Jum was unemployed.

After a full day's surfing at Maroubra Beach, the seven-year-old boy walked down the side passage of the house. He jerked to a stop as the loud squawking of panic-stricken chickens struck his ears.

Six chickens were strung up on the clothes line in readiness for slaughter. Loops of twine around their legs held them captive. One chicken, its throat slashed, was dripping blood. Another was flapping wildly, its cut throat spraying blood in all directions.

The boy stood still, in terrified fascination. Jum, sensing his presence, turned around. He was dressed in a singlet and shorts. He looked at his son, then turned back to his gruesome task. He sliced the necks of the next two birds. His son, who had never become used to the sight of slaughtered chickens, took a few paces towards the squawking mayhem. Jum turned again, his face set in a grim smile. 'Want to do the last one?' He offered his wooden-handled, razor-sharp knife. His singlet, soaked in chicken blood, clung to his chest.

The last bird, screeching in terror, awaited its turn. It was Red Man. Jum grimaced as he sliced the rooster's head off, then he tossed the head with its red comb and open eyes at George, who yelled in fear and panic as the head bounced off his chest, leaving a large bloodstain on his shirt. He ran down the side passage and cowered at the front gate – anywhere to escape the horrible scene.

Jum walked into the back of the house. Alma stood at the fuel stove, filling a large boiler with water.

'All finished?' asked Alma.

'Yeah, all done,' he replied. 'Young George didn't handle it too well, though.'

'What do you mean?' asked Alma as she turned from the stove.

'I gave him the chance to do the last bird, but he ran like buggery.'

'Oh, Jum, how could you be so insensitive? He's only a child,' said Alma, very annoyed. 'Where did he go?'

'Out the front, I think.'

Alma hurried to the front door and walked up to the boy, who was now standing nervously at the front gate. 'It's all right, darling, come to Mum!'

His heart pounding, the boy stood and hugged his mother around the waist. 'Mum, the blood was all over Dad. He was laughing. He wanted me to help him.' George shuddered and began to cry. 'That was old Red Man. He was our favourite!'

Alma held her son and gently stroked his hair. 'Why did Dad have to kill Red Man?' he cried.

Alma smiled sadly. 'Listen to me, my little boy. Sometimes things aren't nice, but they have to be done. Red Man was pecking the other chickens on their heads and hurting them. And he was pecking the eggs the hens were laying. So he had to go.'

Now dry-eyed, the boy asked, 'Couldn't we have put him in his own cage?'

'Yes, but would you like that, stuck in a cage all by yourself?'

The boy shook his head slowly. 'I s'pose not.'

As the sun began to set, mother and son walked into the house and back to the kitchen. Jum had cleaned up and changed. He called gruffly to his son, 'Come and sit with me.' The boy warily sat on his father's knee. Jum's arm encircled him gently. He could feel the strength in his father's arm as he snuggled into his chest.

Alma looked at the pair, Jum softly humming one of his favourite songs as the boy fell into a sound sleep. 'Don't wake him, Jum. Straight to bed, he's very tired.'

Jum rose carefully and carried the sleeping boy to his bedroom. Neatly tucking him in, Jum bent and tenderly kissed his son's head.

1943

Alma sat with her sister, Eda, watching the small boy as he dragged himself across the room. 'He should be taking a few steps, or at least standing,' said Alma.

'Bring him in to the Children's Hospital in Quay Street, near Dad's building,' said Eda.

The following morning, the two sisters stepped down from the tram at Central Railway and walked the 200 yards to the small hospital.

'I'm afraid your infant is suffering from cerebral palsy, Mrs Bevan,' the doctor said quietly.

'What can be done?' asked Alma.

'A leg brace will help, and special exercises daily are what we recommend. That's about all that can be done. The mobility in the child's right leg and arm are impaired. If it's any consolation, I've seen much worse.'

The two women left the hospital and walked 20 yards along the pavement. A polished brass plate with finely chiselled lettering – 'H. G. Johnson, Joinery' – was fixed beside the entrance to the large office.

Eda turned to Alma. 'I told Dad about your boy and that we'd be coming here today. I also told him how hard it is for you now that Jum's finding it impossible to get work, and that he's drinking heavily and has become violent.'

Alma's expression did not change.

Henry Johnson sat at his desk in the quiet office. He had considered what his elder daughter, Eda, had confided to him the previous day.

'Twelve years,' he thought. 'Has it been that long?' Twelve years since he had seen or spoken to his daughter. Had he been too hard on her? She was, after all, as tough as teak. He should have known that she wouldn't give an inch.

His only son, George, thirty-nine years of age, was in action in New Guinea, fighting the Japanese invaders. Both his wives had passed away. But he refused to give in to loneliness.

Alma turned to Eda, then averted her gaze. 'I can't, Ede. He won't speak to me.'

'Yes, he will, Al. Go on in!'

Nervously, Alma walked in. Eda followed, carrying the infant boy. Alma removed her hat, and her eyes adjusted to the light. Henry Johnson, now eighty-two years of age, stood up. He was still 6 feet 4, and straight-backed. With her heart in her mouth, Alma waited. Her father moved forward with his arms outstretched. She fell into his arms. He sank his face into Alma's hair. Soft tears rolled down his face.

'God, what have we done, Al? Twelve years – how could we be so stupid?'

Alma felt the strength of the father she had always loved and admired. She turned to Eda, who said, 'It's about time you two silly buggers spoke to each other.'

Alma smiled as Henry quickly wiped his eyes. The three had much to talk about.

LATE 1943

Bright sunlight heralded the start of another warm spring Saturday. Her chores completed, Alma idly moved through the vegetable garden near the chicken run.

Thanks to Jum's green thumb, the garden was ablaze with colour and growth. Large ripe tomatoes, beans, cauliflower, rhubarb and spinach fought for space.

Alma went to the shed to fetch a trowel so she could clear some weeds.

As she rummaged under the bench, she noticed a cardboard box sitting on a shelf.

Curious, she opened the box. Coloured ribbons and medals, a black diary and three letters were stacked neatly inside. She had seen the medals on many Anzac Days, when Jum, proudly wearing the medals, left early for the dawn service at the Cenotaph and later, the Anzac Day march through the streets of Sydney. The letters she had never seen before.

She opened the first one. It was dated December 1918 and was addressed to 'my Jum'. It was written in a mixture of English and French. The three letters were short and each was signed 'Anna'. She replaced the letters and put the box back on the shelf.

Remarkably sober for a Saturday afternoon, Jum walked up to Alma, standing at the stove. He slid his arms around her waist and kissed her gently on the nape of her neck. At the age of thirty-three, even after five children, Alma had retained a slim, neat figure.

She turned and kissed Jum lightly on the cheek and then asked, 'Jum, who's Anna?'

Jum looked at her, puzzled. 'Anna? I don't know any Anna.'

'I mean the one who wrote to you in French.'

Understanding dawned on Jum's face.

'Oh!' he said. 'That was in 1917–1918, during the fighting. You were – let me see,' he paused, 'all of seven or eight years old.'

'Yes, but who was she? You never mentioned her before.'

Jum looked through the window, his thoughts racing back to Belgium, Passchendaele, to Zillebeke and Ypres. He felt the pain of memories he had suppressed for so long.

'There were two Belgian girls Bob and I met in late 1916.'

Alma knew of Bob's death. She had also heard Jum mention the girl Bob married.

She asked nervously, 'Did you marry this Anna?'

'No, not even close!'

'Were you lovers?'

He paused. 'Yes, I suppose so. The times we were under attack were unbelievable. When we were out of the line on leave, we did anything that would get us back to normal.'

'Was she attractive? asked Alma. 'Beautiful?'

'She was very attractive, but not half as beautiful as you.'

'Did you love her?' Alma waited.

Jum dropped his eyes. 'Al, we did have a relationship, but I love you and only you. Anna and I finished in 1918, six years before you and I met. I haven't spoken to her or written to her since then, and that would be twenty-five years ago.'

Alma hugged Jum fiercely as his strong arms possessively encircled her waist. Her sudden childish jealousy evaporated. 'If ever I lost you, Jum, I think I'd die.'

They stayed locked in their embrace for some time.

EARLY 1944

With tears in his eyes, George pleaded with his mother. 'Please, Mum, please!'

Alma looked at her son. He was distraught. For days, a number of the local boys had hired horses from the small riding school on the vacant land of the Soldiers' Settlement, about half a mile from the Bevan home.

'They're all going, Mum,' he sobbed.

Alma looked sternly at George. 'You had the money, but spent it, didn't you?' she exclaimed crossly. 'Yesterday you had 4 shillings. Today you have nothing.'

George's heart ached. The ice-creams, block of chocolate and Saturday afternoon matinee had been too hard to resist.

'Mum, Reg is going. All the boys are going without me.'

Alma looked at Jum, who nodded slightly. 'Our money's hard to come by, my boy,' said Alma. 'We all have to work hard just to get enough money for food, let alone damned riding-school horses.'

George looked down glumly and shuffled his feet. Alma turned to her cupboard, took out the large tea urn and produced 4 shillings in shining coin. Tears gone, George jumped up and down in glee.

'We've had a good week with the eggs, Jum,' said Alma.

Jum grinned. 'Come on, then, we'll have to hurry!' Jum and his son ran from the house towards the riding school.

As the yard came into view, George's heart sank. 'Hoppy's gone, Dad,' he called in disappointment.

'Who's Hoppy?'

'He's my favourite horse.'

Father and son entered the horse yard, which was about 30 yards square. One horse remained, a new horse to the school. A dark,

377

impressive gelding, he pranced lightly, nostrils flaring, eyes wide open and showing the whites. The fat young yardman turned as George said, 'Where's Hoppy?'

'Gone,' he said. 'Demon's the only horse left.'

Jum studied the horse. His expert eye took in the prancing, the eyes, the head held high.

'I think he's too lively for you, son.'

At the thought of missing out on the ride, George said quickly, 'No, I'll be right, Dad.'

Demon was already saddled. The other yardman, a stooped older man, led the horse to the centre of the yard. George handed over the 4 shillings and nervously took the reins. The old yardman whispered to George, 'Watch him – he's frisky.'

As the boy swung into the saddle, Jum called, 'Keep a tight rein, George!' The right stirrup was 4 inches too long, and George fumbled with his right foot to find it. Demon, feeling the reins ease, snapped his haunches. George floated gracefully over the horse's head, landing on his side in the soft sand.

Jum ran to him. 'You all right, son?' he said as he gently lifted him.

'I think so, Dad. What happened?'

Jum carefully stood his son near the fence. The overweight yardman was grinning, amused by the boy's misfortune.

Jum's face had set in that hard line, the expression that told most men to steer clear of him. Without a word, Jum grabbed Demon's reins. The older yardman moved in. 'Lengthen that left stirrup,' Jum growled. 'Now hold the reins. This bloody saddle is loose.' Jum pulled the girth strap. The horse puffed out his chest.

'Demon, eh? I'll give you fucking Demon!' Still holding the girth strap with his left hand, Jum unleashed a vicious, right-handed punch into the horse's ribs. The horse grunted and exhaled, and Jum snapped the girth strap up a notch.

The old yardman nervously called, 'Watch him! He's a mean one.'

'I've handled bigger and tougher bastards than this one,' snarled Jum.

With nostrils flared and ears back, Demon eyed Jum aggressively. Jum held the reins tight and, in one fluid movement, was in the saddle. He wheeled the horse to the rear of the yard as horse and rider spun around. Jum booted the horse in the ribs and screamed in its ear.

Demon, not prepared for this type of treatment, bounded towards the 4-foot-high gate and cleared it with ease. Jum wheeled the horse and set off at full gallop, up the slight slope of sand and stunted brush.

George and the two yardmen watched in awe as Jum, whooping and yelling, rode the horse at full gallop along the ridge. He soon disappeared from view.

A good four minutes later, Jum and Demon appeared from the opposite direction, still at full gallop. Two hundred yards from the horse yard, Jum eased the gelding to a canter, and then trotted. The older yardman opened the gate. Demon was flecked with foam and breathing hard, and his eyes no longer showed white.

'Over here, Georgie,' said Jum. 'Just adjust the stirrups.'

With the stirrups adjusted, George mounted the horse, smiling and waving as he cantered off to join the main group walking ahead, three-quarters of a mile away.

Jum watched as George disappeared over the crest. He turned to the two yardmen. The older man spoke with respect. 'Where'd you learn to ride like that?' Jum smiled, for at fifty-two years of age he had not sat a horse in twenty-five years. The older man continued, 'You didn't seem scared at all.'

'You blokes don't know what fear is,' said Jum. 'Fear is a German Maxim machine gun spitting bullets up your arse as you try to gallop back to your own lines.'

Then he turned to the fat young yardman. 'You and I need to talk,' he said. The amusement left the young man's face as he took in Jum's glowering countenance. 'For all the trouble you've caused, including possible serious injury to my son, I want a reduction in price.'

The yard man quickly took the 4 shillings from his pocket.

'Two shillings back,' said Jum.

Without a word, the young man quickly handed over the coins.

Jum moved closer. 'Now, three things. Firstly, have a bath, you pig – you smell like shit. Secondly, have a bloody shave! And thirdly, if you ever put my boy on a horse like that again, I'll give you a lot more than I just gave that bastard Demon.'

Jum waved to the older yardman, who was now grinning, shut the gate and whistled as he headed home.

'Where do you reckon he learnt to ride?' said the younger yardman, chastened.

The other man answered, 'I've seen men ride like that before. They were a special breed, great horsemen. Mounted runners in the Great War were that good. They put their lives at stake every day delivering despatches between HQ and the line. Gutsiest bastards you'll ever see.'

Alma looked up as Jum entered the kitchen. 'Did George get away OK?'

'Yeah. We had a small problem, but we fixed it up.' Jum jingled the coins in his pocket.

'What have you done?' Alma asked apprehensively.

'We agreed on a reduction. You know, Al, this 2 shillings,' Jum paused as he took the coins from his pocket, 'would just about get me three schooners of beer.' He grinned.

Alma laughed. 'You've earned it.'

Later that evening, as Jum tucked his son into bed, George said quietly, 'Old Charlie, the yardman, said you must have been a mounted runner in the war to ride like that, Dad.'

Jum smiled. 'Yes, son, I was a mounted runner in France and Belgium. Now off you go to sleep.'

EARLY 1945

The six boys scrambled excitedly up the steep sandy slope. The Sydney sand, a beautiful yellow, was interspersed with root mat from the shrubbery above.

'We'll tunnel here,' said Benny. He was a year older than George and had a slightly larger build.

The mouths of the two tunnels grew as several pairs of hands dug with feverish haste.

'How deep are we, George?' asked Lochy, a neighbour's boy who was the same age as George.

'I think about 4 feet. How are the others going?' Lochy looked into the other tunnel.

'Real deep, I can hardly see Benny.' George peered into the second tunnel.

With a sudden, soft *whomp*, both tunnels collapsed. The boys looked at each other in terror and amazement. Lochy started screaming at the top of his voice. Three of the boys, overcome by fear, ran away.

A neighbour, who had been sitting on his porch, snatched a spade from his garden, leapt his front fence and ran to the sandhill. 'Ring the police, quickly!' he yelled to his wife.

George was digging frantically, trying to reach the buried Benny. The man frantically began hurling shovelfuls of sand down the slope.

Jum Bevan was walking home from the tram stop after work. He saw the flurry of activity on the sandhill and called out, 'What's going on?' He recognised George, ran up the slope and pushed his son out of the way. 'What's happened?'

Panting heavily, the man gasped, 'A boy, a boy buried in there!'

Jum grabbed the spade and furiously hurled sand. A minute went by. The sand caved in again. Jum doubled his efforts. It was now eight minutes since the collapse. Jum struck a soft object. He dropped the spade and fastened onto a small foot and leg. The other rescuer jumped into the trench, the steep sand walls teetering ominously above them. They dragged with all their might.

The limp eleven-year-old Benny slid face up from the tunnel. His mouth and nose were jammed with soft yellow sand. His eyes, open and unseeing, were also thick with sand.

'Roll him over!' yelled Jum as he shook sand from young Benny's mouth and nose. He commenced the rhythmical resuscitation of the era: hands spread on the boy's upper back, Jum started a measured rocking motion to bring air to his lungs.

By this time a crowd of ten or so people had gathered. The police siren sounded thinly in the distance. A young man had pushed through the crowd. 'I'm a doctor, keep going,' he told Jum.

'Pulse, any pulse?' Jum cried out. The doctor gently lowered the boy's wrist. He looked at Jum and slowly shook his head.

Jum kept going. 'Try again, try again!' he yelled in panic. The group of onlookers watched silently. Spittle dripped from his mouth as he kept up the rhythm.

The local police sergeant knelt on the sand and put his hand on Jum's shoulder. 'It's no good, Jum. We're too late.'

Jum slowly lifted the limp body of the lifeless Benny and clutched him to his chest. His moaning was muffled by the boy's body. Benny's head rolled. His eyes, caked with sand, did not move. His mouth, slightly open, rested on Jum's shoulder. Jum stared with horror at the lifeless young boy, his mind numbed. His voice broke in agony. 'Not again! Please, not again!'

The sergeant and the young doctor gently prised Jum's hands from the boy's slight body and laid him back on the sand. Jum slumped to his knees, his head in his hands.

At that moment, Benny's mother arrived. 'Where's my son, where's my son?' she screamed. The police sergeant gently held the hysterical mother as she fought to reach her dead boy.

An ambulance arrived and the two officers raced up the slope. The doctor spoke quietly to them. They fetched a stretcher from the vehicle, lifted the body and battled their way down the steep slope of sand to the ambulance.

Jum had not moved. He was quiet, and his panic had eased. The ambulance had left and the police car with Benny's mother had followed.

George knelt beside his father. 'Just about everyone has gone, Dad,' he said.

Jum turned, and his blank look turned to a glare. 'We'd best be going too,' he snapped.

'Will Benny be all right, Dad?' asked George.

'No, he won't,' Jum said angrily. 'He's finished. It's lucky any of you are still alive!'

The evening meal was quiet. Benny had lived just three houses away. Alma had spent two hours trying to comfort Benny's mother. Her face was tear-stained. She, too, was angry with George.

'That could have been you lying dead in the hospital' she cried out in fury. Everyone was silent. Jum had said nothing, but he had found Alma's cooking sherry. She now had two fewer bottles than she'd had yesterday.

Jum's hands were shaking badly. He threw his knife and fork onto his plate and stamped out.

'What were you doing anyway, you silly boy?' said his mother. 'You know it's dangerous to play in that steep sand.'

George looked at his mother's face. He saw a combination of fear, relief and anger.

'We saw a movie with soldiers digging tunnels,' he said. 'We were playing soldiers and we wanted our own tunnels.'

Jum listened from the doorway. He reached over and dragged George out of his chair. He raised his voice. 'You are never to play soldiers. Soldiers get killed, just like Benny. Do you want to be killed like Benny?' He shook George until the boy's teeth rattled. 'Do you?' he yelled.

Terrified, the boy broke away and ran from the house. The dusk was deepening as George arrived back at the sandhill. He carefully climbed to the two collapsed tunnels. He sat and looked at the place where Benny had been dragged out. The tears started. 'We were only playing,' he thought. 'Why did Dad get so mad at me?' He sat there for a long time.

Sitting in his backyard, Jum had not moved for an hour. The darkness had closed in, and the evening was chilly. The third bottle of sherry, half-empty, rested between his feet.

Alma knelt before him. 'Come inside, Jum. You've been here for hours.'

Jum looked up. Alma could not see his bloodshot, bleary eyes in the dark. He had trouble speaking. 'Was he part of this?'

'Who? What are you talking about?'

Jum slurred, 'George! He was there when Valerie died, and now little Benny. Is he to blame?'

'Are you mad, Jum?' said Alma. 'You're talking about your own son. Do you realise what you're saying?'

Jum's tormented mind demanded explanations for any event he could not understand. He looked for somewhere to lay the blame. The old guilts returned.

His voice was tremulous. 'I'm so mixed up, Al. I don't know what's happening to me.'

Later, when Alma was asleep, Jum held on to the bedroom door for support as he studied his sleeping son. He stood there, swaying slightly, for more than ten minutes. Eventually, he stumbled back to his own room and fell onto the bed in a drunken stupor.

1945

The war in Europe was over, but the rationing of food, clothing and petrol was to continue well into 1947. Jum was once again made redundant. He walked around endlessly, looking for work, but to no avail.

Jum and Alma often missed meals to ensure their four children were well-fed. The small leg of lamb for Sunday lunch ensured the children had full stomachs on the Sabbath. Jum and Alma ate their Sunday lunch after the children had eaten. It was a meal of dry toast with dripping and the hot, piquant taste of nasturtium leaves for flavour.

Jum was drinking more often than not. Late Saturday afternoon was a good time for the children to disappear. But worse than the drinking was the violence. Alma had stopped trying to console Jum during his violent, drunken fits.

The day after one of his escapades, Alma's quiet rectitude would make Jum realise that he had to answer for his behaviour. He was usually desperately embarrassed and sought forgiveness.

The ten-year-old boy tugged at his mother's dress. Alma looked down at her son.

'What's wrong with Dad? Is he sick again?'

'Yes, your father's sick. He's been sick for a long time.'

'Mum, he just lies there looking at the ceiling!'

'Yes, and he doesn't need nosy little boys to disturb him.'

The boy crept into the dim room. His father lay staring at the ceiling. He did not move, nor did he blink. The boy knelt by the bed. He gently laid his small hand on his father's arm. There was no response.

Later, Jum appeared in the kitchen, rubbing his face. 'I'm hungry, Al. We have any food?'

Alma smiled as she reached for the meal she had prepared four hours earlier.

Adele Jenkins sat by the bedside, holding her brother's hand. His eyes fluttered open.

'Is that you, Adele?'

'Yes, Claude. Lie still, I'm here.'

Rector Claude Jenkins's face had lost its colour. His thin, grey hair was limp and damp. The cancer had spread rapidly, and his condition was deteriorating.

Jim Gillies sat on the other side of the bed. Jenkins had refused to go to hospital. 'I will spend my last days in the church I love and worship in,' he had insisted.

The doctor had shaken his head sadly. 'There's nothing we can do. I'll come daily and administer pain relief. If he's happy here, he should stay.'

Adele and the Reverend Jim Gillies each held a hand. Jenkins's speech, now only a whisper, was ragged. 'Are you there, Jim?'

Gillies squeezed his hand. 'Yes, Claude.'

Jenkins spoke again, his voice a trifle stronger. 'Are we going to Zillebeke tonight? Why don't you go round up Jum and Bob and Harold, and Wagga and Ron?'

'Of course, Claude,' said Jim, through tears. 'Anything for you.'

Jenkins's face eased into a wan smile, his eyes closed. 'We'll have a great sing-along. Anna and Jeanne will come, and Jum and I will play.'

Adele lowered her head and sobbed quietly.

Jenkins's breathing became erratic. His grip tightened as his mouth opened slightly, then his hands fell limp as his breathing ceased. Claude Jenkins was now with his God, the God he had loved and worshipped for most of his life. Adele lay her head on her brother's pillow.

Jim Gillies, heartstricken and shaking, found it hard to relinquish Jenkins's hand – the hand that had brought him from the barbaric fanaticism of the Western Front into the pure life of his religious love.

Jum sat at the kitchen table. His hands were shaking uncontrollably. The telegram delivery boy pedalling down the street.

Alma's gaze followed the disappearing cyclist. She hurried into the house and called, 'Jum! Jum! Where are you?' She stopped as soon as she saw his face. 'What is it?' she asked.

He picked up the telegram and held it out to her. It was brief and to the point.

'Rector Claude Jenkins passed away today. Please contact Rev. Jim Gillies.'

'Oh, God, no!' cried Alma. She knew that Jenkins's death would have a savage impact on Jum.

The small Wenden Village church was packed to overflowing. Hundreds of mourners had jammed the church and spread into the neat gardens and out across the gravel street. It was an unprecedented outpouring of grief and admiration for this man of God who had touched scores of people in his lifetime.

Former captains, majors, brigadiers, colonels, corporals, sergeants and privates – they all came. All aged, some stooped, wearing medals and campaign ribbons with pride.

Reverend Jim Gillies conducted the service, broadcast by way of a hastily set up loudspeaker that had seen better days.

Gillies, visibly shaken and saddened, addressed the silent crowd for a full hour. He told the story of how Jenkins had lifted him from a life of despair. He spoke of Jenkins's time in the gun positions; his piano playing with Jum in the *estaminets*; how he had presided at the marriage of Bob Buchannen to Jeanne Ricaud, and later at Bob's funeral.

Gillies conjured vivid memories of Pozières, where Jenkins had spent many nights carrying lighted candles, saying prayers for those who fell at Sausage Gully. He spoke of the cheerfulness, ready ear and understanding that had elevated Jenkins to a special place in the eyes of his men.

Brigadier Robbie Tideswell spoke of the time after Sausage Gully. 'Reverend Jenkins told me he wished to go into the line to experience what the men were handling every day, so he could be on an equal footing with them and understand their pain. I replied that a dead padre was of no use to us. His answer was basically, "Better a dead padre than a live one not carrying out his duties." That was our man,' said Tideswell. 'Courageous, brave, determined. He touched all our lives in some way.'

As the service came to an end, few eyes remained dry.

Jum spoke to Reverend Gillies. 'What are you going to do now, Gill?'

Gillies smiled. 'I'm applying for the position here. Hopefully, I'll be accepted.'

Harold McErbain waited patiently with his wife Lucy. Adele finished her conversation with a grey-haired woman on the church steps then ushered them into the rectory. McErbain took Adele's hand. 'I'm sure you realise, Adele, how much Claude meant to us all.'

'Yes. And you know he always spoke of you as "his boys".'

'He gave me some advice in 1917 in Belgium,' said Harold. 'It took some time for me to accept, but I did follow it eventually. Lucy and I now have a fine family and a strong, committed love for one another.' Lucy squeezed McErbain's hand as he spoke. 'Our family will be forever indebted to your wonderful brother.'

The train ride from Hornsby to Sydney was quiet until some wag in one of the packed carriages started singing, 'Mademoiselle from Armentières.' The tune was picked up, grew, roared and spread throughout the train. It was a heartfelt testimony to a man of the cloth, a small man with the heart of a giant.

DECEMBER 1945

Although the war in Europe had come to an end with Germany's unconditional surrender, the fighting in the Pacific was still ferocious. The American advances were gaining momentum. At any one time, there were thousands of US troops in Sydney awaiting their despatch to the various theatres of war in the Pacific.

Malabar Rifle Range, south of Sydney, was constantly busy, as the young American GIs and marines honed their weaponry skills.

Malabar Primary School was just 400 yards from the guarded entrance to the range. A few of the boys from the school, including George, had spent years searching and exploring the maze of concrete tunnels connecting the range with the large 6-inch gun emplacements on the cliffs between South Maroubra and Malabar.

There was a lot to fascinate ten-year-old boys. Live firing practice, using the 6-inch guns at targets being towed 2 miles out at sea, was unbelievably loud in the concrete bunkers housing the guns. The boys were forbidden entry to these areas, though a few of the artillerymen made exceptions occasionally and allowed the boys to witness a few rounds of firing. The blast and concussion of the guns, followed by the clanging of the shell cases on the concrete floor, was both frightening and thrilling.

The other forbidden activity was to be in the target bays during live practice on the rifle range. But the boys, full of confidence and swagger, moved along the target bays as if they were being paid to be there.

Hauling on the ropes to lift and lower targets was pretty boring work for the marines. The boys eagerly took over, and were paid with chewing gum, hats, insignia and other objects that boys like to collect, whilst the 'Yanks' lounged around smoking their Lucky Strike and Camel cigarettes.

One Wednesday afternoon, Lochy and a few of the fifth and sixth class boys sat around the cricket pitch in front of the school. The Yanks are on the range,' said Lochy. 'Anyone want to go to the butts?'

Three agreed. 'What about you, Bev?' asked Lochy.

George's father had warned him once before that the range was out of bounds. 'Yeah, I'll come,' he said.

It wasn't long before the five boys were in the target bay, taking over the target manipulation. It was the first time in the butts for ten-year-old Alan, a boy who was not usually included in the group's activities. He was nervous for the first few minutes, until he became accustomed to the cracking sound followed by a heavy thud as the bullets smashed into the high back butt.

His curiosity was aroused, and he decided to see where the bullets were coming from. He stepped onto the frame of one target and peered over the edge at the men firing 200 yards away.

A marine sergeant yelled in horror as he ripped Alan from the frame. Not in time though, for an errant bullet had clipped the concrete top of the butt, spraying Alan's face with concrete chips.

The sergeant quickly examined the boy's face, breathing a sigh of relief when he saw that the injuries to Alan's face were minor. A catastrophe had been averted.

Suddenly, the target bay was crowded with officers, American and Australian, attempting to determine what had happened. The five boys were marched to the CO's office in the small block of buildings away from the firing lines.

The local police sergeant arrived with a constable, as the story had been relayed to the police. The sergeant turned to George. 'This is the second time, young Bevan, that I've had to come here, and you've been here both times. You were warned before not to come here during live firing.' He glared at the boys. 'Your parents can handle this.'

The police car deposited each boy at his home. The parents were informed of the boy's escapades. If they were not at home, a note was left.

Alma was not amused. In fact she was livid. 'I'll let your father deal with this,' she said. 'You're getting to be more than I can handle.'

George slunk into his bedroom, fearing the worst.

At 6.30 pm Jum arrived home. He had only had a few beers, but he was in a belligerent mood.

'The police were here today,' Alma said. 'They brought George home. Five boys from the school were on the range today. Apparently one idiot stuck his head up and just missed being shot, but his face is injured from flying stones.'

Suddenly, Jum felt ill. At the thought of his son or a small friend having their head exploded by rifle fire, he broke into a cold sweat and his hands trembled. Jum had seen it all – men climbing out of trenches, their heads blown off by machine-gun fire; lifeless bodies falling back and pinning men down; the screaming of men in agony; Ron's corpse in Wagga's arms ... The memories kept flooding back.

George stood beside his mother. Jum's anger mounted into a cold rage.

'I warned you before about the range.' He strode to his bedroom, reappearing with a 3-foot plaited leather whip, standard issue for mounted runners in the Great War. Stiff and vicious, the whip was designed to force recalcitrant or hard-to-handle horses to obey without question. The whip was never designed for use on a ten-year-old boy.

Jum grabbed George by his upper left arm and held it in a vice-like grip. George pleaded in terror, 'Please, Dad, I won't do it again!'

'I'll teach you a lesson you won't forget.'

Jum slashed the whip across the boy's calves and George let out a scream of agony as the white-hot pain seared through his legs. A second, a third cut. Alma grabbed Jum's wrist, stopping the next stroke. George was struggling madly to free himself, but he had underestimated his father's strength.

'No more, Jum! No more!' yelled Alma.

Jum, wild-eyed, had not finished, but Alma fiercely held on to his wrist and he eased his grip on the boy.

'Run! Run!' screamed Alma.

George needed no more encouragement and ran from the house as if the devil himself were after him. He leapt the low front fence and ran 300 yards down the unmade road. He sat down, crying and in severe pain.

His friend, Lochy, ran up. 'What happened?'

George rolled on his side, sobbing, showing the large red weals that criss-crossed his legs. He couldn't stop crying. Lochy looked on in subdued disbelief.

'Jesus, did he give you some!' Lochy ran to a puddle at the edge of the road that contained thick yellow clay. He quickly applied the soft clay to the weals as George's sobbing subsided. He sat by his friend as the pain diminished.

'What happened to you?' asked George, his voice ragged.

'My old man was too pissed to do anything. He'll have forgotten by tomorrow.'

The boys sat in the street, talking until late that night.

The next day, at school, the teacher on yard duty, John Slater, approached George and said quietly, 'The headmaster wishes to see you in his office, Bevan. Go now.'

George, full of apprehension, knocked on the headmaster's door.

'Come in,' called a voice. Jack Sheridan swivelled in his chair. 'Ah, Bevan.' He paused. 'Show me your legs, son.' George's heart beat furiously as he turned around.

The headmaster ran his hand over George's leg. 'How did this happen?'

'We went to the range yesterday, sir.' He hesitated. 'My father had warned me never to go there again. He was very mad at me.'

George stood quietly as the headmaster completed his handwritten note.

'I want you to take this home to your mother, now, before classes start.' He folded the note and placed it in an envelope, sticking the flap down. George ran home, clutching the letter.

Alma anxiously read the note. 'The headmaster wants to see me immediately. What's happened?'

George hung his head. 'He saw my legs.'

Alma turned to George and looked at his calves. Her hand flew to her mouth. 'My God, I had no idea!' Her face was white.

The headmaster ushered Alma and George into his office.

'Mrs Bevan,' he said, 'I know you're a good mother. Your children are always well-dressed and well-fed, which is more than I can say for some of the more unfortunate children we teach. What happened to the boy's legs?'

Alma, distressed, dabbed her eyes with a handkerchief as she said, 'George has become a handful. He's disobedient and unruly. But this should never have happened.'

'I see George was part of a group on the range yesterday,' said Sheridan. Alma nodded. He continued, 'It was lucky the other boy wasn't killed or badly injured. I have the police report here.'

'George's father was furious. I've never seen him so wild. He told him he'd teach him a lesson he wouldn't forget.'

'I'm glad you came to see me,' the headmaster said. 'Consider this matter closed. But I must warn you, if I see any evidence of this sort of treatment again, I will contact the relevant authorities immediately.'

'Mr Sheridan, I guarantee this will not happen again.'

That afternoon, George went into his parent's bedroom. He found the whip leaning in the corner. He examined it and slashed the double bed before putting it back.

That evening, he refused to look his father in the face. The respect George now had for his father was born of fear, not of love and care. Their relationship had inexorably changed.

The next time George Bevan ventured onto a rifle range was eight years later, during his National Service at Old Holsworthy Army Camp. He had learnt his lesson well.

1946

One Saturday afternoon, low cloud from the south, dark and ominous, scudded across the beaches south of Sydney. Jum watched as the tram came to a stop outside the Doncaster Hotel. He swayed and stared belligerently at the tram guard as he swung into a rear compartment. 'You're too pissed to get on the tram, mate,' said the guard.

Jum handed over the twopence fare as the guard glared at him, then slumped onto a seat. At his stop, he stumbled across the tram tracks. His eyes, glazed and red, told the story of a marathon drinking bout with a few 2nd Division mates from France. He slowly wove his way along the road edge.

The loud backfire of the passing car galvanised Jum into action. He leapt sideways into the brush, his hands covering his head. With a thumping heart, he carefully looked over the bushes. The dusk was slowly descending. He saw nothing. 'Where are you, you Boche bastards?' he muttered. He crouched, then ran across the bitumen road into the hilly paddock, searching for any sign of movement. Eventually, he forgot about the phantom enemy and headed home. His progress was slow and laborious.

Alma stood at the window and watched anxiously as Jum fumbled with the gate latch. He swayed to the front door.

Alma had seen enough. She hurried to the backyard, pulling Reg with her. In the yard, she paused at the clothes line and watched the back door. Jum appeared and stumbled into the yard. She whispered to Reg, 'Hide by the fence, quickly!'

Jum lurched towards Alma. 'Is 'at you, Bob? I think there are some Boche bastards around.'

Alma moved towards him and said, 'Come inside, Jum, out of the cold.'

Jum swayed on his heels in a drunken stupor. 'Boche bastard!' he snarled as he threw a punch at the blurred face before him.

Luckily for Alma, the blow had half its normal power. She felt the bone in her nose crunch as she fell to the ground. Blood ran down her chin.

Her eyes filled with tears as the pain bit home. She scrambled away as Jum, mouthing obscenities, stumbled after her.

Reg ran crying to her and pulled her towards the side passage. Alma fearfully looked over her shoulder and stood on the path, where she had a view of both the backyard and the front gate.

Jum appeared inside at the kitchen window, blearily looking out into the darkness. Whether it was Alma he saw or his own reflection in the window, his reaction was brutal. He punched the glass. As he withdrew his arm, a sharp, spear-shaped piece of glass imbedded itself deep in the underside of his forearm.

Alma carefully approached the smashed window. Jum sat on a tiny stool, holding out his arm as the blood dripped rapidly into an ever-increasing pool around his feet.

'Quickly,' she said to Reg, 'go and see what your father has done. But be careful – he doesn't know what he's doing.'

The boy went in the back door, scooting past the laundry and into the kitchen. His father was counting the drops of blood running down and off his elbow. 'I've cut my arm,' he slurred.

The boy ran outside to his mother, crying in shock. 'Mum, there's blood all over the floor! It's running out his arm!'

Alma ran to the neighbour's house. 'Could you please call an ambulance?' she said. 'Jum's severed an artery in his arm.'

Fifteen minutes passed before the ambulance turned into the street. The two officers quickly followed Alma as she ran into the house. At the sight of the uniforms, Jum became enraged. 'More Boche bastards!' he screamed.

The two men quickly subdued Jum, who was badly weakened by alcohol and blood loss.

'Please don't hurt him!' cried Alma.

The larger officer held Jum's good arm behind his back while the other bandaged the bleeding arm. 'Hurt him! I'll break his bloody arm if he doesn't quieten down!' he said.

Jum sat down on the kitchen chair, quiet at last.

'What's happened to you, love?' the larger officer softly asked Alma.

'Nothing, just a family argument,' she replied, tight-lipped.

The younger man led Jum to the ambulance. 'He'll need that arm sutured. We'll take him to casualty at Prince Henry.'

'Can I come with you?' Alma asked.

'Of course. We'll wait in the ambulance for you.'

Alma sat in the front of the van with one officer while the other watched Jum in the back.

She leant out the window of the ambulance. 'Will you be OK, darling?' she asked Reg. He nodded as the ambulance turned and drove towards the hospital.

The boy was transfixed by the large pool of blood. With his heart in his mouth, he began to clean up the kitchen floor. He could not comprehend the extent and bright redness of the blood.

The following Monday, Alma left home early and went to see the family doctor.

'What happened, Alma?' he asked gently.

Alma, highly embarrassed, began to cry softly. 'It wasn't his fault. He was as drunk as hell and was calling me a "Boche bastard". He punched the air. I just happened to be in the way.' She looked at the doctor in despair. 'What happened to these men in France and Belgium, doctor?'

The doctor drew a deep breath before he said, 'Men suffered awfully on the Western Front,' he said. 'Most won't even talk about their experiences. The mental stress they endured day after day affected a large number of them. I understand your husband was one of these. The medical label given to it was "neurasthenia", and that covered hysteria, shell shock and any other mental condition, including certifiable insanity. But you trained at Broughton Hall, as I recall – you'd have seen many of these conditions.'

'Yes,' said Alma. 'My time at Broughton Hall really opened my eyes. But I thought Jum only drank when he caught up with his wartime mates. He seemed to be normal most of the time early on in our marriage – although because he had no trade, he found work hard to come by, and that did have an effect on him.

'Then he was brought so low by the loss of our little daughter. The depression years were dreadful. So, are you saying that he's

396

still suffering because of the war – not just because of what happened to him when he got back home?'

'Yes, certainly,' answered the doctor. 'Unfortunately, when these men returned to Australia, they were ignored by the government, left to fend for themselves. We've been witnessing the aftermath of this frightful episode for years. It's become a huge problem. Alma, it's obvious that your husband suffered greatly. Without help, he'll only slide deeper into depression. He needs support and counselling.'

'I don't know what to do,' said Alma. 'He won't seek medical help or let me organise any assistance. But we can't go on like this.'

The doctor rose to examine Alma's nose. 'Well, you have some cartilage damage. I'll pack it with tape.'

Alma went home with her nose neatly taped. Jum sat in the kitchen. He was sober. When Alma walked in, he started. He rose from his chair and moved towards Alma, stammering guiltily. 'What happened?'

Alma looked at Jum, searching his face, his blue-grey eyes showing a mixture of pain, embarrassment and disbelief. 'Jum,' she said carefully, 'if you ever touch me again, I'll leave.'

Jum sat with his head in his hands as the realisation hit home. Alma placed her arm around his shoulders. She gently stroked his face as he turned and clutched her desperately, sobbing for forgiveness.

For a time, Jum stopped drinking. He finished various house repairs and projects that he had started long before. He found and planted new runners in the lawn, and trees appeared alongside the boundary fences. The chicken run, shabby and in disarray, was transformed into a neat, tightly wired enclosure.

Six weeks passed. One Saturday evening, Alma heard the singing before she saw the two men at the gate. Jum, lurching, barely able to stand, dragged his companion, who was in a similar state, into the lounge room. Jum's arm rested on his friend's shoulder. The friend wore a silly, lopsided grin.

'Thish's Chicka. Me and 'im were at Lark'ill in '17.'

'Hello, Chicka,' Alma said politely. 'Please have a seat.'

The two men sat down heavily at the dining table, where Alma had set out food. They wasted no time in disposing of their large hot meals. Chicka mumbled his thanks. He stood unsteadily and waved farewell as he left. The freshly opened bottle of sherry was now empty.

Jum swayed as he approached Alma. She glanced behind her to make sure the back door was open. She was not going to be caught again.

'Why'd you send Chicka away?' he asked pugnaciously.

Alma quickly ran into the yard. Jum followed, but stumbled and fell down the back step. Alma grabbed his arm as she helped him to his feet. All Jum's reason had evaporated. His alcohol-fuelled brain reacted with violence, the violence that had been his companion for most of his adult life. His left arm came swinging at Alma.

On this occasion, Alma anticipated the blow and dodged it. She had often watched as Jum trained on the heavy bag in the shed. In admiration she had observed his neat footwork and the telling blows from both hands as he slammed away at the bag. She now danced, as Jum had, then stepped in and, with all her strength, smashed her right fist into Jum's mouth.

'How d'you like that?' she yelled as Jum fell backwards onto the lawn, his split lip bleeding. He looked baffled and unsure as he sat trying to comprehend what had just happened.

Alma ran inside, snatched her coat and ran along the street. She returned two hours later. The children were at home, huddled together listening to the radio. 'Dad's in bed, snoring,' said Reg.

'All right, all wash and into bed,' said Alma.

Jum didn't move throughout the night. Alma's hand felt very sore, though it was with sad satisfaction that she endured the pain.

1947

Alma spoke quietly on the telephone and Henry Johnson listened resignedly at the other end. 'Dad, I thought he was settling down, but his age is against him when he's looking for work now. The returned men from the Second War are young and strong, and they're getting the jobs. He's getting frustrated, drinking heavily and becoming violent. He lies on the bed for hours sometimes, staring and not moving. It's getting to the stage where I'm concerned for my own safety, and the children's. He won't see a doctor about it. I don't know what to do.'

Her father spoke reassuringly. 'If you decide to leave, you can move into the home at Randwick. There's only one tenant upstairs. Take over the ground floor.'

After some discussion, the two sisters, Alma and Eda, finally agreed that the time had arrived. Reg, the eldest boy, had already started at Sydney High School and George was about to begin at Randwick High.

Alma stood beside the truck, staring at the house she had built. 'So much love, so much effort,' she thought, 'all for nothing!' Tears welled in her eyes.

Her seven-year-old daughter, Patricia, hugged her mother's knees. 'Don't cry, Mummy! Please don't cry!'

Mother and daughter climbed into the cabin of the vehicle. Laden with furniture, the truck departed for Randwick. Alma could no longer hold back her tears.

Jum jumped from the tram, his step light. He was excited. The job was his, 4 pounds 10 shillings per week. He was overjoyed and hummed as he hurried home. He stopped by the grassy edge of the road where small yellow dandelions grew in profusion.

Carefully he collected a large handful of flowers, deftly twisting a length of stem around them to make a posy. He was sober and his mind was clear as he inserted his key in the front door.

Dusk made the house dim. He switched on the light and noticed the strange emptiness of the house. Then he saw the note on the table.

Jum,

> *I sit here in tears, with my heart breaking. What I am doing is the hardest thing I have ever done. I'm leaving you, and taking the children.*
>
> *I've fought myself over this decision, but in the end it's the only sensible thing left for me to do. Your drinking and violence towards me, and at times to our son, I can't endure any longer.*
>
> *From the first day I set eyes on you, I adored you. From my early days as a teenager, you were my hero, so strong, so determined, so manly. I loved it when you played and sang to me. I was as enraptured as any young girl could be. I forsook my father, against his wishes, to be with you.*
>
> *In those early years, we did it tough. Very little food, few clothes and no money, but we got by. And then came the soul-destroying loss of our Valerie. I knew, more than you did yourself, what she meant to you. But we had four other children. Maybe that wasn't enough?*
>
> *I know you've fought the demons all our married life. I've watched you struggle with the memories, but with little success.*
>
> *We both know there's no cure for what ails you, except, as a few others have done, to put it all behind you. That's easy for me to say, but it's in your head, not mine.*
>
> *Jum, I have loved you fiercely, but the bright burning candles of my love you have one by one extinguished over the years.*
>
> *I worry endlessly what will become of you.*
>
> *I can't write anymore, I am too distressed.*
>
> *Damn it all, Jum.*

Alma.

He choked in shock as a band of pain constricted his chest. The flowers dropped from his trembling hand. He sat on the tiny stool he had made for his baby daughter, Valerie. He was still holding the note.

In utter desolation, he reread it. He sank to his knees on the floor, and dropped his head into his hands.

With despair, he realised the size of his loss. The person he should have nurtured, cared for and loved like no other was gone.

Devastated by remorse, he lifted his hands, looked up and screamed, 'Almighty God, what have I done?'

LATE 1947

The tram approached Coogee terminus. The early afternoon sun was bright and high in the sky. The tram slowed, its wheels squealing.

The twelve-year-old boy, late for the swimming carnival at the Coogee Aquarium Pool, glanced up. Facing him in the next compartment, behind the glass partition, was his father, staring at him intently. The tram was otherwise empty.

The boy's heart skipped a beat, the hair on his neck stood on end. He felt the chill of fear envelop him. This was the man the family had left months previously. He jumped from the tram as it slowed to a halt. His father called to him, 'Wait, wait! I just want to talk to you!' With fear in his heart, the boy stopped and turned.

Jum walked towards him with his palms outstretched. 'Can we talk?'

The boy looked into his father's face, a face he had grown to fear. He shook his head slowly from side to side. 'That's funny,' he thought, 'you used to be so much taller.'

Terror rose in the boy's throat as his father drew nearer. He turned and ran frantically towards the beach, leaping over the stone wall at the northern end. Without so much as a backward glance, the swimming carnival forgotten, he sprinted along the beach and under the large shark tower, fear making his feet fly.

He reached the southern end of the beach and slumped exhausted to the sand, panting heavily as his towel and togs fell out of his bag. He threw a backward glance along the beach, fully expecting his father to be close behind him. But the beach was empty.

'What are you doing, running like that?' A dark-haired boy about his age stood in front of him.

'Nothing, just having a run, that's all.'

'Come on, then, I'll race you to the shark tower,' the dark-haired boy challenged.

The dark-haired boy won easily. He said, through gulps of air, 'See that shed under the promenade, over there? The blokes in the Surf Club leave their boards and skis in there. When it gets near dark, we take them out and crack a few waves. It's great fun!'

'What if they find out?'

'They'll kick our arses,' he laughed, 'but don't worry, they can't catch us.'

The blond boy asked, 'What's your name?'

'John, John LeMarseny, but just call me Lemmo. What's yours?'

'George Bevan.'

'Well, with that silly haircut, I'll call you Ugly.' Lemmo and George laughed together as George rubbed his blond crewcut. The boys talked, as boys will do, about all and sundry. Eventually the conversation turned to their fathers.

'Was your old man in the war?' asked John.

George felt a pang of shock. Only an hour earlier, he had run in abject terror from his father. He knew his father had been in a war a long time ago. He remembered his father on Anzac Days, wearing his ribbons and medals, proudly marching with the other thousands of similarly decorated men, swinging along George Street, Sydney, preceded by the proudly borne brigade banner. George's excitement would always rise as he watched his father smile and wave.

Sometimes he would run under the barricade and march a few yards, holding his father's hand. It was hard not to be proud of his father during these moments. But then he thought of the nights when his mother would push him from their house with a warning. 'Quick! Go into the yard, your father's in one of his moods. Come back later.'

And yet on some occasions, his father would sit him on his knee and describe photographs in his wrestling book. 'Big Chief Little Wolf', with his white feathered headband, was George's favourite. He ached to be proud of his father.

'Yeah, my old man was in the war – the first one, not the one that's just finished,' he said to his new friend.

The boys looked at the surf.

'So was mine. My real father's name was Ernie Buckleton,' said John. 'He died a long time back. He got very sick after the war. He used to say the gas had got him. Anyway, I hardly remember him. He was sick with TB and died in Prince of Wales Hospital. My mum married my new dad years ago. Denis is his name. He's a good bloke.'

'My father's name is Jum. We left home a few months ago. We don't see him anymore.'

John jumped up. 'Let's have a swim before it gets too cold.'

They hit the water together, the fair-haired boy easily first past the break where the small surf curled and broke. They laughed as they splashed water in each other's faces.

They had a lot in common, and one thing in particular: neither would ever see his father again.

1949

Alma divorced Jum Bevan in 1949. The judge cited the causes as physical cruelty, drunkenness and a constant threat of violence.

Alma, in tears, stood outside the court supported by her sister Eda. Jum was 20 feet away, holding onto the steel picket fence for support. He was breathing heavily, staring at Alma, trying to comprehend the situation.

Alma, shocked at his appearance, said, 'Oh, Ede, he looks so small and lost! And he's wearing that awful tie.' She turned away, desperately trying to control herself.

Eda walked over to Jum and put her hand on his shoulder. 'How are you, Jum?'

Jum's face was pallid and lined, his blue-grey eyes full of emotional pain. 'I've been better, thanks, Ede.'

'Well, Jum, I guess it's all over now,' she said sadly. 'If it's any consolation, I've always said you were a good man and a hard worker. But you did drink too much!'

'I know,' Jum said wrily. 'I had a great apprenticeship in France and Belgium.'

Eda leant forward and kissed him lightly on the cheek, then walked back to Alma.

'For God's sake, get me out of here, Ede,' said Alma. 'Otherwise I'll make a complete fool of myself.'

Eda looked around and spied a vacant taxi. 'Come on, we're going by cab.'

'I haven't the money, you know that.'

'I have, so don't argue.'

Once in the cab, Alma sobbed. Eda put her arm around her younger sister and cried.

Jum watched, unable to move, as the cab drove off.

At that moment he realised that it was finished. He sagged, and the sun glistened on the faint sheen of sweat on his forehead. His grey hair, now thin, was still neatly combed.

He walked unsteadily in the midday sun to Elizabeth Street. The tram rattled its way south past Maroubra Junction, with Jum the only passenger.

As the taxi passed Centennial Park, Alma, now recovered enough to talk, said, 'Do you think Dad was right from the start that Jum was wrong for me?'

Eda reflected. 'He may have been tough on you, but he was smart. Truth be told, Al, you were tough on Dad.'

Alma looked at Eda. 'Do you think the problem was me being so young, and Jum being much older?'

'Yes, Al, part of it. Remember that Dad dealt with men all his life – not only his employees, but his customers too. He could read a man backwards. I think Dad knew at the start that Jum had been damaged by the war, and he knew that returned soldiers had problems coming back into civilian life. Also the drinking – you know Dad's a virtual teetotaller.'

Alma smiled. 'Well, Jum certainly made up for Dad.'

She sat in silence for a moment, then said, 'What about Beatrice Wenban? Do you think Dad sent her round to scare me before we got married?'

'I honestly don't know, Al. Dad never mentioned it to me, and he told me everything.'

Alma sat watching the trees slide past. 'I wonder what Jum would have been like with no war to turn his mind.'

Eda did not answer.

This man had been strong and determined, so kind at times, a passionate lover. He had always tried to work.

She remembered one evening in the late 1930s, after he had been tramping the streets searching endlessly for work, any work. The soles of his shoes were worn through. George had cut hard cardboard inner soles for his father, but the uppers of the shoes were polished and shining. Jum had always said, 'Looking for a job requires neatly combed hair, a clean-shaven face, nice clothes and polished shoes.'

Now, twenty-three years later, their union was over.

She still had her four children. Her father had let her move into the residence at Randwick. Her main concern was to raise her children in a loving, peaceful home. With dry eyes, she faced the future with fierce determination.

RANDWICK, 1950

Alma stretched up to the clothes line and squeezed the last peg onto the sheet. It was late afternoon and the sun, still hot and fiery, hung in the sky. She would have to hurry: the publican at the Royal Hotel was annoyed by lateness and this was a job she could not afford to lose.

Alma turned to the house.

'Hi, Al.'

Her heart thumped at the voice. Jum stood 10 feet away on the path. She had not seen him for over a year, not since the divorce had been finalised.

'Hello, Jum.' Her voice sounded strange. 'I didn't expect to see you again.'

Jum, neatly attired, looked much better than the last time she had seen him, although his complexion was still pale and unhealthy. Alma searched his face, her breath catching as she met his blue-grey eyes.

'I don't think this is a good idea, Jum, you coming to my house.'

'That's the reason I'm here, Al.' He lowered his eyes. 'I miss you and the family beyond belief. I'm here to tell you I'll do anything to patch up our marriage, our relationship.'

Alma paused, then answered firmly, 'No, Jum. There's no going back. I've made a new life here. It just wouldn't work.'

He raised his eyes, the pain, hurt and loneliness never more apparent than now. His voice broke slightly.

'I love you, Al, more than life itself. My life is meaningless without you!'

She just stood there, motionless.

'I'm begging you to give it another go. Please, let's try again.'

Alma glanced at the hills where she had played as a child, remembering herself as a teenager, infatuated with the man before her. This man had taught her much about life – how to laugh, to enjoy their union, and be happy through the worst of times.

Then she thought of the violence, the drunkenness, the abuse. She dared not even contemplate a return to that situation.

Her voice hardened as she fought back tears. 'No, Jum, it's over, all over. I'm late for work. I must be going.'

Jum's shoulders slumped. 'Can I see you again?' he asked softly.

'Jum, there's no point, nothing to be gained. Please don't come around again.'

Jum turned and walked to the street. Alma did not see his face, which was etched with pain and despair.

Alma shut the back door and lay on her bed. She sobbed as she had not done for years, not since her baby, Valerie, had died, fifteen years before. She sobbed for the marriage they had lost, the agonies they had suffered, and, finally, she sobbed for the man she still loved, walking slowly up the street, away and out of her life forever.

COOGEE BEACH, JANUARY 1951

At 8.30 am, a warm westerly breeze greeted the early Sunday morning surfers at Coogee Beach. A sprinkling of swimmers stood watching in awe. Not one was brave enough to leave the safety of the beach.

A cyclonic disturbance had generated a massive swell. It rose alarmingly at the shallow bank 200 yards from the beach, where it instantly reared into monstrous dumpers that expended their brutal energy in a fearsome display.

Bright sunlight on the faces of six nervous young lifesavers did little to warm the chilling scene as the dumpers thunderclapped their way to shore and the white water roared its way halfway up the beach. Even the most intrepid surfers watched from the sand.

A few Surf Life Saving Association officials in traditional white had arrived to oversee the bronze examination of six members of the Coogee Surf Life Saving Club. The squad of six youths stood anxiously waiting as the huge swell alarmingly increased in size.

George Bevan and John LeMarseny, both sixteen years of age, were in the squad. They had been trained by fellow club member Rusty Peters.

George Johnson, 'Johnno' to all who knew him, said to Peters, 'You think the young blokes'll handle this?' He glanced at the sea. As chief examiner, he was responsible for judging whether the conditions were safe.

'I don't know, Johnno. It's bloody big!' replied Rusty.

George Johnson was no stranger to big seas. In 1931, at Bronte Beach in Sydney, a surf carnival was held, with disastrous consequences. On that occasion, there was a heaving southerly swell.

Gigantic seas were breaking well out past the swimming buoys, 300 yards from the beach, with an occasional monster wave breaking on the boat buoys, some 500 yards from shore. Disaster had beckoned as junior belt-swimmers, under eighteen years of age, became entangled in surf lines and swamped surf boats. Over thirty people were rescued that afternoon. The carnival had become a nightmare. Without aid, George Johnson carried out seven heroic rescues in the boiling sea. Amazingly, no lives were lost during that calamitous afternoon.

While Johnson had no desire to go easy on youths about to become lifesavers, it was with reluctance that he finally said to the squad, 'The test will proceed.'

George Bevan, a nephew and namesake of George Johnson, said nervously, 'Uncle George, are you really sending us out in that shit fight?'

Johnson said sternly, 'What if next week there's some poor bugger drowning in that shit fight? Are you just going to sit on your arse on the beach while that poor bastard drowns?'

George Bevan drew the first swim as patient, with John LeMarseny as beltman.

These were the days before the quick-release surf belt was introduced to surf lifesaving. The belt, attached to the usual 400 yards of line, was a tightly sewn, wide canvas strap, incorporating a neck band that had obviously once been an army haversack. Once secured in this contraption, it was impossible to get out without help.

John was a great surf-ski competitor, but he really preferred sunbaking to swimming. He was only too aware of this himself, and the thought of what lay ahead in the wretched belt in this horrendous surf made his knees tremble.

With fluttering stomachs and dry mouths, the pair hit the white water and were instantly washed back up the beach. After a few more attempts, they fought their way to the treacherous sand bank, about 200 yards out. Great heart-stopping, curling dumpers, higher than the clubhouse roof, greeted them.

After being smashed into the sand for the fourth time, George's ears were ringing and his mouth was full of seaweed. He managed a quick look at John. The veins in John's neck bulged as he strove to make headway – three strokes forward, one yard back. There was no let-up, and his line did not move.

George screamed encouragement between dumpers, with John eventually forcing his way past the break. He was totally exhausted – the 250-yard swim had taken its toll.

'I'm buggered,' he gasped.

George grabbed the line behind him – it was dead tight. 'Fifty yards, Lemmo, come on!' he yelled.

Stroke by stroke, John ploughed his way through the massive swells. By now they could see the marker buoy that was their goal. Rising on the huge swell, they would glimpse the buoy, then plunge down again into the trough. George wondered how much longer John could endure this punishment.

George grabbed the line again – it was still dead tight. Eventually, coughing and spluttering, John approached the buoy, reached out and grabbed the anchor line. He looked at George and gasped 'Ugly, I made it!'

The 300-yard swim had taken eighteen minutes.

How he had made it, they never knew, for as the squad reeled the line into the beach, they found great clumps of seaweed attached to it. The effect was like a massive sea anchor, dragging on the line.

For the rest of the morning, the sea softened as the swell dropped on the tide change. The remainder of the swims became relatively easy.

After the examination, George Johnson approached the squad. 'Everyone in the squad exceeded the allowable time limit for the swim, which means a fail.' His eyes twinkled. 'But given the sea conditions, I've extended the time limit and you buggers have all passed.'

John Fitzroy LeMarseny had climbed his Mount Everest in a terrifying situation, an effort he'd thought well beyond his capability. Not surprising, really – for, after all, he was the son of Ernie Fitzroy Buckleton.

6 MARCH 1953

The darkened room was musty, the drawn curtains denying the warm sunlight entry. A small figure lay on the unmade bed. Several empty wine and sherry bottles lay scattered across the floor.

Rolling over slowly, Jum eased to a sitting position. His once muscular, lean frame was desperately thin. His ribs showed clearly under his skin. His face, dissipated by years of heavy drinking, held two sunken, bloodshot eyes.

With great difficulty, he moved across the room to the half-empty bottle of whisky on the side table. Resting his left arm on the table for support, he raised the bottle to his lips and greedily gulped the liquid.

The doctor had tried to bring him to his senses. 'You realise, Jum, that if you continue to drink in this fashion and don't eat properly, you'll most certainly become gravely ill?'

Jum had nodded dumbly. His voice, hoarsened by years of alcohol abuse, sounded foreign, even to himself. 'I still can't get over Alma and the kids leaving me,' he admitted, hanging his head.

'You must understand that your liver is really in an advanced stage of disease and your general health is appalling. You're desperately undernourished. I'm seriously considering admitting you to hospital.'

The doctor looked closely at him. 'How old are you now, Jum?'

'Sixty, I think.'

'Pull your shirt up, Jum.' Jum slowly slipped his shirt over his head and shoulders. 'Are you still smoking?' the doctor asked, as he slid his stethoscope over Jum's back. Jum nodded. 'I told you five years ago you had to stop, remember?'

Jum turned his head, a mischievous glint in his reddened eyes. 'Never was much good at taking orders, Doc, remember?'

At sixty-five years of age, Doctor Stanley Davies certainly remembered.

He also remembered the blood and pain and mud and all the horrors of mutilation he had dealt with. His hands had stopped moving over Jum's back as he lost himself momentarily in the hell of France in 1918. He shook his head as he tried to erase those years of senseless destruction. His focus returned to the pitiful patient before him.

Scars across his back – shrapnel, of course. The doctor parted Jum's thin, grey hair, running his finger along the scar he had sutured in the field, near Fleurbaix, so many years ago.

'All OK, Doc?'

The doctor moved back to his desk. 'Yes. Put your shirt on, Jum. You don't remember the scar on your head, do you?' Then he answered himself. 'Of course not, you were unconscious when they got you to the CCS.'

Jum raised his hand and felt the scar. 'I don't remember the blast, just my horse going down.'

'Well, you were certainly lucky that day. The three who ran with you on the stretcher saved your life for sure.'

Jum's face clouded. 'Bob and the Wagga boys – three good men. They went much too early.'

Stanley Davies pretended to write in Jum's medical history. He wasn't writing because he couldn't. The pen slipped from his shaking hand as the appalling images, so long suppressed, flooded his mind. With great effort he composed himself. It wasn't too often he lost control. It was mostly when one of the old group came to see him.

He had thought long and hard about the conflict. Who were better off – Bob Buchannen and Ron Roberts, who graced the French soil with their youthful immortality? Or the sad wrecks often sitting before him who had suffered mental anguish and declining physical health for the past thirty years or more? Alcoholism, violence, depression, broken marriages and, in many cases, suicide were rampant among returned soldiers who had been cheered as winners and heroes after the Great War.

'I want to see you again in one week's time. If you haven't improved, I'll have to admit you to Concord Repatriation Hospital.'

The doctor looked at Jum with deep sadness. 'Your wife and family left you, Jum, because of your violence and constant drunkenness. You have only yourself to blame.'

Jum's head hung despondently. 'So much has gone wrong in my life, doctor. There seems to be nothing more to live for.'

Doctor Davies knew most of the story of Jum's life. His voice broke in pity for the man before him. 'You must eat, Jum – you must!'

Jum nodded as he stood up, his frame tiny beneath the long-sleeved shirt. He left the surgery and began the slow, pain-filled walk back to his miserable, lonely lodgings. He closed the door and slowly made his way to the bedroom. His steps were faltering, his breathing laboured.

The whisky bottle seemed to beckon him tauntingly. He quickly grabbed the bottle and gulped the contents. Then he pushed the empty bottle away and slumped across the bed. His body heaved as the whisky took effect; a trickle of blood ran from his nose. His body stilled and his breathing became shallower; the trickle increased.

Alma, the woman who had loved him for nearly thirty years and borne him five children, was the image he held softly in his mind. His baby daughter, Valerie, with her head of blonde, tousled curls, smiled at him. The tiny white coffin disappeared into the open grave.

His body convulsed. His left arm, hanging down the side of the bed, shook and trembled. His unseeing eyes stared at the ceiling.

His fingers stopped twitching. The powerful aura of Claude Jenkins filled his mind. He was aware of a voice. 'Come, Jum, come with me. There is a God.'

The jimjams had gone; the demons had fled.

2002

My mind drifted. This intense journey with my father through his troubled life, with all its tragedy, had ended. What this man had suffered and endured had eluded not only me, but also most who came into contact with him.

He had been cast adrift in a sea of waste – wasted opportunities and a wasted life – where he was left to flounder and fend for himself as best he could. Like so many others, he failed to leave the nightmare of the Western Front behind.

I had trodden the path with my father that I had never dared tread before. I now accepted him for what had once been unacceptable.

Finally, I was at peace with my father.

EPILOGUE, 2006

I sat on the sands of Coogee Beach with John LeMarseny, my close friend of sixty years.

We studied the small surf curling and dumping on the sand at the beach we had surfed together for so many years. John turned to me. 'Do you think our fathers were mates in the war?'

I let the fine sand run through my fingers as I thought about his question carefully. 'Well, Lem, they were within 500 yards of each other at Broodseinde Ridge in late 1917.' I paused. 'But we really don't know, and I guess we never will.'

The seagulls screeched overhead as the white water crashed across Wedding Cake Island.

Notes and Acknowledgments

I would like to thank Colin Gillard Tours, of Martinpuich, France. Also the Commanding Officer of the Royal School of Artillery at Larkhill, Wiltshire, England, and his adjutant, for the tour of their establishment late in 2004.

The quote at the beginning of the Prologue is from Winston Churchill's The World Crisis 1911–1918. *Also used as reference was C. E. W. Bean's* Official History of Australia in the War of 1914-1918, *volumes 1–4, and various other works on World War I.*

Ernie Fitzroy Buckleton and Lieutenant Cecil Daniel Lockhart are not in Jum's diary, but they were in Jum's war. Ernie Buckleton was the father of my closest friend, John LeMarseny. Ernie courageously won his Military Medal on Broodseinde Ridge in Belgium, and survived the war. Lieutenant Lockhart was the father of Bob, a close friend of mine. Lieutenant Lockhart was an Officer of the 9th Machine Gun Company, which fought to the bitter end at Villers-Bretonneux – there are details to be found in C. E. W. Bean's account, which I have dramatised here. Lieutenant Lockhart also survived the war.

Murray 'Muzza' Stewart, the intrepid Coogee fisherman, is alive, agile and well. At eighty-three years of age, he lives in Tweed Heads, New South Wales, and is clear and adamant regarding the controversial events of 1935 (involving a shark and an arm) described in this book. 'Muzza' went on to become a member of the Coogee Surf Life Saving Club Relay Team, which won the Australian Beach Relay Championship in 1947.

While this book is loosely based on factual events, certain characters and events have been fictionalised.

First published in 2007 by Murdoch Books Pty Limited

Murdoch Books Australia
Pier 8/9, 23 Hickson Road, Millers Point NSW 2000
Phone: +61 (0) 2 8220 2000 Fax: +61 (0) 2 8220 2558
www.murdochbooks.com.au

Murdoch Books UK Limited
Erico House, 6th Floor, 93–99 Upper Richmond Road,
Putney, London SW15 2TG
Phone: +44 (0) 20 8785 5995 Fax: +44 (0) 20 8785 5985
www.murdochbooks.co.uk

Chief Executive: Juliet Rogers
Publishing Director: Kay Scarlett

Commissioning Editor: Diana Hill
Design concept: Reuben Crossman
Design: Heather Menzies
Production: Monique Layt

Text copyright © George Bevan 2007
Design copyright © Murdoch Books Pty Limited 2007

All rights reserved. No part of this publication may be reproduced, stored in a retrieval system or transmitted in any form or by any means, electronic, mechanical, photocopying, recording or otherwise, without the prior written permission of the publisher.

National Library of Australia Cataloguing-in-Publication Data
Bevan, George E.
Jum's War: Finding my Father
ISBN 9 781 92120 837 9 (pbk)
1. Bevan, Jum (William Charles). 2. World War, 1914–1918 –
Personal narratives, Australian. 3. World War, 1914–1918 –
Veterans – Australia – Biography. 4. Soldiers – Australia –
Biography. 5. Fathers and sons – Australia – Biography.
I. Title.
940.48194

Printed by i-Book Printing Ltd in 2007. Printed in China.